A BOYS' TREASURY OF
SEA STORIES

The *Adventure Galley*

A BOYS' TREASURY OF SEA STORIES

Illustrated by

WILL NICKLESS

PAUL HAMLYN
London : New York : Sydney : Toronto

First published 1966
Second impression 1967
Third impression 1968

Published by
THE HAMLYN PUBLISHING GROUP LTD
London : New York : Sydney : Toronto
Hamlyn House · The Centre · Feltham · Middlesex
for Golden Pleasure Books Ltd

CONTENTS

Famous Ships

by

FRANK KNIGHT

The Adventure Galley *of Captain Kidd the Pirate, 1696*

There have always been pirates. Julius Caesar was once captured by them. King Alfred and many other English kings had to build ships to drive them out of the Channel. In Queen Elizabeth I's time pirates from Algiers used to raid English towns, and once sailed right into the Thames.

But the great days of pirates were from about 1650 to 1720, and their chief hunting grounds were among the West Indies and off the coasts of North America.

They came because Spain refused to let ships of other nations trade with her American colonies. Many seamen defied the ban, and the Spaniards called them pirates. Most of them, however, had commissions from their governments, as Drake did. Strictly, they were privateers, or private warships, not pirates.

Elizabeth issued many such commissions. But James I, anxious to make peace with Spain, cancelled them. Many seamen who held them decided to remain in the West Indies to become real pirates.

They had chosen a hard life. No ports would receive them.

For food they caught wild cattle, roasting the meat over wood fires in the open. The Spanish-Indian word for such a fire was boucan, and so the pirates came to be called boucaniers, or buccaneers.

But their numbers grew. They were joined by runaway slaves, deserting seamen and soldiers, and unemployed seamen from Europe. They took possession of some islands which were almost deserted, such as St Kitts, Antigua, Tortuga. Many English pirates went to Jamaica, which Oliver Cromwell's ships captured from the Spaniards. One famous buccaneer, Henry Morgan, became governor of Jamaica, with the task of putting an end to piracy!

Pirates, like burglars, can only make a living if they can sell the goods they steal. The pirates' best customers were the colonists, Spanish in the south, English in the north.

England made the same mistake as Spain. Only British ships were allowed to trade with British colonies. But few ships came, and the pirates captured many that did. Then the pirates sold their cargoes to the hungry colonies much cheaper than honest merchants would have done.

In return the colonists welcomed pirate ships to their harbours. The pirates spent their money in the growing American towns such as New York, Boston, Philadelphia. Some pirates built fine houses there and lived like lords. They made friends with colonial governors and got bankers to invest money in their voyages. Piracy became big business.

Soon the pirates became more ambitious. They made longer voyages. From their American homes they went all the way to the Indian Ocean and Persian Gulf. They took possession of the island of Madagascar and set their own 'king' to rule it.

Incredibly rich cargoes went home to America. In 1694 Thomas Tew sailed into Boston with a cargo worth £1000,000. Two years later Henry Avery came in with goods worth £300,000.

This sort of thing could not last. Many of the goods had been stolen from the powerful East India Company, or from their Indian friends. They told the British government it must send out warships to stop the traffic.

Britain was at war with France and could not spare a warship. The government told the Earl of Bellomont, who was governor in chief of the American colonies, he must do something about it from his side of the Atlantic. Bellomont decided to send out a private warship, a privateer.

The ship he chose was called *Adventure Galley*, an armed merchant ship of about 300 tons, mounting thirty guns. She was a sailing ship, but was called 'galley' because she also had big oars for moving her in harbour or in a flat calm. She was not a galley at all in the old-fashioned sense of a rowing ship.

The man he chose to command her was a retired merchant skipper named Captain Kidd, a most respectable man by all accounts, who had lived in New York for many years.

Captain Kidd sailed. Little was heard of him for almost a year. And then, suddenly, came the news that instead of catching pirates, Kidd was indulging in piracy himself. The East India Company angrily demanded that real warships be sent out — and this time they went.

Meanwhile Captain Kidd was on his way home with the *Adventure Galley*. He sailed innocently into New York, and was promptly arrested, and was then sent to England for trial.

Was he really a pirate? His crew said he was, and he had forced them to be pirates too. One man who refused was killed by Captain Kidd 'with a bucket worth eightpence'.

Captain Kidd said he was not. He said his crew mutinied and forced him to seize other ships. And, in any case, two ships he took were carrying French cargoes, which made them enemies. He said he had given the French papers of those ships to the Earl of Bellomont.

But the Earl of Bellomont had died and the papers could not be found. After more than two years of argument Captain Kidd was tried, found guilty, and hanged. Right to the end he protested: 'I am the innocentist person of them all, only I have been sworn against by perjured persons.'

Perhaps he was. Two hundred years after his death those French papers were found in the Public Records Office in London.

Nobody believed him innocent at the time. In fact the newspapers and story-writers of his day turned him into the greatest pirate who ever lived, which he certainly was not. Horrible crimes were invented for him. Books were written about his career, quite untrue. His imaginary life was even acted on the stage.

In fact much of the nonsense written about pirates began with these stories of Captain Kidd.

The truth is that pirates were not very romantic. They were not even particularly bloodthirsty. They never killed people if they could avoid it, for they knew they would be hanged for it if they were caught. Captain Kidd was hanged for killing that man with a bucket, not for piracy. Piracy was sometimes pardoned, but not murder.

Pirates did not make people walk the plank. Some story-writer invented that. Nor did pirates fight if they could avoid it. Even the famous Blackbeard Teach, who loved to decorate himself with cutlasses and pistols, fireworks and lighted candles, was only in one serious fight. It was with a young naval officer, and Blackbeard was killed.

Pirates did not make a habit of burying their treasure. They spent it on gay living. But they did sometimes pretend they had buried it when they were captured, so that their lives might be spared. They hoped to be given a chance to dig it up; in other words a chance to escape. Captain Kidd tried that, but nobody believed him.

Some later pirates were much more bloodthirsty: the pirates of the China Sea, Borneo and Java, for instance. They killed for the love of killing. And there was the famous Benito de Soto who was a pirate in the Atlantic not much more than a hundred years ago. He once locked all the passengers of a sailing-ship under hatches, opened the sea-cocks, and set fire to the ship as well. Captain Kidd would never have done that.

The Victory
Nelson's flagship at Trafalgar, 1805

The old wooden sailing-ships had long lives. Merchant ships might remain in service for a hundred years. Even warships might last fifty years.

Nelson's *Victory* was ordered to be built in 1758, the year of Nelson's birth. She was launched in 1765, forty years before Trafalgar. She was kept afloat in harbour for 120 years after that. Now she is preserved in a dry-dock, but she is still an admiral's flagship, as she was during most of her active life.

The best ships were built of oak. But oak is an expensive timber. An oak tree must grow for a hundred years before it is ready for cutting. In those days nearly all oak trees were reserved for the use of the Navy, and were marked with the Government's 'broad arrow'. Some old trees may still be seen bearing this mark.

Admiral Collingwood, who was second in command to Nelson at Trafalgar, used to carry acorns in his pocket and plant them in any likely spot. He did not dream that long before his trees had grown, all warships would be built of iron or steel.

Because oak was valuable, and scarce, ships could not be scrapped when they became old-fashioned. Even when a ship was rotten and falling to pieces, any good timber in her was carefully removed and used again. That happened in the case of the *Royal George*, and with many others.

Nor did ships easily become old-fashioned. Drake's *Revenge* was not very different from the frigates of Nelson's day, more than two centuries later. Sails and rigging had improved, and so had guns; but the hulls were very similar. There was no machinery of any kind to become out of date. Drake could have sailed the *Victory*, or Nelson the *Revenge*. Both men would have been lost aboard the steamers which came only a few years after Trafalgar.

The *Victory* was practically rebuilt twice in her fifty years of active life. This was partly because she was such a popular ship. Many admirals besides Nelson chose her for their flagship, including Admiral Kempenfeldt who went down with the *Royal George*, Admiral Keppel who had been one of Anson's midshipmen aboard the *Centurion*, Lord Howe, Lord Hood, and Lord St Vincent.

Once the Admiralty converted the *Victory* into a prison ship; but such a shout of protest arose that they had to fit her out as a flagship again. And that was before Nelson made her famous at Trafalgar.

When Nelson heard she was to be his flagship he wrote to a friend, 'I am very pleased, for I know the weight of the *Victory* in the Mediterranean.' That is, even her name added something to the importance of his appointment as Admiral in Command. Friends and enemies alike knew that whoever flew his flag in the *Victory* must be an important man.

Nelson's job in the Mediterranean was to keep the French fleet shut up in Toulon, or to fight it if it came out. For Napoleon was hoping to invade Britain, but could not do so without his warships.

In the summer of 1803 Nelson vowed 'never to go into port till after the battle, if they make me wait a year'. But they made him wait much longer than that. Next summer he was writing, 'If I should miss these fellows my heart will break.' And in another letter he said that the French admiral 'sometimes plays bo-peep in and out of Toulon, like a mouse at the edge of a hole.'

But at Christmas 1804 they did slip out, and Nelson missed them in bad weather.

His own ships were terribly battered by then. Most of them had not been in dock for two years. Some of the best had gone to watch the Spanish fleet, for Spain was also at war with Britain.

Rumours and false reports came in. Someone said the French had gone to Italy. Nelson chased them there, but did not find them. Then he thought they might have gone to Egypt, so he went there to look for them. Not until March did he learn that they had passed Gibraltar, bound out into the Atlantic.

The wind turned against him. He fretted and fumed, and after weeks managed to reach Gibraltar. More delays — and then the wind changed and off Nelson went, not even bothering to wait for the ships' laundry to come back from the shore.

He guessed now that the French meant to attack the West Indies, and he was right. His fleet crossed the Atlantic in twenty-four days, and so frightened the French that they hurried back across the Atlantic again.

This time they escaped into Spanish ports. The British frigates could see the combined French and Spanish fleets in Cadiz harbour. But Napoleon wanted both fleets in the English Channel, and said he would sack the admiral in command if he did not make a move.

They made a move on October 19, 1805. The watching

The *Victory* (right)

frigates saw their topsails being hoisted. Nelson prepared for battle.

The British fleet formed into two parallel lines, one led by Nelson in the *Victory*, the other by Collingwood in the *Royal Sovereign*. But there was scarcely any wind. Not until the morning of October 21 could Nelson get his ships near enough to open fire. The *Victory* was moving at about two knots.

Nelson's plan was to smash the long enemy line in two places, and so break the big fleet up into small groups. The plan worked perfectly. The two British lines sailed majestically on, ignoring the French guns, until they crashed in among the enemy ships. The *Victory* came under fire from seven or eight French ships at once. From one came the bullet which killed Lord Nelson in his hour of triumph.

Every history book tells of the Battle of Trafalgar. But here is a letter from a young sailor who took part in it, written to his father just after the battle.

'This comes to tell you that I am alive and hearty except three fingers; but that's not much, it might have been my head. I told brother Tom I should like to see a great battle, and I have seen one, and we have peppered the enemy rarely; and for matter of that, they fought us pretty tightish for French and Spanish. Three of our mess are killed, and four more of us winged.

'How my fingers got knocked overboard I don't know; but off they are, and I never missed them till I wanted them. You see by my writing it was my left hand, so I can write to you, and fight for my King yet. We have taken a rare parcel of ships, but the wind is so rough we cannot bring them home, else I should roll in prize-money. So we are busy smashing 'em, and blowing 'em up wholesale.

'Our dear Admiral Nelson is killed, so we have paid pretty sharply for licking 'em. I never set eyes on him, for which I am both sorry and glad; for, to be sure, I should like to have seen him. But then, all the men in our ship who have seen him are such soft toads, they have done nothing but blast their eyes and cry ever since he was killed. God bless you, chaps that fought like the Devil, sit down and cry like a wench.

'I am still in the Royal Sovereign, but the Admiral has left her. He is in a frigate so that he may be here and there and everywhere. For he's as cute and bold as a lion, for all he can cry! I saw tears with my own eyes, when the boat hailed and said my Lord was dead. So no more at present — Sam.'

The Mary Celeste
Heroine of the most famous
sea mystery, 1872

She was a very ordinary little sailing tramp, owned in the U.S.A., built in Nova Scotia, of about 230 tons. Her skipper, Captain Benjamin Briggs, was also part-owner of her. He was a very respectable man, by all accounts, and religious.

The *Mary Celeste* sailed from New York for Genoa, Italy, on November 7, 1872. She had a cargo of oil and raw alcohol in barrels. Captain Briggs had his wife and two-year-old daughter with him. There were a mate, second mate, cook and four seamen.

Twenty-eight days later, on December 5, the *Mary Celeste* was found drifting helplessly about 600 miles west of Gibraltar, with no one on board.

Why? A court of enquiry was held, books have been written about it, men have puzzled about it ever since. Nobody knows.

She was found by the brig *Dei Gratia* which had been in New York with her. In fact Captain and Mrs Briggs had dined with Captain Morehouse of the *Dei Gratia* just before sailing. So Captain Morehouse sent his mate on board the mystery ship.

The mate found very little wrong. The sails were set, though some were torn and one had been let down on deck, perhaps in a hurry. It had not been stowed away. There was water in the ship's bilges, but not a lot. She was not sinking. The ship's only small boat was missing.

Some hatch covers were off, but the cargo in the hold seemed undamaged. The cabin skylight was open, and everything was wet inside, from rain or spray. But on the whole things were in good order.

The ship's log was in the mate's cabin. It showed no unusual entry. But the ship's other papers and the captain's navigation instruments were missing.

There was plenty of food on board, and water. There was no sign of fire or other calamity. In short there was nothing to show why the ship had been abandoned.

Yet she had been, and in a hurry. The seamen had left their pipes and tobacco in the fo'c'sle, and their oilskins. Why had that sail been dropped in haste? On the other hand the captain had had time to collect his papers and instruments.

The mate of the *Dei Gratia* sailed the *Mary Celeste* to Gibraltar. There she was handed over to the port authorities. Captain Morehouse claimed salvage money in the usual way.

Of course everyone expected the *Mary Celeste's* crew to turn up somewhere. But they never did. No trace of their boat was ever found.

Those are the plain facts. Unfortunately they were much too

plain for some people. 'Experts' busied themselves with the mystery, and found sinister clues.

There was a cut in the ship's rail which must have been made with an axe. Why? There were two long scratches in the ship's bow planking. How did they get there? There were some nasty brown stains on deck which must be blood. There was actually a bloodstained sword in the captain's cabin, which someone had tried to clean! Biggest mystery of all, the clock in the cabin was hanging upside down.

Alas for the 'experts', most of these clues came to nothing. The axe cut might have been made years ago. The scratches in the planking were merely where splinters had been torn away by the sea. A doctor said the blood was not blood, whatever else it might be.

As for the sword, it was an ancient curio, no more than an ornament. Its stains were only rust; and the person who had tried to clean it was the mate of the *Dei Gratia*, to pass the time away. He had also tried to get the clock going, but could not, so put it back on the wall in disgust, not noticing and not caring that it was upside down.

Naturally the experts were annoyed at having their clues blown away like this. They bullied the mate of the *Dei Gratia* unmercifully, almost accusing him of murder. As to the remaining owner of the *Mary Celeste*, who had come from America to give evidence, he wrote to a friend:

'They were going to arrest me for hiring the crew to make away with the officers. I did not know but they might do it, as they seem to do just as they like. So I decided to come home.'

In despair the experts of the court of enquiry gave up. But not so the amateurs. The mystery was too intriguing to be dropped. Strange theories were put forward, none of which fitted the facts.

One was that an octopus had removed the crew one by

The *Marie Celeste*

one — and presumably the boat as well! But why an octopus should need navigation instruments nobody explained.

Another was that plague had broken out. Or the captain had gone mad and killed everybody, including himself. Or the entire crew had gone swimming, and the ship had sailed away from them.

Most fantastic, one theory was that the baby on board was really a baby-grand piano. It had broken adrift and so frightened the crew that they all jumped overboard.

Other investigators picked on Captain Morehouse and his crew. They were mere pirates, who had killed the crew of the *Mary Celeste* for the sake of the salvage money. Or perhaps a gang of toughs joined the *Mary Celeste* in New York and did away with the regular crew.

There were even 'confessions' of stories like that, published in newspapers as coming from 'survivors'. But strangest of all, perhaps, are the details which have been invented to make the mystery more mysterious.

The mate of the *Dei Gratia* said clearly enough that there was nothing on the cabin table except the racks, or 'fiddles', to keep things from sliding off in bad weather. And the ship had been in bad weather, for everything was wet.

But someone invented the story that there was a meal on the table, ready to be eaten. Says one writer, 'Three cups of tea were standing on the table. They were still warm!' And the same writer tells how newly washed shirts were hanging on a line, and there was a chicken frying on the galley stove.

Another writer has 'a phial of sewing-machine oil still standing upright by a reel of cotton and a thimble'.

All this is nonsense. But the mystery remains. What did happen? The answers given by two practical seamen are worth quoting.

One was the mate of the *Dei Gratia*. He said that when someone on board the *Mary Celeste* tested the depth of water in her bilge that morning, water had surged up the pipe, giving an entirely false reading. He said it had happened to him sometimes, when the ship was rolling. The water surged up and the reading on the line became ten or twelve feet instead of two or three. So the crew panicked, thinking the ship was sinking under them, and left her.

The other man was the part-owner of the *Mary Celeste*, himself an old seaman. He thought gas from the cargo of alcohol might have caused an explosion which blew those hatch covers off. So the crew hastily took to the boat in case a worse explosion was to follow.

In either case, then, the ship must have sailed away on her own, and the boat been swamped by the bad weather which came soon afterwards.

It is a tame ending to a mystery story, but at least it fits the facts. And the other mystery of the *Mary Celeste* remains. Why pick on her? Why has she become the most famous mystery ship of all time?

The Titanic
The unsinkable ship, 1912

The White Star Line boasted that their great ship was unsinkable. Her bottom was divided into sixteen separate watertight compartments. If any one became holed it could be shut off from the rest, and the ship would still float.

But on her maiden voyage an iceberg ripped through five of those compartments, and she did sink. More than 1,500 people were drowned.

She was the biggest and most luxurious liner that had yet been built: 46,000 tons, 880 feet long, she could carry 2,000 passengers besides her crew of 800. Her speed was 24 knots, and on this first voyage she was trying to break the Atlantic speed record.

Famous and wealthy people, American and British, had booked passages in her. But in addition there were hundreds of poor emigrants from Europe, going to America to find new homes and fortune.

It happened on a fine, calm, but very cold night, April 14, 1912. Icebergs were about, as the captain of the *Titanic* had been told by wireless — and not many ships had wireless in those days. But the *Titanic* rushed on, out to break the record. And, of course, she was unsinkable.

Suddenly, just before midnight, the look-outs shouted that there was an iceberg right ahead. The helm was put over, the engines reversed. But it was too late. The berg slid along the ship's side, slopping tons of ice on to her decks.

Not many people heard or felt the shock. Most people were in bed. A few who happened to be on deck thought it was a great joke, and began playing with the ice. But far down below stokers were horrified to see the Atlantic water pouring in.

Half an hour later Captain Smith realised the awful truth. The unsinkable *Titanic* was sinking. He ordered the boats to be got ready, the passengers mustered on deck. The first wireless call for assistance went out.

Captain Smith knew what the passengers did not. There were only half enough boats to go round. Moreover there had been no boat-drill on board. Even the crew did not know to which boats they were supposed to go. As to the passengers, they were only annoyed at being turned out on deck in the cold. Many refused to go. The ship was unsinkable.

In their cabin high on the bridge the two wireless operators were having trouble, too. Other ships heard their distress call, but refused to believe it. They thought it was a leg-pull and refused to wake their captains.

One ship, the *Californian*, a big cargo liner, could actually see the *Titanic*. Sensibly, she had stopped because there was so much ice about, and was waiting for daylight. Her wireless operator was asleep, and her captain. Her officers watched the big ship arrive, and also stop. Later, when the *Titanic* fired distress rockets, the *Californian's* people thought they were fireworks to amuse the passengers! When the *Titanic's* lights went out they thought she had steamed away.

In fact only one ship took the *Titanic's* calls seriously. She was the small and old Cunarder *Carpathia*, bound from New York on a sunshine cruise to the Mediterranean.

The *Carpathia* was built to do fourteen knots. That night her aged engines pushed her along at seventeen. Steam was cut off from the passengers' radiators to give more for the engines. But she was sixty miles away from the *Titanic* when she heard the call.

The *Titanic's* passengers refused to worry. They played cards in the saloon. The band was playing. But down below third-class and emigrant passengers found the water rising in their cabins. They rushed about blindly, not even knowing where the boat-deck was. The huge ship seemed a maze of alleyways and staircases leading nowhere.

The first boats were lowered almost empty. The first-class passengers refused to leave the warm saloon. But the officers knew the boats must be put in the water, even if they went empty. Better that than let them go down with the ship.

Then the ship began to tilt, and suddenly people realised the matter was serious. Now they rushed for the boats, and the trouble was to keep them back. Men tried to crowd in with the women and children. But some women refused to leave their menfolk, preferring to drown with them.

By that time, too, people were finding their way up from far below. Officers had to bring out their revolvers. A few shots were fired into the air. The last boat was lowered, and there were still about 1,600 people on board the ship. Hundreds were still trying to find the boat-deck.

Two hours after hitting the berg the ship's foredeck dipped under water. The band began playing hymns. Officers and seamen struggled desperately to clear collapsible boats and rafts so that they would float when the ship sank. Inside the ship furniture and fittings began to slide.

At two o'clock the captain told the two wireless operators to save themselves. They ignored him and went on working. But a few minutes later they heard the sea swishing over the top bridge. Then they went.

People fought their way towards the stern, which was rising high into the air as the ship stood on her head. Everything inside slid down in a tremendous avalanche. One of the four huge funnels toppled over.

At twenty minutes past two the *Titanic* vanished. The unsinkable ship had sunk — in less than three hours. On board the *Californian* an officer noted that the big ship's lights had disappeared. Twenty-seven miles to the southward the *Carpathia* was racing on.

The water felt like ice. Second Officer Lightoller said it felt like a thousand knives when he was plunged into it. He had just been sucked down into one of the sinking ship's big ventilators, and blown out again by a blast of hot air. He grabbed a collapsible boat with about thirty other men. The junior wireless operator fought his way out from underneath it and joined them.

Fifth Officer Rowe took one boat back to look for survivors. He found four. No other boat went back, but most of them held only women and children. In any case nobody could live long in that icy water.

At four in the morning the *Carpathia* arrived. Captain

The *Titanic*

Rostron had to take his ship to the lifeboats, for the frozen people in them could not row to the ship.

The *Carpathia* took on board 705 people. There had been 2,207 on board the *Titanic*. 1,502 were missing, for none was picked up by any other ship. At just about this time the White Star Line man in New York was telling newspaper reporters, 'We place absolute confidence in the *Titanic*. We believe her to be unsinkable.'

The truth horrified the world. Laws were hastily passed about lifeboats, boat-drills, wireless. Such a thing must never be allowed to happen again.

Perhaps it will not. At any rate nobody is likely to boast again that a ship is unsinkable.

Amyas and the Armada
from Westward Ho!

by
CHARLES KINGSLEY

Westward Ho! *tells of the exciting adventures of Amyas Leigh on the Spanish main in the years 1575—1588. Amyas' hatred of the Spanish is patriotic, but also personal. His lady-love was carried off by a Spanish cavalier named Don Guzman, who married the girl, but then left her to burn to death, along with Amyas' brother, at the hands of the Spanish Inquisition. The desire to revenge these deeds leads Amyas into the famous battle which is the climax of the book — the defeat of the Invincible Spanish Armada.*

The Spaniards are dispirited and battered, but unbroken still; and as they slide to their anchorage in Calais Roads on the Saturday evening of that most memorable week, all prudent men know well that England's hour is come, and that the bells which will call all at Christendom to church upon the morrow morn, will be either the death-knell or the triumphal peal of the Reformed faith throughout the world.

But where is Amyas Leigh all this while? Day after day he has been seeking the *Sta. Catharina* in the thickest of the press, and cannot come at her, cannot even hear of her; one moment he dreads that she has sunk by night, and balked him of his prey; the next, that she has repaired her damages, and will escape him after all. He is moody, discontented, restless, even (for the first time in his life) peevish with his men. He can talk of nothing but Don Guzman; he can find no better

27

employment, at every spare moment, than taking his sword out of the sheath, and handling it, fondling it, talking to it even, bidding it not to fail him in the day of vengeance.

Amyas called for a boat and went on board Drake's ship to ask for news of the *Sta. Catharina*, and listened scowling to the loud chants and tinkling bells, which came across the water from the Spanish fleet. At last Drake was summoned by the Lord Admiral, and returned with a secret commission, which ought to bear fruit that night; and Amyas, who had gone with him, helped him till nightfall, and then returned to his own ship as Sir Amyas Leigh, Knight, to the joy and glory of every soul on board, except his moody self.

So there, the livelong summer Sabbath day, before the little high-walled town and the long range of yellow sand-hills, lie those two mighty armaments, scowling at each other, hardly out of gun-shot. Messenger after messenger is hurrying towards Bruges to the Duke of Parma, for light craft which can follow these nimble English somewhat better than their own floating castles; and above all, entreating him to put to sea at once with all his force. He returns for answer; first, that his victual is not ready; next, that his Dutch sailors, who have been kept at their post for many a week at the sword's point, have run away like water; and thirdly, that over and above all, he cannot come so 'strangely provided of great ordnance and musketeers' as those five-and-thirty Dutch ships, in which round-sterned and stubborn-hearted heretics watch, like terriers at a rat's hole, the entrance of Nieuwport and Dunkirk.

Lord Henry Seymour has brought Lord Howard a letter of command from Elizabeth's self; and Drake has been carrying out so busily all that Sunday long, that by two o'clock on the Monday morning, eight fire-ships 'besmeared with wildfire, brimstone, pitch and resin, and all their ordnance charged with bullets and with stones,' are stealing down the wind straight for the Spanish fleet, guided by two valiant men of Devon, Young and Prowse. (Let their names live long in the land!) The ships are fired, the men of Devon steal back, and in a moment more, the heaven is red with glare from Dover Cliffs to Gravelines Tower.

And then breaks forth one of those disgraceful panics which so often follow overweening presumption; and shrieks, oaths, prayers, and reproaches make night hideous. Cutting all cables, hoisting any sails, the Invincible Armada goes lumbering wildly out to sea, every ship foul of her neighbour.

The largest of the four galliasses loses her rudder, and drifts helpless to and fro, hindering and confusing. The duke, having (so the Spaniards say) weighed his anchor deliberately instead of leaving it behind him, runs in again after a while and fires a signal for return; but his truant sheep are deaf to the shepherd's pipe, and swearing and praying by turns, he runs up the Channel towards Gravelines, picking up stragglers on his way, who are struggling as best they can among the flats and shallows: but Drake and Fenner have arrived as soon as he. When Monday's sun rises on the quaint old castle and muddy dykes of Gravelines town, the thunder of the cannon recommences, and is not hushed until the night. Drake can hang coolly enough in the rear to plunder when he thinks fit: but when the battle needs it none can fight more fiercely, among the foremost; and there is need now, if ever. That Armada must never be allowed to re-form. If it does, its left wing may yet keep the English at bay, while its right drives off the blockading Hollanders from Dunkirk port, and sets Parma and his flotilla free to join them, and to sail in doubled strength across to the mouth of the Thames.

So Drake has weighed anchor, and away up the Channel with all his squadron, the moment that he saw the Spanish fleet come up; and with him Fenner burning to redeem the honour, which indeed he had never lost; and ere Fenton,

Beeston, Crosse, Ryman and Lord Southwell can join them, the Devon ships have been worrying the Spaniards for two full hours into confusion worse confounded.

But what is that heavy firing behind them? Alas for the great galliasse! She lies, like a huge stranded whale, upon the sands where now stands Calais pier: and Amyas Preston is pounding her into submission, while a fleet of hoys and drumblers look on and help, as jackals might the lion.

Soon, on the southwest horizon, loom up larger and larger two mighty ships, and behind them sail on sail. As they near a shout greets the *Triumph* and the *Bear*; and on and in the Lord High Admiral glides stately into the thickest of the fight.

True, we have still but some three-and-twenty ships which can cope at all with some ninety of the Spaniards, but we have dash, and daring, and the inspiration of utter need. Now, or never, must the mighty struggle be ended. We worried them off Portland; we must rend them in pieces now; and in rushes ship after ship, to smash her broadsides through and through the wooden castles 'sometimes not a pike's-length asunder,' and then out to reload, and give place meanwhile to another. The smaller are fighting with all sails set; the few larger, who once in, are careless about coming out again, fight with topsails loose, and their main and foreyards close down on deck, to prevent being boarded. The duke, Oquenda and Recalde, having with much ado got clear of the shallows, bear the brunt of the fight to seaward; but in vain. The day goes against them more and more, as it runs on. Seymour and Winter have battered the great *San Philip* into a wreck; her masts are gone by the board: Pimintelli in the *San Matthew* comes up to take the mastiffs off the fainting bull, and finds them fasten on him instead; but the Evangelist, though smaller, is stouter than the Deacon, and of all the shot poured into him, not twenty 'lackt him through.' His masts are tottering; but sink or strike he will not.

'Go ahead, and pound his tough hide, Leigh,' roars Drake off the poop of his ship, while he hammers away at one of the great galliasses. 'What right has he to keep us all waiting?'

Amyas slips in as best he can between Drake and Winter; as he passes he shouts to his ancient enemy —

'We are with you, sir; all friends today!' and slipping round Winter's bows, he pours his broadside into those of the *San Matthew*, and then glides on to reload; but not to return. For, not a pistol shot to leeward, worried by three or four small craft, lies an immense galleon; and on her poop — can he believe his eyes for joy? — the maiden and the wheel he has sought so long!

'There he is!' shouts Amyas, springing to the starboard side of the ship. The men, too, have already caught sight of that hated sign; a cheer of fury bursts from every throat.

'Steady, men!' says Amyas in a suppressed voice. 'Not a shot! Reload, and be ready; I must speak with him first'; and silent as the grave, amid the infernal din, the *Vengeance* glides up to the Spaniard's quarter.

'Don Guzman Maria Magdalena Sotomayor de Soto!' shouts Amyas from the mizzen rigging, loud and clear amid the roar.

He has not called in vain. Fearless and graceful as ever, the tall mail-clad figure of his foe leaps up upon the poop-railing, twenty feet above Amyas's head, and shouts through his vizor —

'At your service, sir! whosoever you may be.'

A dozen muskets and arrows are levelled at him; but Amyas frowns down. 'No man strikes him but I. Spare him, if you kill every other soul on board. Don Guzman, I am Captain Sir Amyas Leigh; I proclaim you a traitor and a ravisher, and challenge you once more to single combat, when and where you will.'

'You are welcome to come on board to me, sir,' answer

'I proclaim you a traitor and a ravisher, and challenge you to combat.'

the Spaniard in a clear, quiet tone, 'bringing with you this answer, that you lie in your throat,' and lingering a moment, out of bravado, to arrange his scarf, he steps down slowly again behind the bulwarks.

'Coward!' shouts Amyas at the top of his voice.

The Spaniard reappears instantly. 'Why that name, Senor, of all others?' asks he in a cool, stern voice.

'Because we call men cowards in England, who leave their wives to be burnt alive by priests.'

The moment the words had passed Amyas's lips, he felt that they were cruel and unjust. But it was too late to recall them. The Spaniard started, clutched his sword-hilt, and then hissed back through his closed vizor —

'For that word, sirrah, you hang at my yard-arm, if Saint Mary gives me grace.'

'See that your halter be a silken one, then,' laughed Amyas, 'for I am just dubbed knight.' And he stepped down as a storm of bullets rang through the rigging round his head; the Spaniards are not as punctilious as he.

'Fire!' His ordnance crash through the stern-works of the Spaniard; and then he sails onward, while her balls go humming harmlessly through his rigging.

Half an hour has passed of wild noise and fury; three times has the *Vengeance*, as a dolphin might, sailed clean round and round the *Sta. Catharina*, pouring in broadside after broadside, till the guns are leaping to the deck-beams with their own heat, and the Spaniard's sides are slit and spotted in a hundred places. And yet, so high has been his fire in return, and so strong the deck defences of the *Vengeance*, that a few spars broken, and two or three men wounded by musketry, are all her loss. But still the Spaniard endures, magnificent as ever; it is the battle of the thresher and the whale; the end is certain, but the work is long.

A puff of wind clears away the sulphurous veil for a moment; the sea is clear of ships towards the land; the Spanish fleet are moving again up Channel, Medina bringing up the rear; only some two miles to their right hand, the vast hull the *San Philip* is drifting up the shore with the tide, and of somewhat nearer the *San Matthew* is hard at work with her pumps. They can see the white stream of water pouring down her side.

In the meanwhile, long ere the sun had set, comes down the darkness of the thunderstorm, attracted, as to a volcano's mouth, to that cast mass of sulphur-smoke which cloaks the sea for many a mile; and heaven's artillery above makes answer to man's below. But still, through the smoke and rain, Amyas clings to his prey. She too, has seen the northward movement of the Spanish fleet, and sets her topsails; Amyas calls to the men to fire high, and galleys, having forced their way at last over the shallows, coming flashing and sputtering up to the combatants, and take his fire off the galleon. Amyas grits his teeth, and would fain hustle into the thick of the press once more, in spite of the galley's beaks.

'Most heroical captain,' says Cary, pulling a long face, 'if we do, we are stove and sunk in five minutes; not to mention that Yeo says he hasn't twenty rounds of great cartridge left.'

So, surely and silent, the *Vengeance* sheers off, but keeps as near as she can to the little squadron, all through the night of rain and thunder which follows. Next morning the sun rises on a clear sky, with a strong west-north-west breeze, and all hearts are asking what the day will bring forth.

They are long past Dunkirk now; the German Ocean is opening before them. The Spaniards, sorely battered, and lessened in numbers, having during the night regained some sort of order. The English hang on their skirts a mile or two behind. They have no ammunition, and must wait for more. To Amyas's great disgust, the *Sta. Catharina* has rejoined her fellow during the night.

'Never mind,' says Cary; 'she can neither dive nor fly, and as long as she is above water, we — What is the Admiral about?'

He is signalling Lord Henry Seymour and his squadron. Soon they tack, and come down the wind for the coast of Flanders. Parma must be blockaded still; and the Hollanders are likely to be too busy with their plunder to do it effectually. Suddenly there is a stir in the Spanish fleet. Medina and the rearmost ships turn upon the English. What can it mean? Will they offer battle once more? If so, it were best to get out of their way for we have nothing wherewith to fight them. So the English lie close to the wind. They will let them pass, and return to their old tactic of following and harassing.

'Goodbye to Seymour,' says Cary, 'if he is caught between them and Parma's flotillas. They are going to Dunkirk.'

'Impossible! They will not have water enough to reach his light craft. Here comes a big ship right upon us! Give him all you have left lads; and if he will fight us, lay him alongside, and die boarding.'

They gave him what they had, and hulled him with every shot, but his huge side stood silent as the grave. He had not wherewithal to return the compliment.

'As I live, he is cutting loose the foot of his mainsail! the villain means to run.'

'There go the rest of them! Victoria!' shouted Cary, as one after another, every Spaniard set all the sail he could.

There was silence for a few minutes throughout the English fleet; and then cheer upon cheer of triumph rent the skies. It was over. The Spaniard had refused battle, and thinking only of safety, was pressing downward toward the Straits again. The Invincible Armada had cast away its name, and England was saved.

'But he will never get there, sir,' said old Yeo, who had come upon deck to murmur his *Nunc Domine*, and gaze upon that sight beyond all human faith and hope: 'Never, never will he weather the Flanders shore, against such a breeze as is coming up. Look to the eye of the wind sir, and see how the Lord is fighting for His people!'

Yes, down it came, fresher and stiffer every minute out of the grey northwest, as it does so often after a thunderstorm; and the sea began to rise high and white, till the Spaniards were fain to take in all spare canvas, and lie-to as best they could; while the English fleet, lying-to also, awaited an event which was in God's hands and not in theirs.

'They will all be ashore on Zealand before the afternoon,' murmured Amyas; 'and I have lost my labour! Oh, for powder, powder, powder! to go in and finish it at once!'

'Oh, sir,' said Yeo, 'don't murmur against the Lord in the very day of his mercies. It is hard; but His will be done.'

'Could we not borrow powder from Drake there?'

'Look at the sea, sir!'

And indeed, the sea was far too rough for any such attempt. The Spaniards neared and neared the fatal dunes, which fringed the shore for many a dreary mile; and Amyas had to wait weary hours, growling like a dog who has had the bone snatched out of his mouth, till the day wore on; when, behold, the wind began to fall as rapidly as it had risen. A savage joy rose in Amyas's breast.

'They are safe! safe for us! Who will go and beg us powder? A cartridge here and a cartridge there? — anything to set to work again!'

Cary volunteered, and returned in a couple of hours with some quantity: but he was on board again only just in time, for the southwester had recovered the mastery of the skies, and the Spaniards and the English were moving away; but this time northward. Whither now? To Scotland? Amyas knew not, and cared not, provided he was in the company of Don Guzman de Soto.

The Armada was defeated, and England saved.

Yes, it is over; and the great Armada is vanquished. As the medals struck on the occasion said, 'It came, it saw, and it fled!' And whither? Away and northward, like a herd of frightened deer, past the Orkneys and Shetlands, catching up a few hapless fishermen as guides; past the coast of Norway, there, too, refused water and food by the brave descendants of the Vikings; and on northward ever towards the lonely Faroes, and the everlasting dawn which heralds round the Pole the midnight sun.

Their water is failing; the cattle must go overboard and the wild northern sea echoes to the shrieks of drowning horses. They must homeward at least, somehow, each as best he can. Let them meet again at Cape Finisterre, if indeed they ever meet. Medina Sidiona, with some five and twenty of the soundest and best victualled ships, will lead the way, and leave the rest to their fate. He is soon out of sight; and forty more, the only remnant of the mighty host, come wandering wearily behind, hoping to make the southwest coast of Ireland, and have help, or at least, fresh water there, from their fellow-Romanists. Alas, for them! for now comes up from the Atlantic, gale on gale; and few of that hapless remnant reached the shores of Spain.

And where are Amyas and the *Vengeance* all this while?

At the fifty-seventh degree of latitude, the English fleet, finding themselves growing short of provision, and having been long since out of powder and ball, turned southward toward home. A few pinnaces are still sent onward to watch their course: and the English fleet, caught in the same storms which scattered the Spaniards, 'with great danger and industry reached Harwich port, and there provided themselves of victuals and ammunition,' in case the Spaniards should return; but there is no need for caution. The Armada is away on the other side of Scotland, and Amyas is following in its wake.

For when the Lord High Admiral determined to return, Amyas asked leave to follow the Spaniard; and asked too, of Sir John Hawkins, who happened to be at hand, such ammunition and provision as could be afforded to him, promising to repay the same like an honest man, out of his plunder if he lived, out of his estate if he died; after which, Amyas, calling his men together, reminded them once more of the story of the Rose of Torridge and Don Guzman de Soto, and then asked —

'Men of Bideford, will you follow me? There will be plunder for those who love plunder; revenge for those who love revenge; and for all of us (for we all love honour) the honour of having never left the chase as long as there was a Spanish flag in England's seas.'

And every soul on board replied that they would follow Sir Amyas Leigh around the world.'

It was now the sixteenth day of the chase. They had seen, the evening before, St David's Head, and then the Welsh coast round Milford Haven, looming out black and sharp before the blaze of the inland thunderstorm.

In vain, they had strained their eyes through the darkness, to catch, by the fitful glare of the flashes the tall masts of the Spaniard. Of one thing at least they were certain, that with the wind as it was, she could not have gone far to the westward; and to attempt to pass them again and go northward was more than she dare do.

Amyas paced the sloppy deck fretfully and fiercely. He knew that the Spaniard could not escape; but he cursed every moment that lingered between him and that one great revenge which blackened all his soul. The men sat sulkily about the deck and whistled for a wind; the sails flapped idly against the masts; and the ship rolled in the long troughs of the sea, till her yard-arm almost dipped left and right.

So the morning wore away, without a sign of living thing,

not even the passing gull; and the black melancholy of the heaven reflected itself in the black melancholy of Amyas. Was he to lose his prey after all? The thought made him shudder with rage and disappointment. It was intolerable. Anything but that.

'No, God!' he cried, 'let me but once feel this in his accursed heart, and then — strike me dead, if Thou wilt!'

'The Lord have mercy on us,' cried John Brimblecombe. 'What have you said?'

'What is that to you, sir? They are piping to dinner. Go down. I shall not come.'

And Jack went down, and talked in a half-terrified whisper of Amyas's ominous words. All thought that they portended some bad luck, except old Yeo.

'Here she is!' thundered Amyas from the deck; and in an instant all were scrambling up the hatchway as fast as the frantic rolling of the ship would let them.

Yes, there she was. The cloud had lifted suddenly and to the south a ragged bore of blue sky let a long stream of sunshine down on her tall masts and stately hull, as she lay rolling some four or five miles to the eastward; but as for land, none was to be seen.

The weary day wore on. The strip of blue sky was curtained over again, and all was dismal as before, though it grew sultrier every moment; and now and then a distant mutter shook the air to westward. Nothing could be done to lessen the distance between the ships, for the *Vengeance* had had all her boats carried away but one, and that was much too small to tow her; and while the men went down again to finish dinner, Amyas sharpened his sword, looking up every now and then suddenly at the Spaniard, as if to satisfy himself that it was not a vision which had vanished.

About two, Yeo came up to him.

'He is ours safely now, sir. The tide has been running to

the eastward for this two hours, and there comes the breeze.'

'And there the storm, too.'

And with that strangely accelerating pace which some storms seem to possess, the thunder, which had been growling slow and seldom far away, now rang peal on peal along the cloudy floor above their heads.

'Here comes the breeze. Round with the yards, or we shall be taken aback.'

The yards creaked round; the sea grew crisp around them; the hot air swept their cheeks, tightened every rope, filled every sail, bent her over. A cheer burst from the men as the helm went up, and they staggered away before the wind, right down upon the Spaniard, who lay still becalmed.

'There is more behind, Amyas,' said Cary. 'Shall we not shorten sail a little?'

'No. Hold on every stitch,' said Amyas. 'Give me the helm, man. Boatswain, pipe away to clear for fight.'

It was done, and in ten minutes the men were all at quarters, while the thunder rolled louder and louder overhead, and the breeze freshened fast.

'The dog has it now. There he goes!' said Cary.

'Right before the wind. He has no liking to face us.'

'He is running into the jaws of destruction,' said Yeo. 'An hour more will send him either right up the Channel, or smack on shore somewhere.'

After two hours more, the four miles had diminished to one, while the lightning flashed nearer and nearer as the storm came up; and from the vast mouth of a black cloud-arch poured so fierce a breeze that Amyas yielded unwillingly to hints, which were growing into open murmurs, and bade shorten sail.

On they rushed with scarcely lessened speed, the black arch following fast, curtained by one flat grey sheet of pouring rain, before which the water was boiling in a long white line; while every moment behind the watery veil, a keen blue spark leapt down into the sea, or darted zigzag through the rain.

'We shall have it now, and with a vengeance; this will try your tackle, master,' said Cary.

The functionary answered with a shrug, and turned up the collar of his rough frock, as the first drops flew stinging round his ears. Another minute and the squall burst full upon them, in rain, which cut like hail — hail which lashed the sea into froth, and wind which whirled off the heads of the surges, and swept the waters into one white seething waste. And above them, and behind them, and before them, the lightning leapt and ran, dazzling and blinding, while the deep roar of the thunder was changed to sharp ear-piercing cracks.

On they swept, gaining fast on the Spaniard.

'Call the men up, and to quarters; the rain will be over in ten minutes.'

Yeo ran forward to the gangway; and sprang back again, with a face white and wild —

'Land right ahead! Port your helm sir! for the love of God, port your helm!'

Amyas, with the strength of a bull, jammed the helm down, while Yeo shouted to the men below.

She swung round. The masts bent like whips, crack went the foresail like a cannon. What matter? Within two hundred yards of them was the Spaniard; in front of her and above her, a huge dark bank rose through the dense hail, and mingled with the clouds; and at its foot, plainer every moment, pillars and spouts of leaping foam.

'What is it, Mort? Hartland?'

'It might be anything for thirty miles.'

'Lundy!' said Yeo. 'The south end! I see the head of the Shutter in the breakers! Hard a-port yet, and get her close-hauled as you can, and the Lord may have mercy on us still! Look at the Spaniard!'

Yes, look at the Spaniard!

He, too, had seen his danger, and tried to broach-to. But his clumsy mass refused to obey the helm; he struggled a moment, half hid in foam; fell away again, and rushed upon his doom.

'Lost! Lost! Lost!' cried Amyas madly, and throwing up his hands, let go the tiller. Yeo caught it just in time.

'Sir, what are you at? We shall clear the rock yet.'

'Yes!' shouted Amyas in his frenzy; 'but he will not!'

Another minute. The galleon gave a sudden jar, and stopped. Then one long heave and bound, as if to free herself and then her bows lighted clean upon the Shutter.

An awful silence fell on every English soul. They heard not the roaring of wind and surge. They saw not the blinding flashes of the lightning; but they heard one long ear-piercing wail to every saint in Heaven rise from five hundred human throats; they saw the mighty ship heel over from the wind, and sweep headlong down the cataract of the race. Plunging her yards into the foam and showing her whole black side even to her keel, till she rolled clean over and vanished forever and ever.

'Shame!' cried Amyas, hurling his sword far into the sea, 'to lose my right, my right! when it was in my very grasp! Unmerciful!'

A crack which rent the sky, and made the granite ring and quiver; a bright world of flame and then a blank of utter darkness, against which stood out, glowing red-hot, every mast and sail, and rock, and Salvation Yeo as he stood just in front of Amyas, the tiller in his hand. All red-hot, transfigured into fire; and behind, the black, black night.

Strange Tales of the Coast

by

GEORGE GOLDSMITH-CARTER

'The Greate Storme'

The shores of Britain have always been noted for wild weather — indeed, Spanish sailors of long ago christened the Thames' approaches 'The Black Deeps', because they so feared the fierce winds and furious currents. Nevertheless, in all our long history of tempest and shipwreck, there has never been such a fearful night as that of 23rd November, 1703.

There had been a full gale blowing from the south-west for nearly ten days previously but, on the night in question, the wind suddenly changed to the north-north-west, where it swiftly increased in fury from a mere gale to a hurricane — and then to a living, bellowing wall of fury which sent men, women and children cowering to their cellars.

Nothing could withstand the insane force of that killer-wind. Thousands of houses and buildings were reduced to piles of rubble; tiles hurtled through the air with such velocity that they were afterwards found buried *eight inches deep in the earth;* tens of thousands of great trees were torn out by the roots; and hundreds of people were killed by flying debris. The Bishop of Bath and his wife were killed instantly in the Bishop's Palace at Wells, Somerset, when a great chimney crashed through the roof; *fifteen thousand* sheep were hurled into the River Severn and drowned as a result of the wind-force; and, so great was the general carnage, Queen Anne called the entire nation to prayer and fasting in order to appease the Wrath of God.

Yet, terrible as things were on land, they were infinitely worse at sea. A few days previous to the hurricane, the famous engineer Henry Winstanley had finished his new Eddystone Lighthouse, and had decided to spend a few days in it to test its strength. Before he went, Winstanley was heard to say that he hoped to be in his lighthouse 'In the greatest storme under the Face of Heaven', such was his confidence in his work. His presumptuous wish was granted in the most terrible manner for, the day after 'The Greate Storme', watchers from Plymouth were horrified to see the dangerous Eddystone rocks swept clean by the great, smoking seas; the lighthouse — together with Winstanley, his workmen and the lighthouse-keepers — had been smashed into oblivion. In the meantime, *whole fleets* of merchant ships and warships had been hurled to destruction, the bodies of *8,000 drowned seamen* being ulti-mately cast up along our beaches.

The worst scene of the entire catastrophe, however, was on the Goodwin Sands. A few days before the killer-wind had struck, Admiral Basil Beaumont's fleet of thirteen men o' war had just returned from the Mediterranean, and were at anchor between the mainland and the Goodwin Sands. The sudden fury of that awful wind ripped the fleet from its moorings and blew the ships either ashore on the mainland, or on to the deadly Goodwins. Three 70-gun ships — the *Mary*, *Stirling Castle* and *Restoration* — were driven on to the Goodwins and totally wrecked, with the loss of nearly 2,000 officers and men, including Admiral Beaumont.

Daylight dawned on 24th November, to reveal a fearful scene of death and disaster. Boatmen watching from Deal beach saw survivors from the three wrecks, racing madly up and down the sands, waving frantically for help before the returning tide swept them to death. The local men's boats were not seaworthy enough to face the enormous seas which were still running, so Simon Pritchard, leader of the boatmen, went to the Preventive Inspector with a request to be allowed to use the large and seaworthy Customs boats to snatch the pitiful survivors from the cruel sands before it became too late. The inhuman Customs official refused the request, however, saying that 'Her Majesty's boats are not for rescuing pressed scum, who would be better dead, anyway!'

Thomas Powell — the tough little Mayor of Deal — had other ideas about this matter, however. Taking the local boatmen in a body to the sheds where the big Customs boats were kept, he ordered them to break down the doors and launch off immediately, telling the protesting Customs officer, at the same time, that he, the Mayor, would assume full responsibility for the use of the boats.

Thanks to the determination of Thomas Powell, and the courage and magnificent seamanship of Simon Pritchard and his men, the shipwrecked sailors were snatched from the Goodwins just as the tide was about to carry them away.

So greatly did the townsfolk of Deal admire both Thomas Powell and Simon Pritchard, that their names have never been forgotten in the vicinity.

The Ghost Ship

A few years ago, lightshipmen aboard lightships stationed round the Goodwin Sands reported that strangely human cries were coming from the dreaded Goodwins. The source of these eerie sounds was never discovered; the incident was but one of many similar weird occurrences which, during the course of the centuries, have given this 10 by 4-mile grave-yard of ships and men the reputation of being a haunted area.

The Goodwins — which, in just over 500 years, are estimated to have swallowed some 50,000 human lives — abound in ghost stories; but undoubtedly the most uncanny of all is the story of the ghostly schooner *Lady Lovibond*, which was seen every fifty years, over a period of two centuries — in each instance on 13th February.

On this day, in the year 1748, the three-masted schooner *Lady Lovibond*, carrying general cargo for Oporto, and commanded by Captain Simon Read, sailed down the Thames and around the North Foreland. Captain Read was a very proud and happy man, for he had just married a young and lovely girl; his bride, together with her mother and a small party of friends, were aboard the schooner. As the fine vessel sped through the water, the captain's cabin was the scene of happiness and revelry as people toasted the happy couple. On deck, however, the scene was a different one, for the first mate, John Rivers, was pacing the planks like an angry tiger. The reason was a simple one — namely, that he had been a rival for the hand of the captain's lovely wife, and he boiled with jealous anger to hear the happy laughter coming from the cabin below. True, he had been best man at the wedding, but this in no way eased the bitterness of his thoughts.

Glancing away to eastward, where the great breakers of the Goodwins rolled in smoky thunder, John Rivers suddenly conceived a devilish plan. Casually drawing a heavy, club-like belaying pin from the rail, the mate walked softly up behind the man at the steering wheel and felled him to the deck with one crushing blow. As the helmsman rolled into the scuppers, Rivers seized the steering wheel and, with a mad laugh, drove the speeding schooner hard on to the wicked sands, which are as hard as rock at low tide.

The captain was too occupied with his bride and wedding guests to notice the sudden change of course and, with a terrible grinding crash, and the awful tumult of rending timbers and toppling masts, the once proud schooner broke her back. Listening to the terrified screams of the trapped people in the flooded cabin below, John Rivers threw back his head and laughed with crazy triumph. He knew that he would die, too, but what matter — his vengeance was complete!

It was late evening when this awful tragedy occurred and, at daybreak the next day, there was nothing to be seen of the *Lady Lovibond*, her passengers or her crew, for the Goodwins had engulfed them.

Later, at an official enquiry into the incident, John Rivers's sorrowing mother, giving evidence, admitted that she had heard her son say that he would get even with Simon Read, even if it cost him his life.

The tragedy was nearly forgotten, but, in the year 1798, on 13th February, Captain James Westlake, of the trading brig *Edenbridge*, had a strange and terrifying experience. While skirting the Goodwins at the exact spot where Rivers had driven the *Lady Lovibond* to her doom, he saw a three-masted schooner with all sails set driving down on his vessel at fantastic speed. Cursing the captain of the hurtling schooner as a madman, Westlake ran to the wheel of his brig, and he and the helmsman put the helm hard over just in time to avert collision. As the schooner sheered past, Westlake and his helmsman both heard the sound of revelry and laughter coming from the schooner's cabin. By this time the entire crew of the *Edenbridge* had rushed on deck and, to their horror, they saw the schooner strike the nearby Goodwins *and instantly vanish from sight*. This was no mere hallucination for, at a subsequent enquiry into the matter the crew of a fishing smack which had been nearby supported Captain Westlake's evidence, saying that they, too, had seen the schooner strike. They had lowered a boat as fast as they could to rescue survivors, but had had the unnerving experience of finding nothing but empty sand and sea.

Again the fearful incident was almost forgotten, until the day of 13th February, 1848, when Deal boatmen saw a schooner run aground on the identical spot where the *Lady Lovibond* had been lost. Launching their speedy sailing galleys to the rescue, the hardy boatmen were utterly confounded when they found — nothing! Again the frightening occurrence had been no mere hallucination, for the crew of a big American clippership, which had been passing near the spot, swore that they, too, had seen the schooner strike the sands and then vanish into thin air.

The last time the tragic phantom schooner was seen was on 13th February, 1898, when Deal boatmen again saw a three-masted vessel strike the fatal sands at the same ill-omened spot. Launching off at a speed for which they are still famous, the Deal boatmen again found nothing but the hard sand and empty sea.

The phantom of the *Lady Lovibond* has not been seen since that day, and the mystery of the ghostly schooner has remained unsolved. The Goodwins keep their secrets well.

Dogger Bank

On 5th March, 1883, a huge fleet of sailing trawlers, ranging from 40 to 80 tons burthen, and hailing from Hull, Grimsby, Yarmouth, Lowestoft and Colchester, lay becalmed off the northern extremity of the Dogger Bank. It was a place rich in fish, but very dangerous, for here, during northerly gales, huge seas burst in fury on the steep sides of the bank, creating a dangerous maelstrom which North Sea fishermen grimly named 'The Cemetery'.

Day had dawned with a leaden sky and, although there was no wind, an ugly surf was thundering across 'The Cemetery'. At 11 o'clock that night, the wind rose sufficiently to fill the sails of the becalmed smacks, giving them just enough speed to pull their cumbersome trawl nets along the bottom. Just before midnight, the light breeze increased with terrifying speed to a howling blizzard, which chopped the crests of the waves into flying spindrift and blotted everything from sight in a blinding mantle of whirling snow.

From mere gale force the north-east wind increased to hurricane force and, with stunning violence, it struck the huddle of unprepared fishing smacks, snapping their heavy trawl ropes like cotton threads and driving many of them into the frightful fury of 'The Cemetery'. The crews of those frail and tiny sailing craft had no chance whatever; men were swept headlong from the decks by giant masses of water topped with ghostly white surf, their cries unheard amid the roaring of wind and sea. Brother was torn from the side of brother, sons from the sides of their fathers and, incredible as it may seem, some lucky men were swept from the decks of sinking smacks on to the decks of craft which miraculously survived the dreadful carnage.

Other incredible things happened, too. One Grimsby smack, in spite of being ballasted by heavy stones, was rolled completely over by the giant seas, coming upright again with the stones, her catch and the wrecked ironwork of her keep all unbelievably mixed up — and not a single member of her crew harmed. Churned and tossed remorselessly in the cauldron of 'The Cemetery', smack after smack crammed on all the sail they could carry and vainly sought to sail clear of the smashing waves. All in vain, for many were smashed to matchwood by the fury of the waves, some being literally burst asunder by the weight of water which fell on them. Others were just sailed right under the water by their panic-stricken crews. The luckier ones wallowed off into the night, some dismasted, some with bare masts, and some with tiny storm sails set. In the terror of that raging night, one could not see, much less help, his neighbour. It was a case of every man and every ship for themselves.

Grey daylight brought no relief to the scene for, in those days, there was no radio to bring swift aid. As far as the eye could see, there was nothing in all the raging seas but wallowing, mastless hulks to which men grimly clung, the bottoms of upturned vessels, shattered spars and floating bodies. Some of the vessels just vanished without trace, but the fate of others has been recorded.

The 72-ton smack, *North Sea*, of the famous Red Cross Fleet, while sailing on the port tack, was seen to be hit by a huge sea which ripped out her masts and decking, leaving her to fill and sink within eight minutes. Only three of her crew were picked up.

The 72-ton smack *John Harker* of Grimsby, was seen with her sails ripped away, bulwarks and boat gone and her crew clinging to the sinking wreck shouting for help. Before help could be given, a driving snow-squall blotted the smack from sight and when it was gone, the *John Harker* had vanished.

The smack *Thomas and Florry*, her hatches stove-in, mizzen-mast and bulwarks ripped away, and 16 feet of her starboard side torn out, was abandoned by her crew. They were picked up from their sinking small boat in the nick of time by another smack, aptly named *Blessing*, then transferred to the smack *Energy*, of Grimsby, which eventually landed them at Hull on 8th March. Such were but a very few of the incidents which were observed. A great many of the trawlers were just driven away into the howling darkness never to reappear.

Day after day, damaged and undamaged trawlers sailed into the east-coast fishing ports, some crammed with survivors, some towing dismasted vessels. As the terrible extent of the disaster gradually became known, the fishing ports of the east coast were besieged by frantic women seeking amid the battered smacks for news of husbands, sons, brothers and sweethearts who had been out at sea.

After several weeks had passed, the appalling casualties of this one dreadful night became known. Forty-five trawlers had been lost in 'The Cemetery', some having been seen to sink, others just vanishing forever. Seven smacks had been abandoned by their crews, 38 had been badly damaged and 51 slightly damaged.

The total loss of life was truly shocking, for 255 men and boys had been drowned. Such was the effect of the disaster on many of the survivors, that they became shattered wrecks of their former robust selves, never daring to face the sea again.

A maritime disaster of such magnitude inevitably led to an official enquiry, which revealed that the majority of the smacks that had survived the fury of the Dogger Bank had been able to use their big trawl-nets as sea-anchors on which to ride out the fury of the sea and wind. Others had ridden out the hurricane-force wind on enormous lengths of stout rope attached to stockless anchors, which the crews had been

naged to drop clear of the fury of 'The Cemetery'. The majority
of the lost vessels had crammed on all sail in a desperate and
losing race to gain sea-room before they were overwhelmed.
Their crews had made the fatal blunder of imagining that
they could outsail the very elements and, in making the attempt, had driven their smacks clean under.

At the same time of the disaster, the famous 'Short Blue'*
fleet of smacks, sailing under the direction of senior skipper
Skinley, was working on the southern edge of the Dogger
Bank, and these smacks rode out the gale with very little
damage. This was, indeed, a remarkable fact that emphasised
the truly terrible reputation of 'The Cemetery'.

*So called from the short blue pennant these trawlers flew from the
masts. Each fleet in the days of the sailing trawlers flew their own
company flag.

The Wreck of the Indian Chief

Aided by a strong wind from the north-west, the 1,238-ton,
full-rigged ship *Indian Chief*, bound from Middlesbrough to
Yokohama with a general cargo, roared down the North Sea,
the foam boiling under the graceful forefoot. At 2.30 a.m. on
5th January, 1881, the look-out sighted the swinging rays of
the Kentish Knock light-vessel. Not long after this, the north-
west wind flew to the eastward, bringing icy, snow-laden rain
squalls — death in dreadful form to seventeen of the crew
of the *Indian Chief*, and an awful suffering to those who survived.

52

With the sudden and deadly change of wind, the deeply-laden ship began to drift down on to the Longsand, which lay hard-a-lee. The early morning was as black as the pit, and the eerily-piping wind as bitter as death. Although the helm of the ship was instantly altered, the mainbraces of the mainsail suddenly fouled and, in turn, caused the spanker-boom to catch the steering wheel, which made the great sailing ship strike the Longsand broadside on.

Captain Fraser, the ship's master, ordered a large red distress flare to be burned and rockets to be fired. Cheered by the answering rockets, which mounted from the Kentish Knock and Sunk lightships, the crew went to the shelter of the deckhouse, confident that the lifeboat would rescue them within a few hours.

The savage, icy day turned to night, while the *Indian Chief*, her sails now in tatters and drumming like devil's coach whips, slowly beat her life out on the uncaring sands. In the deck-house, the still-confident crew waited without warmth or hot food, not knowing that the Aldeburgh and Harwich lifeboats had been launched, only to be beaten back into the raging surf by the ferocity of the ice-laden easterly wind. However, as dawn broke, one of the crew gave a hoarse cry of hope and staggered across the already-breaking deck planks. Half-blinded by spray which froze to ice pellets as it struck, the rest of the drenched crew went to the rail. They saw a small ship backing and filling just below the boiling, smashing surf that was hammering their great ship to kindling. Putting her helm over, the little vessel vanished into the welter. With despairing groans, the crew of the wrecked ship tottered back into the miserable shelter of the deckhouse. They thought that the little craft they had seen so briefly had been the lifeboat, and that they had callously been left to die. Actually, the vessel had been a small sailing coaster whose master, realising his inability to effect a rescue, did the next best thing and, clapping on all the sail he dared to carry, headed at speed to Ramsgate to call out the lifeboat there.

Slowly the bitter day passed and, as the tide rose, it gave brutal strength and weight to the awful seas which were hammering at the wreck. At midnight the wind and sea eased a trifle but, as the old sailors say in all truth: 'An easterly wind has more lives than a cat.'

Red and cruel, the bitter sun rose in a sky unnaturally clear, bringing with it a vicious and snowladen gale, and seas more wicked than ever.

Suddenly, amid the awful sounds of rending timber and groaning masts, there was a shattering report, followed by a series of horrifying rumbles from the heart of the dying ship.

Captain Fraser looked at the faces of his crew, haggard in the greenish glow of that terrible dawn. 'She's broken her back, lads, and the pressure is blowing her decks out. We'd better try to launch the boats.'

Three boats were lowered; the first, with two men in it, was instantly engulfed by the roaring sea; the other two filled and sank immediately. The remainder of the crew fled back to the disintegrating deckhouse, while cruel green water, rolling unchecked from stem to stern, battered savagely at their frail shelter.

A five o'clock that afternoon there rose a giant sea, whose terrible might dwarfed all that had gone before. Roaring into smoking surf, it thundered like a watery avalanche across the vanishing ship, sweeping away the deckhouse and leaving nothing but a few uprights to which the half-drowned, frozen men clung with a death-grip. The once-proud *Indian Chief* was a dead ship now, the mainmast a tottering ruin, the gaping holds filled with lapping water, and great, black watery gulfs where the decks had blown out. 'Take to the mizzen-mast,' Captain Fraser told his men. 'When the mainmast falls, it will take the foremast with it!' Some men did not hear his orders in the roar of the wind and sea. They scrambled into the foremast rigging, and thereby saved themselves from a ghastly death. Seventeen men, already doomed but unaware of it, took to the mizzen top-mast while Captain Fraser and his young brother Howard, the second mate, lashed themselves securely to the lower part of the mizzen-mast.

Night came again, bringing no relief from the deadly wind which gnawed the frozen faces of the survivors like a savage dog and, at three o'clock in the morning, the ferocious sea struck its most awful blow. A seething mountain of water ripped away the mizzen topmast, to which seventeen men had pinned their only hope of survival, tossing it like a twig overboard, to dangle by its rigging in the smashing surf.

Too weak to free themselves, seventeen men kicked away their lives, drowning slowly in the great surges beneath the horrified eyes of their shipmates, who were lashed helplessly to the foremast. Below the jagged break of the mizzen-mast, Howard Fraser spoke comforting words to his elder brother, who stared mutely ahead through a mask of brine and ice.

Suddenly a survivor croaked in a wild voice: 'A light — a light!' Exposed to the vicious elements, men sometimes suffer from delusions — but this time it was no fantasy. The light was that of the paddle tug *Vulcan*, of Ramsgate, with the Ramsgate lifeboat *Bradford* in tow.

The sight of the sturdy *Vulcan* and the stalwart, life-jacketed figures in the wallowing, plunging *Bradford*, rising triumphantly from each watery valley of death, brought strength to the frozen limbs of the survivors. Somehow they cut themselves free from their lashing and, knotting a number of ropes together, they lashed the end to a piece of shattered timber, letting it drift down to the lifeboat. Soon, they were hauling back a massive hawser which meant all the difference between life and death.

Magnificent old Charles Fish, the giant coxswain of the

Bradford, pointed to a figure lashed to the splintered butt of the mizzen-mast — a figure which appeared to be making frantic but unavailing efforts to free itself. 'Help that man!' he thundered, in a voice which beat down even the raging of the wind and sea. 'No good...' came back the terrible cry. 'It's Captain Fraser... been dead for hours... we'll try to get his brother...!' *The awful shuddering and jarring of the wreck had imparted a macabre motion to Fraser's frozen corpse — movements so life-like that they had deceived even the hawk-eyes of Coxswain Fish.*

Somehow, the survivors managed to cut Howard Fraser from his last refuge against the sea. He was still alive but quite mad, crying like a child and struggling feebly as they took him from his dead brother's side. Gently the dedicated lifeboatmen laid him in the lifeboat's bottom, chafing his frozen limbs and trying to give him sips of rum. All in vain, for he died in half an hour. One by one, the survivors of the *Indian Chief* dropped into the tossing lifeboat, averting their eyes from the awful figure of their dead captain, his head crushed by a falling yard, his ice-rimed body lashed to the splintered mast, watching sightlessly for the help which came too late for him.

Even when the last survivor had been taken off, together with the captain's body, the danger was still fearful. The *Bradford* buried by the great seas which tumbled in smoking ruin across the Longsand, seemed in imminent danger of sinking. One survivor said afterwards that he was even more terrified in the lifeboat than he had been aboard the wreck, for it seemed quite impossible for the tiny, gallant craft to survive the terribly crippling weight of the monstrous seas.

Slowly, with her freight of half-drowned and frozen men, the *Bradford* was towed clear of the maelstrom by the labouring *Vulcan*, and back to Ramsgate. Watchers on the breakwater of Ramsgate Harbour marvelled when they saw the two rescue vessels enter safe water. The paint had literally been washed from the lifeboat, and the *Vulcan* was a near-wreck, both sponsons and half her wheelhouse gone.

One by one, the survivors of the *Indian Chief* were helped ashore and supported by Captain Brain, the Harbour Master, and members of his staff, they stumbled along the breakwater to shelter, warmth and food. Shivering with bowed heads and flaccid limbs, they were helped from sight — the pitiful flotsam of Britain's most awful shipwreck.

Author's Note. In 1947, while aboard the Trinity House Vessel *Ready* which was servicing the Longsand Head Buoy, an ancient, worm-eaten and barnacle-covered topmast and yard was pulled up in the mooring chain of the buoy. Was it part of the fatal mast which, seventy-nine years ago, carried seventeen men to a fearful death in this terrible shipwreck?

Jackdaw Baits the Trap

by

JOHN E. EDWARDS

'Deck below! Squadron's making off, sir!'

Perched high in the rigging of the sloop of war *Jackdaw*, Midshipman Peter Busby, fourteen years old and on his first war patrol, balanced his brass-bound telescope against a handy stay and took another anxious look across the blue-white, sunlit Caribbean Ocean. Three British frigates, the fighting backbone of the West Indies Station and the most powerful squadron afloat in those waters, were spreading enormous wings of white canvas and skimming away like giant gulls towards the distant horizon. From the signal yard of the leading frigate a tiny cluster of brilliant colours burst suddenly against the cobalt background of the tropical blue sky.

'Flagship's signalling, sir' Peter frantically pictured to himself the diagrammed pages of the signal book over which he had pored for hours during the last few months. 'Good luck,' he read off loudly. 'You'll need it!'

'Acknowledge that signal!' The voice of Lieutenant Thatcher, captain of the *Jackdaw*, sharply addressed a seaman from the quarterdeck. There was a swift rush of hoists and a red swallowtail climbed to the *Jackdaw*'s peak.

'Well, Mr Busby. What are you lying aloft like a dead cat on a yard for?' called Thatcher. 'Report to the deck in two seconds, or I'll take my sword and chase you three times round the world!'

Peter banged shut his telescope, scalded his hands in skidding down a stay and sprinted for the quarterdeck. Lieutenant Thatcher, tall, lean and darkly brooding, with hands clasped behind and head lowered in an habitual attitude of pessimism, awaited his arrival with impatience.

'So we're playing guessing games are we, Mr Busby?' said Thatcher, piercing eyes under thick, dark brows transfixing Peter as though he had committed some mortal sin. 'You wish me to hazard a guess as to what sail rig the squadron carried? Tempt me to a wager, perhaps, on what compass course the flagship's steering?'

'N-no, sir. 'Course not, sir.' Peter breathlessly hastened to complete his report. 'Squadron's settled to a nor'westerly course under full spread of sail.'

'Deserting us, you might say.' Thatcher sucked hollows in his cheeks and nodded gloomily. 'Abandoning us to the first powerful raider that slips from Cartagena harbour to blow us clear out of the water. You'd say that, now, wouldn't you, Mr Busby?'

'Abandoning us?' Peter gave a startled look towards the rapidly disappearing frigate group, now discernible only by the flash of sunlight on their white sails. To the southward, a purple smear on the horizon marked the Spanish fortress of Cartagena. In that moment, there seemed something ominous in the hiss of the trade wind about his ears and the shadows of the weather rigging swinging relentlessly back and forth over the deck. 'It — it would seem so, sir.'

The *Jackdaw* was a fifty ton sloop, an adapted merchantman; a good seaboat of small size and shallow draft, handy for dodging among the shoals and reefs of the Caribbean islands; a useful dogsbody to the West Indies Fleet, with four six-pounders and a crew of sixteen. But all the same a tiny force to be left on solitary guard against the guns and galleons concentrated in Cartagena harbour.

'And that would be your best estimate of our present situation?' Thatcher pressed him for an answer.

'I — I suppose it would, sir.'

'Aha!' said Thatcher abruptly. 'That's 'cos you're a fool, lad.' He gave his tricorne hat a thump to settle it more firmly on his head, hitched at his blue, knee-length coat and strode off across the quarterdeck.

Peter fell in beside him, vainly trying to match his steps, and settling finally for a trot that at least kept him abreast as Thatcher swung about at the port-side rail in a flurry of coat-tails and marched back across the quarterdeck.

'Now listen carefully, lad, and be swift with your answers. What's the reason for this squadron being at sea?'

Peter thought quickly. 'Attacks upon Spanish shipping — search and chase operations — destruction of Spanish raiders.'

'You do not have to remind me that England is at war with Spain,' said Thatcher testily. 'I myself have twice been sunk in frigates of the line, and endured months of imprisonment in stinking Spanish dungeons on the island of Cuba, before escaping with such useful information that my Lords of Admiralty were put to the painful embarrassment of recalling me to England and promoting me to my present command.' He checked at the starboard tail, twirled high on his toes and came down with a ringing crash of heels upon the deck. 'You'll tell me next it's May 3rd in the year 1710, and nigh on seven bells in the afternoon watch. Think again, Mr Busby!'

Peter jerked to a halt. Sturdily built for his age, with a stubborn jaw and a mop of copper-coloured hair tied behind with a black ribbon, he glared up at his captain with recklessly mutinous grey eyes. It was the same look he had given his own father when demanding to be allowed to join the British Navy. Peter's father, a prosperous Bristol merchant, had argued vainly against the hardships and dangers of the naval

60

service, then finally given way and procured him a berth as midshipman aboard the sloop of war *Jackdaw*, newly-commissioned at Portsmouth.

Peter's joy at realising his sea-going ambitions was somewhat dampened by his first meeting with Thatcher, a moody lieutenant of thirty-two, with neither family nor fortune, little hope of advancement, and an unfortunate reputation for being unlucky. Thatcher had been wearily amused by Peter's brand-new sea-chest, his much-prized telescope, and his most treasured keepsake, a captured Spanish flag given him by an Avonmouth captain, which he kept carefully stowed in waterproof wrappings. Nothing Thatcher said was ever hurtful or vicious; he was a good officer and the *Jackdaw* was a trim ship; but he had a discomfiting tongue that had more than once stirred Peter's temper.

'I am grateful for your efforts to teach me my duties,' said Peter angrily, 'but how can I be expected to know the contents of your secret sailing instructions?'

'Stop being so stiff, lad.' Thatcher stood over him, looking steadily down his long nose. But his voice was softer now, with a hint of approval in it. 'You're the nearest thing to an officer I possess aboard this lugger. Should I fall in the fighting, you must take command. Now tell me — what's the 'tween-deck buzz?'

Peter blinked. Like every vessel afloat, the *Jackdaw* was a hot-bed of sailors' gossip. But how on earth could the rumours of the lower deck be of any concern to her captain?

'There's — there's talk that we're hunting a renegade raider,' he began haltingly. 'Fast and heavily gunned — a ghost brig called *Sinbad*, impossible to capture.' He could feel his face crimsoning as he recounted these far-fetched scraps of seamen's yarns, but in response to Thatcher's grave nod he went on: 'Commanded by a bloodthirsty lunatic — bribed by Spanish gold to destroy English ships and ravage her colonies.'

'Quite right in every respect,' said Thatcher promptly. 'Let this be a lesson to you, lad. Forget your fancy notions about spies and ciphers and suchlike. My Lords Commissioners at Whitehall have been at great pains and much expense to discover what the *Jackdaw's* fo'c'sle could have told them for nothing.'

'You mean it's all true?' Peter's voice rose in astonishment.

'Every rum-soaked word of it. When war with Spain first broke out, most buccaneers and pirates in the Caribbean got letters of marque from one or other of the colonies' Governors, authorising them to loot Spanish shipping.' Thatcher's face hardened. 'Save for one — Jack Bendigo, master of the *Sinbad*, whose crimes were so foul and whose nature was so vicious that not even his fellow seawolves would run with him. After a year or two of lean pickings, with every man's hand against him, Bendigo quit these waters and took the *Sinbad* to Madagascar, where he terrorised the East India merchants — until a few months ago, when...'

'...when he returned to the Caribbean,' broke in Peter excitedly. 'But why did Bendigo come back?'

Thatcher shrugged. 'For gold, and the protection of Spanish bases from which to strike. Spain has bought herself a deadly weapon in Bendigo. He is mad for revenge against us. Already he has ravaged the colonies of the Windward Islands.'

'I still don't understand why —' Peter checked himself and looked southwards at the distant hump of Cartagena harbour towards which they were heading under light sail. 'Then Bendigo is lying at Cartagena,' he said in a rush of understanding. 'We've got him bottled up!'

'Not quite, Mr Busby.' Thatcher's voice was a silken purr. 'I am flattered by your confidence in my ability, but this lone sloop could hardly prevent Bendigo from breaking out of Cartagena whenever he had a mind to.'

'Then what are we doing here?' asked Peter. 'Why have the frigates gone off and left us alone?'

'To lay a trap for a ghost, of course.'

'Eh?' Peter stared at him with rounded eyes.

'They call *Sinbad* the ghost ship,' explained Thatcher, 'because she's so elusive — too speedy to be caught by heavy frigates, and too powerfully gunned to be fought by smaller vessels fast enough to catch her. Only thing left to do is to tempt Bendigo into a trap.'

'But the frigates will have been sighted from Cartagena's watchtowers,' said Peter.

'They will indeed, lad. Bendigo'll have seen them come, and watched them go away again.'

'Then he must know there's only the *Jackdaw* left to bar his way,' said Peter.

'Which will not strike Jack Bendigo as peculiar,' said Thatcher cynically, 'because he's profited all his rotten life from the Admiralty's patriotic notion that one British ship can do the work of a squadron.'

'But — but where's the trap?' asked Peter.

'That lies with the frigates, lad. Once their tops'ls have dipped below the horizon, they'll beat back to windward under cover of darkness and sweep inshore by first light. We've heard from friendly Indian tribes ashore that Bendigo's finished refitting and is now ready for sea. The Dons'll not pay him to sit in harbour. Besides which, Bendigo will leap at the chance of destroying a British sloop before the eyes of his Spanish paymasters.'

'Then Bendigo will bring out the *Sinbad*,' said Peter.

'On the flood tide at dawn tomorrow,' added Thatcher. 'And to make absolutely certain he does so...'

'We bait the trap with the *Jackdaw*?'

'But of course,' said Thatcher drily. 'What could be more dispensable than this tiny sloop and her miserable captain?'

'And when Bendigo comes to blow us out of the water,' said Peter, his spirits soaring at the prospect of action, 'the frigates will swoop down and batter him into submission.'

'While you and I are feeding the sharks in a welter of wreckage,' said Thatcher. 'Well done, Mr Busby. We'll make a Flag Officer of you yet — should you live so long!'

'It's a good plan,' said Peter, ignoring Thatcher's wry humour, 'but wouldn't it be even better if we stood in towards Cartagena and fired some challenging shots from our guns?'

Thatcher smiled and jerked his thumb forward. Peter glanced down the deck of the *Jackdaw* and saw to his surprise that the port-side forward six-pounder was already primed and about to be fired. The gun's-crew, burly, light-footed men, sun-bronzed and pigtailed, were scampering about with rope-tackles to take up the recoil. The lighted linstock, a long iron plated pike staff with a forked prong at the end which held a rope match soused in saltpetre, already glowed in the mastergunner's hand.

'Quartermaster, I'll trouble you for a touch of starboard helm!' Thatcher turned and called to the poop. 'Lightly now, or I'll have you flogged round the sloop!'

The *Jackdaw* was steered by the wheel, as was now becoming the fashion, instead of the cumbersome tiller. Peter saw white teeth flash in a nut-brown face as the grinning quartermaster showed his appreciation of Thatcher's blood-curdling threat. The wheel-spokes blurred and steadied, and the *Jackdaw's* bowsprit swung gracefully over a serene ocean only lightly troubled by the easterly trades.

'Fire when you bear on the town!' Thatcher shook his fist at the gun's crew. 'A guinea apiece if you knock down the bell tower — a fortnight's hard tack if you miss!'

Peter heard the men chuckle as they crouched around the breech of their gun. He clasped his hands firmly behind and stiffened his legs to ramrod straightness, determined to show no reaction to the explosion. Practice guns fired during their Atlantic crossing from England had caused him to jump involuntarily. Thatcher had gaily offered to wager that the first broadside fired in anger would send 'Mr Leapfrog Busby' clear across Jamaica. He would give him no second chance to display his irritating wit.

But a more urgent thought made Peter swallow nervously as he stood on the deck. He would soon be in the thick of his first sea-fight. Thatcher would be strictly honest in the report he would make about him. A moment's hesitancy, a hint of cowardice, and there would be no second chance for Peter to redeem himself.

He looked at the vast loneliness of blue ocean that lay behind the tiny *Jackdaw*, then at the threatening ridge of the enemy coastline that they were approaching. He wondered if all men felt like this, putting on an outward show of courage when inside they felt weak and helpless.

The gun muzzle swung steadily in answer to the sloop's movement, traversing tiny dots of palms clusters and the low, humped shapes of buildings, settling finally upon the barely visible walls of Cartagena harbour. There was a stab of red flame. The six-pounder leaped back madly against its tackles, bellowing like a monster. A cloud of grey smoke hazed the shuddering deck for a moment, then swirled away before the breeze. The iron ball hummed away like an angry hornet and battered a huge spray of water out of a wavetop, woefully short of the Spanish fort.

'Ah, well,' said Thatcher pleasantly. 'The thought was there, and that's what counts.'

But when an answering growl of iron thunder came back from Cartagena, and balls from heavy guns raised distant but menacing plumes from the sea between, Thatcher became brusque and business-like.

'Bendigo's snuffling at the bait, Mr Busby. We must flirt

with him a little closer. I shall stand by the helm. Kindly put a good man in the bow chains, take constant soundings and relay them back to me. These are shoal waters we are entering, and we'd look foolish stranded on a sandbank just now!'

While a huge, blood-red sun rainbowed the western ocean and threatened them with the imminent downrush of tropical darkness, the *Jackdaw*, under easy sail, threaded a tortuous course over the treacherous waters before Cartagena harbour. Peter stood by the bow-rail. Below him, feet braced in the leadsman's chains, a seaman was swinging the leadline in wide circles, casting it forward into the sea, then reading off the depths when the sloop's passage brought the leadline vertical beneath him.

'By the mark four!' called the leadsman.

Peter cupped his hands and called back the sounding to the poop deck. They were in dangerously shoal water already. Thatcher was looking anxious.

'And a half two!'

Peter chewed at his lip. An abrupt change of depth, and now only fifteen feet of water below them. He conjured up a frightful vision of the *Jackdaw*, her mainmast snapped by the force of a sudden grounding, sails and shrouds trailing down. The next sounding would be crucial...

A sudden jar shook the *Jackdaw* along her length. Planking groaned below. The sloop heeled sickeningly, jib and mainsail flapping like the wings of a wounded bird. Then, with an audible sucking sound and a flurry of brown water along her sides, she broke clear and righted herself again.

Remembering to look down and assure himself that the leadsman, cursing and spluttering and fighting to regain his foothold in the chains, was safe, Peter faced the poop and made a jubilant thumbs-up signal. Thatcher smiled grimly and stabbed a finger stubbornly forward.

The leadsman was changed at half-hourly intervals, but

Peter, determined to show Thatcher what he was made of, kept to his station through the curiously chill hours of a jet-black tropical night. They beat backwards and forwards beneath a weirdly glowing moon and a glazed sprinkling of stars. Now and then an ominous vibration went through the *Jackdaw* as she grazed a sandbank. With nothing to guide them but the hoarse chanting of depths from the bows, they flitted like a grey moth over strangely lead-like, sullen waters.

But their luck held good. When Peter, cramped and shivering at the bow-rail, saw the eastern sky shimmer into pale light, he cheered himself with the thought that in an hour or two, under the stimulus of blazing sun, he would fling himself into his first fighting action. Thatcher was a pessimist. They would cover themselves in glory. He could almost see the despatches now. He bit thankfully into the slice of cold beef and the ship's biscuit that a seaman thrust into his hand. It was then that day broke, and he saw that their luck had disastrously run out.

The whole sea-scape was shrouded in a clammy white mist. They could see little farther than their bowsprit. They were blind and helpless as a moth in a paper bag.

Thatcher appeared suddenly beside him, three-cornered hat askew, bony face drawn with dismay.

'A typical stroke of fortune, Mr Busby,' he said bitterly. 'It is not for nothing, you see, that I am called the Jonah of the West Indies Fleet. God, what a mess!'

Peter frowned at him in puzzlement. What other naval officer but Lieutenant Thatcher would express his feelings so openly before a midshipman? But then, Thatcher broke every rule of behaviour. He harangued and threatened his crew — and they loved him for it, and served him willingly and well. He had driven and lashed his only midshipman with a cutting tongue — yet Peter found himself admiring and liking the man, even now feeling a sort of sympathy for him. Not that he would dare express it, but a show of confidence might not come amiss. Particularly with Thatcher's career threatened with dishonourable extinction at the failure of their mission.

'I'm ready to obey your orders, sir,' he said quietly.

'Recalling me to my duty, are you?' growled Thatcher in miserable indignation. 'You misbegotten midshipman. Utter another word and I'll drop you over the side!'

Peter's own disappointment at the frustration of their plan now broke his self-control.

'But you can't have it both ways, sir,' he said heatedly. 'Last night you were fuming about this being a suicide mission — now you're in a rage because Bendigo can't come out and attack us.'

For a moment it seemed that he had gone too far. Thatcher whipped round. He thrust his face close to Peter's.

'What would you have me do, Mr Busby? Put about like a whipped cur? Make for the open sea, seek out the waiting frigates, pay my respects to the Commodore and tell him I cannot accomplish my task 'cos the weather's turned foul?'

'N-no, of course not.' Peter was horrified.

'Then what's the alternative?' rapped Thatcher.

'Stand in for the shore, regardless — I suppose,' said Peter doubtfully. 'Force Bendigo out and —'

He staggered as Thatcher fetched him a resounding thump on the shoulder.

'My own thoughts precisely! Well done, Mr Busby!' Like magic, his mood of depression was instantly transformed into delight. 'We're already steering for the harbour mouth, lad.' He bent over the bow-rail and spoke to the chanting leadsman. 'Stop that silly racket, or I'll cut your tongue out! Get back aboard, my man, and dry your feet.' He turned back to Peter. 'We'll be in the harbour channel directly. Keep a sharp lookout forward. Scream your head off if you sight anything.'

Stiffly erect at the sharp angle of the bow-rail, Peter searched the mist through which they were creeping. At any moment death might strike at them — out of roaring carronades from the fortress walls towards which they were blindly groping; or from the reeking gun muzzles of the *Sinbad*, if Bendigo, infuriated by the *Jackdaw's* insolent invitation to a duel, should even now quit harbour with a Spanish pilot and steal out through the mist to destroy them.

He jumped when a seaman clapped his shoulder and thrust a pistol and cutlass into his hands. Stuffing the pistol into his coat pocket and wrapping his fingers about the cold cutlass-grip, he became aware of the intense activity on the deck behind him. Bare feet padded the boards. Gun truckles grumbled as all four six-pounders were cleared for action. Wraith-like figures, looking more like witches on Hallowe'en than naval gunners, swung lighted linstocks in gentle arcs to keep them glowing in the clammy atmosphere.

A sudden sound ahead of them sent alarm signals racing through his body. Leaping to the top of the bow-rail, he balanced against a slanting fore-stay, forcing himself to listen through and beyond the subdued mutter of the seamen, the noisy slap of sea against the *Jackdaw's* side, the creak and groan of the sloop's gear. Then it came again — the sound of high, nasal voices thinly penetrating the muggy air.

Peter twisted like a cat and gave a low hail towards the poop. He heard Thatcher rap a command. Blocks screeched as fore- and main-sail were hoisted to their limits, scooping every ounce of thrust from the wayward breeze that was tormenting the mist into fantastic patterns. There was a shrill, musical chatter from the bows beneath him. The sloop leaned slightly and sharpened her speed.

'Craft dead ahead!' The words ripped out of Peter's throat when the prow of a strange vessel took shape in the mist. The *Jackdaw's* bowsprit lunged towards her enemy. Thatcher was going to ram!

Peter dropped to the deck and wrapped one arm about the teak rail, leaving his cutlass hand free. A sudden chorus of shouts told him that they had been sighted. A fore-and-aft rigged vessel, much of the *Jackdaw's* size, collapsed her main-sail in a panic and sheered away — but too late. With a crunch of shattered timber, the *Jackdaw's* bow sliced like an eagle's beak into her enemy's port quarter.

Peter's body slammed against the rail. The port-side six-pounders thundered together, stabbing red flame. There was a rattle of musket fire from the *Jackdaw* as the two ships, locked in a rending agony of splintering planks and snapping cordage, swung their lengths around. Men screamed shrilly and slumped upon the strange craft's deck in grotesque attitudes of death.

Perched high in the *Jackdaw's* bows, Peter found himself rail to rail with their adversary's raised stern. Blinking the powder-haze out of his eyes, he desperately parried a ringing cutlass stroke from a swarthy villain fighting with lunatic energy and mouthing curses at him. He recovered, feeling as though his wrist were broken, and slashed back in a frenzy. A gaping red line striped down the bearded face and it dropped out of his blurred vision like a nightmare.

Pain flamed through his arm as another steel blade, hacking through the powder-streaked air, clashed upon his cutlass and beat it out of his hand. Peter thumbed back the heavy hammer, of his pistol, jammed the muzzle against a heaving chest and jerked at the trigger. The man's mouth flung open in a sound-less cry, his eyes rolled whitely in his head and he fell across the rail like a sack.

The six-pounders roared again, and this time, with a grinding wrench, the two ships parted. Peter's last sight of their stricken foe was the huge red and gold banner of Spain that drooped and fell when the sea rushed in through her riven hull and she sank stern-first.

'Dammit, we've turned about!' Thatcher was glaring up at

his sail spread when Peter came on to the poop deck to make his report. The steep, triangular areas of canvas were bulging tautly to a breeze that came fresher now from the starboard side. 'Now where the devil's Cartagena got to? Astern of us, for a wager. Blast this confounded mist!'

Peter had hoped for some congratulatory word after their successful action. It was, after all, his first taste of sea-fighting. But their victory seemed to have landed them in an even more dangerous predicament. They were now completely lost. All the same, he did have something to report.

'That was a Spanish vessel,' he said. 'I spotted her colours.'

'I did not believe her to be a Barbary corsair,' replied Thatcher coldly.

'But she wasn't cleared for action,' went on Peter. 'Her guns didn't fire. I think she was a pilot boat leading something out of harbour.'

'Leading something...?' Thatcher's eyes lighted with a sudden idea. He whirled to the taffrail and peered astern through the clammy grey curtain of mist at which the eager fingers of the lifting breeze were already tearing. 'God save us, boy, you were right! Look there!'

Peter turned. Less than a cable's length astern, revealed by a movement in the mist and then instantly obscured again, he made out the tall, pale ghost of a ship gliding towards them.

'It's Bendigo, right enough,' cried Thatcher. 'He's bringing the *Sinbad* out after us. And here we are, turned wrong ways round in the harbour channel with no room to manoeuvre!' He dashed his hat against the taffrail in a burst of bitter anger. 'My luck holds good, you will observe, Mr Busby!'

But Peter had already left his side. Winged by a sudden inspiration, he rattled down the 'tween-decks companionway, grabbed a precious bundle out of his sea chest, and was back on the poop before Thatcher had finished cursing his misfortune. He ripped back the wrappings and wordlessly thrust before Thatcher's astonished face the gold and crimson folds of the Spanish flag that was his treasured keep-sake.

'You're mad, Mr Busby; It'd never work.' Thatcher's response was predictably pessimistic, and then his quick intelligence asserted itself. 'I don't know, though. The mist's thick enough. I reckon I can still recall some of my prison dungeon Spanish.'

Taking this for an order, Peter raced to the signal halyards, lowered the British colours and hauled to the *Jackdaw's* peak the billowing red and gold of Spain.

'Shorten sail and shut your mouths!' Thatcher's command was low but incisive. 'Steady as she goes, quartermaster. Keep by me, Mr Busby. This was your idea, as I recall. Should Bendigo mislike my Spanish accent and fire off his bow-chasers, then I shall have the consolation of dying in your company.'

'It — it would be an honour,' said Peter, half in retort and half meaning it. To his surprise, Thatcher gave a dry chuckle before clapping his tricorne hat firmly upon his lean head and stepping up to the taffrail.

'Amigos!' he yelled, muffling his voice with the flat of one hand held before his mouth, and addressing the looming outlines of the *Sinbad* in garbled Spanish. 'Follow us closely — make more speed!'

A hoarse voice from the *Sinbad* demanded to know what the devil was happening.

'British sloop — we sink her — clear water ahead,' shouted back Thatcher, and quietly to Peter. 'The *Sinbad* draws a fathom more of water than we do. Please God we skid over a sandbank and run the renegade aground!'

Peter gripped his arm. 'Look sir. The mist is clearing!'

It was true. The freshening breeze was shredding the vapours into nothing. To seaward was a glint of dazzling sunshine and a prospect of blue and white ocean.

72

'Oh my God, that's torn it! They'll sight us now.' Before Thatcher could hail the *Sinbad* again, a ragged chorus of howls broke from the brig. 'Luff her, quartermaster. Take all the wind you can get. We'll have to run for it, Mr Busby. I'll trouble you to take the waist.'

'Aye, aye, sir.' Peter leaped down to the deck and stationed himself amidships. He was now in command of the sloop's battery of six-pounders. Should dire necessity demand that they fight the *Sinbad* ship to ship, it would be his responsibility, while Thatcher manoeuvred the sloop, to maintain a disciplined and accurate fire from all guns that would bear on their target.

There was a great crash from the *Sinbad*, and jets of orange flame shot out from her bow'-chasers. Almost instantly, so close behind them was Bendigo's white mountain of canvas, the air seemed filled with a savage, hurtling sound. There was a thunderous shock amidships. Great slivers of wood were torn from the *Jackdaw's* sides and waterline. The deadly whine of splinters scythed across their topdeck. Peter winced and staggered, clapping a hand to the sear of pain like a sharp nail being dragged across his forehead. His limbs trembled with nausea, and he struggled to stay erect with blood streaming down his cheek.

'Hard-a-starboard!' yelled Thatcher from the poop. 'Wear ship!'

The *Jackdaw* flung across wind and scurried away on the port tack. Peter clenched his teeth. This manoeuvre of Thatcher's would lay them open to the scalding weight of the *Sinbad's* starboard broadside. He peered through a hail of spray and readied his own gun's-crews, fiercely resolved to give back what fire he could.

'Ready to go about! Port your helm — wait for it, man — now!'

With a squeal and snap of gear, the boom mainsail thundered

over and took the wind on the opposite tack. The *Jackdaw* spun and checked and then darted back across the *Sinbad's* black, thrusting bows. Peter shook his head. They were fluttering aimlessly about the ocean like a sparrow hunted by a hawk. Enlightenment came with Thatcher's next shout.

'Satan's curse on you! Show yourselves, dammit!' Arms outstretched, the captain of the *Jackdaw* was bitterly eyeing the sun-dazzled waters over which they sped. His voice rang out beseechingly. 'Sandbanks ahoy!'

So that was it. They were still in shoal water, with Bendigo in hot pursuit. Thatcher was trying to run the renegade brig aground. If ever a captain needed luck...

Peter lurched headlong to the deck as a jarring blow struck their bottom. The sloop heeled steeply. Planking groaned under an unbearable strain and her mainmast quivered like a bowstring. With a shriek and thunder of truckles, the port-side guns hurtled backwards down the tilting deck and battled like stampeding elephants against their restraining tackles. Thatcher had succeeded too well — they were stuck fast.

The next instant, a heavy salvo from the *Sinbad's* bowchasers, double-shotted for close range fighting, smashed along their sides. Giant spouts of water, brown-stained with sand, leaped into the air. A heavy ball punched into their stern. Blindly obeying the impulse to rally his gunners for a last despairing defiance, Peter staggered to his feet — and then pitched across a hatch coaming when the *Jackdaw*, levered off the clutching sandbank by the very shots that were aimed to sink her, skidded into clear water again and groped for the singing breeze.

Peter scrambled to the starboard rail and looked behind them. For one moment the *Sinbad*, her bows creaming majestically and her rigging dotted with triumphantly howling men, bore down on them like a fury. Then she struck the sandbank in their wake.

74

The force of the collision killed the *Sinbad* as a fighting ship.

She might have collided with a mountain. Main and fore-topmast, with yards and sails, broke off and tumbled down in a dreadful tangle. She lifted in a great rending of timber, and canted sideways to bury her lee-rail in a welter of broken water. Men dropped from her rigging like flies. The force with which she had hit the sand had killed the *Sinbad* as a fighting ship. Bendigo was beaten.

'I'll not have my deck cluttered up by blood-stained midshipmen. We're a sorry enough looking sight as it is!'

Peter became aware that Thatcher was standing beside him. 'Here, take this, Mr Busby, and make yourself presentable.'

Peter accepted the handkerchief that Thatcher held out to him and wiped his face.

'The frigates, by some quaint error in the Commodore's reckoning,' went on Thatcher, lightly sarcastic, 'are close to hand and even now bearing down to surround the *Sinbad* — as you will observe, Mr Busby, if you can bear to leave off prettying yourself for one moment and cast your eyes to starboard.'

Peter looked. The three frigates had returned as promised to close the trap, and were now backing sail to form a crescent of doom about the stricken renegade.

'It would seem that my fortunes have changed at last,' said Thatcher pleasantly. 'I wonder whether the Commodore will run aground before my very eyes — but perhaps that is asking too much.' He turned his gaze upon Peter. 'They will promote me for this, you know — give me a bigger command, I mean. You have done very well today Mr Busby. I should —' He struggled in a mixed mood of new-found confidence and unaccustomed shyness. 'I should take it very kindly if you would consent to accompany me.'

Peter grinned at him. 'I'd like that very much, sir.'

Thatcher gave a satisfied nod. Then he looked away, and his eyes hardened. 'The flagship's signalling us, Mr Busby.

Smartly with your telescope, now. Read what she has to say.'

Peter levelled his telescope at the flagship's signal yard, where a string of coloured bunting fluttered gaily against the sun-bleached, blue sky.

'Strike — your — colours — this — instant,' he read slowly. A moment's puzzlement, then he glanced up at the *Jackdaw's* peak, where the flamboyant banner of Spain still flew arrogantly to the breeze. He looked at Thatcher. 'Beg to report, sir, that we're sailing under the enemy's flag.'

'Indeed, indeed — I had quite forgotten. Make what reply you will, Mr Busby. Those are your colours, and I fancy it's your day.'

It took Peter some time to assemble the correct flags, but when he finally bent to the halyard and hoisted the bunting aloft, he was well satisfied with his answer.

'Trophy — of — war,' was the signal he sent.

Midshipman Peter Busby was not lowering his colours that day — not even for a Commodore.

The Pirates

from Captain Singleton

by

DANIEL DEFOE

I shipped myself, in an evil hour to be sure, on a voyage to Cadiz, in a ship called the —, and in the course of our voyage, being on the coast of Spain, was obliged to put into the Groyn, by a strong southwest wind.

Here I fell into company with some masters of mischief; and, among them, one, forwarder than the rest, began an intimate confidence with me, so that we called one another brothers, and communicated all our circumstances to one another. His name was Harris. This fellow came to me one morning, asking me if I would go on shore, and I agreed; so we got the captain's leave for the boat, and went together. When we were together, he asked me if I had a mind for an adventure that might make amends for all past misfortunes. I told him, yes, with all my heart; for I did not care where I went, having nothing to lose, and no one to leave behind me.

He then asked me if I would swear to be secret, and that, if I did not agree to what he proposed, I would nevertheless never betray him. I readily bound myself to that, upon the most solemn imprecations and curses that the devil and both of us could invent.

He told me, then, there was a brave fellow in the other ship, pointing to another English ship which rode in the harbour, who, in concert with some of the men, had resolved to mutiny the next morning, and run away with the ship; and that, if we could get strength enough among our ship's company, we might do the same. I liked the proposal very well, and he got eight of us to join with him, and he told us, that as soon as his friend had begun the work, and was master of the ship, we should be ready to do the like. This was his plot; and I, without the least hesitation, either at the villainy of the fact or the difficulty of performing it, came immediately into the wicked conspiracy, and so it went on among us; but we could not bring our part to perfection.

Accordingly, on the day appointed, his correspondent in the other ship, whose name was Wilmot, began the work, and, having seized the captain's mate and other officers, secured the ship, and gave the signal to us. We were but eleven in our ship, who were in the conspiracy, nor could we get any more that we could trust; so that, leaving the ship, we all took the boat, and went off to join the other.

Having thus left the ship I was in, we were entertained with a great deal of joy by Captain Wilmot and his new gang; and, being well prepared for all manner of roguery, bold, desperate (I mean myself), without the least checks of conscience for what I was entered upon, or for anything I might do, much less with any apprehension of what might be the consequence of it; I say, having thus embarked with this crew, which at last brought me to consort with the most famous pirates of the age, some of whom have ended their journals at the gallows, I think the giving an account of some of my other adventures may be an agreeable piece of story; and this I may venture to say beforehand, upon the word of a pirate, that I shall not be able to recollect the full, no, not by far, of the great variety which has formed one of the most reprobate schemes that ever man was capable to present to the world.

I that was, as I have hinted before, an original thief, and a pirate, even by inclination before, was now in my element, and never undertook anything in my life with more particular satisfaction.

Captain Wilmot (for so we are now to call him) being thus possessed of a ship, and in the manner as you have heard, it may be easily concluded he had nothing to do to stay in the port, or to wait either the attempts that might be made from the shore, or any change that might happen among his men. On the contrary, we weighed anchor the same tide, and stood out to sea, steering away for the Canaries. Our ship had twenty-two guns, but was able to carry thirty; and besides, as she was fitted out for a merchant-ship only, she was not furnished either with ammunition or small-arms sufficient for our design, or for the occasion we might have in case of a fight. So we put into Cadiz, that is to say, we came to an anchor in the bay; and the captain, and one whom we called young Captain Kidd, who was the gunner, landed, and some of the men who could best be trusted, among whom was my comrade Harris, who was made second mate, and myself, who was made a lieutenant. Some bales of English goods were proposed to be carried on shore with us for sale, but my comrade, who was a complete fellow at his business, proposed a better way for it; and having been in the town before, told us, in short, that he would buy what powder and bullet, small-arms, or anything else we wanted, on his own word, to be paid for when they came on board, in such English goods as we had there. This was much the best way, and accordingly he and the captain went on shore by themselves, and having made such a bargain as they found for their turn, came away again in two hours' time, and bringing only a butt of wine and five casks of brandy with them, we all went on board again.

The next morning two *barcos longos* came off to us, deeply laden, with five Spaniards on board them, for traffic. Our captain sold them good pennyworths, and they delivered us sixteen barrels of powder, twelve small rundlets of fine powder for our small-arms, sixty muskets, and twelve fuses for the officers; seventeen ton of cannon-ball, fifteen barrels of musket-bullets, with some swords and twenty good pair of pistols. Besides this, they brought thirteen butts of wine (for we, that were now all become gentlemen, scorned to drink the ship's beer), also sixteen puncheons of brandy, with twelve barrels of raisins and twenty chests of lemons; all which we paid for in English goods; and, over and above, the captain received six hundred pieces of eight in money. They would have come again, but we would stay no longer.

From hence we sailed to the Canaries, and from thence onward to the West Indies, where we committed some depredation upon the Spaniards for provisions, and took some prizes, but none of any great value, while I remained with them, which was not long at that time; for, having taken a Spanish sloop on the coast of Carthagena, my friend made a motion to me, that we should desire Captain Wilmot to put us into the sloop, with a proportion of arms and ammunition, and let us try what we could do; she being much fitter for our business than the great ship, and a better sailer. This he consented to, and we appointed our rendezvous at Tobago, making an agreement, that whatever was taken by either of our ships should be shared among the ship's company of both; all which we very punctually observed, and joined our ships again, about fifteen months after, at the island of Tobago, as above.

We cruised near two years in those seas, chiefly upon the Spaniards; not that we made any difficulty of taking English ships, or Dutch, or French, if they came in our way; and particularly, Captain Wilmot attacked a New England ship bound from the Madeiras to Jamaica, and another bound from New York to Barbados, with provisions; which last was a very happy supply to us. But the reason why we meddled as little with English vessels as we could, was, first, because, if they were ships of any force, we were sure of more resistance from them; and, secondly, because we found the English ships had less booty when taken, for the Spaniards generally had money on board, and that was what we best knew what to do with. Captain Wilmot was, indeed, more particularly cruel when he took any English vessel, that they might not too soon have advice of him in England; and so the men-of-war had orders to look out for him. But this part I bury in silence for the present.

We increased our stock in these two years considerably, having taken 60,000 pieces of eight in one vessel, and 100,000 in another; and being thus first grown rich, we resolved to be strong too, for we had taken a brigantine built at Virginia, an excellent sea-boat, and a good sailer, and able to carry twelve guns; and a large Spanish frigate-built ship, that sailed incomparably well also, and which afterwards, by the help of good carpenters, we fitted up to carry twenty-eight guns. And now we wanted more hands, so we put away for the Bay of Campeachy, not doubting we should ship as many men there as we pleased; and so we did.

Here we sold the sloop that I was in; and Captain Wilmot keeping his own ship, I took the command of the Spanish frigate as captain, and my comrade Harris as eldest lieutenant, and a bold enterprising fellow he was, as any the world afforded. One culverdine* was put into the brigantine, so that we were now three stout ships, wellmanned, and victualled for twelve months; for we had taken two or three sloops from New England and New York, laden with flour, peas, and barrelled beef and pork, going for Jamaica and Barbados; and for more beef we went on shore on the island of Cuba, where we killed as many black cattle as we pleased, though we had very little salt to cure them.

Out of all the prizes we took here we took their powder and

*a large cannon

bullet, their small-arms and cutlasses; and as for their men, we always took the surgeon and the carpenter, as persons who were of particular use to us upon many occasions; nor were they always unwilling to go with us, though for their own security, in case of accidents, they might easily pretend they were carried away by force.

We had one very merry fellow here, a Quaker, whose name was William Walters, whom we took out of a sloop bound from Pennsylvania to Barbados. He was a surgeon, and they called him doctor; but he was not employed in the sloop as a surgeon, but was going to Barbados to get a berth, as the sailors call it. However, he had all his surgeon's chests on board, and we made him go with us, and take all his implements with him. He was a comic fellow indeed, a man of very good solid sense, and an excellent surgeon; but, what was worth all, very good-humoured and pleasant in his conversation, and a bold, stout, brave fellow too, as any we had among us.

I found William, as I thought, not very averse to go along with us, and yet resolved to do it so that it might be apparent he was taken away by force, and to this purpose he comes to me. 'Friend,' says he, 'thou sayest I must go with thee, and it is not in my power to resist thee if I would; but I desire thou wilt oblige the master of the sloop which I am on board to certify under his hand, that I was taken away by force and against my will.' And this he said with so much satisfaction in his face, that I could not but understand him. 'Ay, ay,' says I, 'whether it be against your will or no, I'll make him and all the men give you a certificate of it, or I'll take them all along with us, and keep them till they do.' So I drew up a certificate myself, wherein I wrote that he was taken away by main force, as a prisoner, by a pirate ship; that they carried away his chest and instruments first, and then bound his hands behind him and forced him into their boat; and this was signed by the master and all his men.

Accordingly I fell a-swearing at him, and called to my men to tie his hands behind him, and so we put him into our boat and carried him away. When I had him on board, I called him to me. 'Now, friend,' says I, 'I have brought you away by force, it is true, but I am not of the opinion I have brought you away so much against your will as they imagine. Come,' says I, 'you will be a useful man to us, and you shall have very good usage among us.' So I unbound his hands, and first ordered all things that belonged to him to be restored to him, and our captain gave him a dram.

'Thou hast dealt friendly by me,' says he, 'and I will be plain with thee, whether I came willingly to thee or not. I shall make myself as useful to thee as I can, but thou knowest it is not my business to meddle when thou are to fight.' 'No, no,' says the captain, 'but you may meddle a little when we share the money.' 'Those things are useful to furnish a surgeon's chest,' says William, and smiled, 'but I shall be moderate.'

In short, William was a most agreeable companion; but he had the better of us in this part, that if we were taken we were sure to be hanged, and he was sure to escape; and he knew it well enough. But, in short, he was a sprightly fellow, and fitter to be captain than any of us. I shall have often an occasion to speak of him in the rest of the story.

Our cruising so long in these seas began now to be so well known, that not in England only, but in France and Spain, accounts had been made public of our adventures, and many stories told how we murdered the people in cold blood, tying them back to back, and throwing them into the sea; one half of which, however, was not true, though more was done than is fit to speak of here.

The consequence of this, however, was, that several English men-of-war were sent to the West Indies, and were particularly instructed to cruise in the Bay of Mexico, and the Gulf of

Florida, and among the Bahama islands, if possible, to attack us. We were not so ignorant of things as not to expect this, after so long a stay in that part of the world; but the first certain account we had of them was at Honduras, when a vessel coming in from Jamaica told us that two English men-of-war were coming directly from Jamaica thither in quest of us. We were indeed as it were embayed, and could not have made the least shift to have got off, if they had come directly to us; but, as it happened, somebody had informed them that we were in the Bay of Campeachy, and they went directly thither, by which we were not only free of them, but were so much to the windward of them, that they could not make any attempt upon us, though they had known we were there.

We took this advantage, and stood away for Carthagena, and from thence with great difficulty beat it up at a distance from under the shore for St Martha, till we came to the Dutch island of Curaçao, and from thence to the island of Tobago, which, as before, was our rendezvous; which, being a deserted, uninhabited island, we at the same time made use of for a retreat. Here the captain of the brigantine died, and Captain Harris, at that time my lieutenant, took the command of the brigantine.

Here we came to a resolution to go away to the coast of Brazil, and from thence to the Cape of Good Hope, and so for the East Indies; but Captain Harris, as I have said, being now captain of the brigantine, alleged that his ship was too small for so long a voyage, but that, if Captain Wilmot would consent, he would take the hazard of another cruise, and he would follow us in the first ship he could take. So we appointed our rendezvous to be at Madagascar, which was done by my recommendation of the place, and the plenty of provisions to be had there.

Accordingly, he went away from us in an evil hour; for, instead of taking a ship to follow us, he was taken, as I heard afterwards, by an English man-of-war, and being laid in irons, died of mere grief and anger before he came to England. His lieutenant, I have heard, was afterwards executed in England for a pirate; and this was the end of the man who first brought me into this unhappy trade.

We parted from Tobago three days after, bending our course for the coast of Brazil, but had not been at sea above twenty-four hours, when we were separated by a terrible storm, which held three days, with very little abatement or intermission. In this juncture Captain Wilmot happened, unluckily, to be on board my ship, to his great mortification; for we not only lost sight of his ship, but never saw her more till we came to Madagascar, where she was cast away. In short, after having in this tempest lost our fore-topmast, we were forced to put back to the isle of Tobago for shelter, and to repair our damage, which brought us all very near our destruction.

We were no sooner on shore here, and all very busy looking out for a piece of timber for a topmast, but we perceived standing in for the shore an English man-of-war of thirty-six guns. It was a great surprise to us indeed, because we were disabled so much; but, to our great good fortune, we lay pretty snug and close among the high rocks, and the man-of-war did not see us, but stood off again upon his cruise. So we only observed which way she went, and at night, leaving our work, resolved to stand off to sea, steering the contrary way from that which we observed she went; and this, we found, had the desired success, for we saw him no more. We had gotten an old mizzen-topmast on board, which made us a jury fore-topmast for the present; and so we stood away for the isle of Trinidad, where, though there were Spaniards on shore, yet we landed some men with our boat, and cut a very good piece of fir to make us a new topmast, which we got fitted up effectually; and also we got some cattle here to eke out our provisions; and calling a council of war among ourselves, we resolved to quit those seas for the present, and steer away for the coast of Brazil.

The first thing we attempted here was only getting fresh water, but we learnt that there lay the Portuguese fleet at the bay of All Saints, bound for Lisbon, ready to sail, and only waited for a fair wind. This made us lie by, wishing to see them put to sea, and accordingly as they were with or without convoy, to attack or avoid them.

It sprung up a fresh gale in the evening at S.W. by W., which, being fair for the Portugal fleet, and the weather pleasant and agreeable, we heard the signal given to unmoor, and running in under the island of Si—, we hauled our mainsail and foresail up in the brails, lowered the topsails upon the cap, and clewed them up, that we might lie as snug as we could, expecting their coming out, and the next morning saw the whole fleet come out accordingly, but not all to our satisfaction, for they consisted of twenty-six sail, and most of them ships of force, as well as burthen, both merchantmen and men-of-war; so, seeing there was no meddling, we lay still where we were also, till the fleet was out of sight, and then, stood off and on, in hopes of meeting with further purchase.

It was not long before we saw a sail, and immediately gave her chase; but she proved an excellent sailer, and, standing out to sea, we saw plainly she trusted to her heels — that is to say, to her sails. However, as we were a clean ship, we gained upon her, though slowly, and had we had a day before us, we should certainly have come up with her; but it grew dark apace, and in that case we knew we should lose sight of her.

Our merry Quaker, perceiving us to crowd still after her in the dark, wherein we could not see which way she went, came very dryly to me. 'Friend Singleton,' says he, 'dost thee know what we are a-doing?' Says I, 'Yes; why, we are chasing yon ship, are we not?' 'And how dost thou know that?' says he, very gravely still. 'Nay, that's true,' says I again; 'we cannot be sure.' 'Yes, friend,' says he, 'I think we may be sure that we are running away from her, not chasing her. I am afraid,' adds he, 'thou art turned Quaker, and hast resolved not to use the hand of power, or art a coward, and art flying from thy enemy.'

'What do you mean?' says I (I think I swore at him). 'What do you sneer at now? You have always one dry rub or another to give us.'

'Nay,' says he, 'it is plain enough the ship stood off to sea due east, on purpose to lose us, and thou mayest be sure her business does not lie that way; for what should she do at the coast of Africa in this latitude, which should be as far south as Congo or Angola? But as soon as it is dark, that we would lose sight of her, she will tack and stand away west again for the Brazil coast and for the bay, where thou knowest she was going before; and are we not, then, running away from her? I am greatly in hopes, friend,' says the dry, gibing creature, 'thou wilt turn Quaker, for I see thou art not for fighting.'

'Very well, William,' says I; 'then I shall make an excellent pirate.' However, William was in the right, and I apprehended what he meant immediately; and Captain Wilmot, who lay very sick in his cabin, overhearing us, understood him as well as I, and called out to me that William was right, and it was our best way to change our course, and stand away for the bay, where it was ten to one but we should snap her in the morning.

Accordingly we went about-ship, got our larboard tacks on board, set the top-gallant sails, and crowded for the bay of All Saints, where we came to an anchor early in the morning, just out of gunshot of the forts; we furled our sails with rope-yarns, that we might haul home the sheets without going up to loose them, and, lowering our main and foreyards, looked just as if we had lain there a good while.

In two hours afterwards we saw our game standing in for the bay with all the sail she could make, and she came innocently into our very mouths, for we lay still till we saw her almost within gunshot, when, our foremast gears being stretched fore and aft, we first ran up our yards, and then hauled home the top-sail sheets, the rope-yarns that furled them giving way of themselves; the sails were set in a few minutes; at the same time slipping our cable, we came upon her before she could get under way upon the other tack. They were so surprised that they made little or no resistance, but struck after the first broadside.

We were considering what to do with her, when William came to me. 'Hark thee, friend,' says he, 'thou hast made a fine piece of work of it now, hast thou not, to borrow thy neighbour's ship here just at thy neighbour's door, and never ask him leave? Now, dost thou not think there are some men-of-war in the port? Thou hast given them the alarm sufficiently; thou wilt have them upon thy back before night, depend upon it, to ask thee wherefore thou didst so.'

'Truly, William,' said I, 'for aught I know, that may be true; what, then, shall we do next?' Says he, 'Thou hast but two things to do: either to go in and take all the rest, or else get thee gone before they come out and take thee; for I see they are hoisting a topmast to yon great ship, in order to put to sea immediately, and they won't be long before they come to talk with thee, and what wilt thou say to them when they ask thee why thou borrowedst their ship without leave?'

As William said, so it was. We could see by our glasses they were all in a hurry, manning and fitting some sloops they had there, and a large man-of-war, and it was plain they would soon be with us. But we were not at a loss what to do; we found the ship we had taken was laden with nothing considerable for our purpose, except some cocoa, some sugar, and twenty barrels of flour; the rest of her cargo was hides; so we took out all we thought fit for our turn, and, among the rest, all her ammunition, great shot, and small-arms, and turned her off. We also took a cable and three anchors she had, which were for our purpose, and some of her sails. She had enough left just to carry her into port, and that was all.

Having done this, we stood on upon the Brazil coast, southward, till we came to the mouth of the river Janeiro. But as we had two days the wind blowing hard at S.E. and S.S.E., we were obliged to come to an anchor under a little island, and wait for a wind. In this time the Portuguese had, it seems, given notice over land to the governor there, that a pirate was upon the coast; so that, when we came in view of the port, we saw two men-of-war riding just without the bar, whereof one, we found, was getting under sail with all possible speed, having slipped her cable on purpose to speak with us; the other was not so forward, but was preparing to follow. In less than an hour they stood both fair after us, with all the sail they could make.

Had not the night come on, William's words had been made good; they would certainly have asked us the question what we did there, for we found the foremost ship gained upon us, especially upon one tack, for we plied away from them to windward; but in the dark losing sight of them, we resolved to change our course and stand away directly for sea, not doubting that we should lose them in the night.

Whether the Portuguese commander guessed we would do so or no, I know not; but in the morning when the daylight appeared, instead of having lost him, we found him in chase of us about a league astern; only, to our great good fortune, we could see but one of the two. However, this one was a great ship, carried six-and-forty guns, and an admirable sailer, as appeared by her outsailing us; for our ship was an excellent sailer too, as I have said before.

When I found this, I easily saw there was no remedy, but

we must engage; and as we knew we could expect no quarter from those scoundrels the Portuguese, a nation I had an original aversion to, I let Captain Wilmot know how it was. The captain, sick as he was, jumped up in the cabin, and would be led out upon the deck (for he was very weak) to see how it was. 'Well,' says he, 'we'll fight them!'

Our men were all in good heart before, but to see the captain so brisk, who had lain ill of a calenture ten or eleven days, gave them double courage, and they went all hands to work to make a clear ship and be ready. William, the Quaker, comes to me with a kind of a smile. 'Friend,' says he, 'what does yon ship follow us for?' 'Why,' says I, 'to fight us, you may be sure.' 'Well,' says he, 'and will he come up with us, dost think?' 'Yes,' said I, 'you see she will.' 'Why, then, friend,' says the dry wretch, 'why dost thou run from her still, when thou seest she will overtake thee? Will it be better for us to be overtaken farther off than here?' 'Much as one for that,' says I; 'why, what would you have us do?' 'Do!' says he; 'let us not give the poor man more trouble than needs must; let us stay for him and hear what he has to say to us.' 'He will talk to us in powder and ball,' said I. 'Very well, then,' says he, 'if that be his country language, we must talk to him in the same, must we not? or else how shall he understand us?' 'Very well, William,' says I, 'we understand you.' And the captain, as ill as he was, called to me, 'William's right again,' says he; 'as good here as a league farther.' So he gives a word of command, 'Haul up the mainsail; we'll shorten sail for him.'

Accordingly we shortened sail, and as we expected her upon our lee-side, we being then upon our starboard tack, brought eighteen of our guns to the larboard side, resolving to give him a broadside that should warn him. It was about half-an-hour before he came up with us, all which time we luffed up, that we might keep the wind of him, by which he was obliged to run up under our lee, as we designed him; when we got him upon our quarter, we edged down, and received the fire of five or six of his guns. By this time you may be sure all our hands were at their quarters, so we clapped our helm hard a-weather, let go the lee-braces of the maintop sail, and laid it a-back, and so our ship fell athwart the Portuguese ship's hawse; then we immediately poured in our broadside, raking them fore and aft, and killed them a great many men.

The Portuguese, we could see, were in the utmost confusion; and not being aware of our design, their ship having fresh way, ran their bowsprit into the fore part of our main shrouds, as that they could not easily get clear of us, and so we lay locked after that manner. The enemy could not bring above five or six guns, besides their small-arms, to bear upon us, while we played our whole broadside upon him.

In the middle of the heat of this fight, as I was very busy upon the quarter-deck, the captain calls to me, for he never stirred from us, 'What the devil is friend William a-doing yonder?' says the captain; 'has he any business upon deck?' I stepped forward, and there was friend William, with two or three stout fellows, lashing the ship's bowsprit fast to our main-mast, for fear they should get away from us; and every now and then he pulled a bottle out of his pocket, and gave the men a dram to encourage them. The shot flew about his ears as thick as may be supposed in such an action, where the Portuguese, to give them their due, fought very briskly, believing at first they were sure of their game, and trusting to their superiority; but there was William, as composed, and in as perfect tranquillity as to danger, as if he had been over a bowl of punch, only very busy securing the matter, that a ship of forty-six guns should not run away from a ship of eight-and-twenty.

This work was too hot to hold long; our men behaved bravely: our gunner, a gallant man, shouted below, pouring in his shot at such a rate, that the Portuguese began to slacken

The Portuguese ran their bowsprit into our main shrouds.

their fire; we had dismounted several of their guns by firing in at their forecastle, and raking them, as I said, fore and aft. Presently comes William up to me. 'Friend,' says he, very calmly, 'what dost thou mean? Why dost thou not visit thy neighbour in the ship, the door being open for thee?' I understood him immediately, for our guns had so torn their hull, that we had beat two portholes into one, and the bulk-head of their steerage was split to pieces, so that they could not retire to their close quarters; so I gave the word immediately to board them. Our second lieutenant, with about thirty men, entered in an instant over the forecastle, followed by some more with the boatswain, and cutting in pieces about twenty-five men that they found upon the deck, and then throwing some grenadoes into the steerage, they entered there also; upon which the Portuguese cried quarter presently, and we mastered the ship, contrary indeed to our own expectation; for we would have compounded with them if they would have sheered off: but laying them athwart the hawse at first, and following our fire furiously, without giving them any time to get clear of us and work their ship; by this means, though they had six-and-forty guns, they were not able to fight above five or six, as I said above, for we beat them immediately from their guns in the forecastle, and killed them abundance of men between decks, so that when we entered they had hardly found men enough to fight us hand to hand upon their deck.

The surprise of joy to hear the Portuguese cry quarter, and see their ancient struck, was so great to our captain, who, as I have said, was reduced very weak with a high fever, that it gave him new life. Nature conquered the distemper, and the fever abated that very night; so that in two or three days he was sensibly better, his strength began to come, and he was able to give his orders effectually in everything that was material, and in about ten days was entirely well and about the ship.

In the meantime I took possession of the Portuguese man-of-war; and Captain Wilmot made me, or rather I made myself, captain of her for the present. About thirty of their seamen took service with us, some of which were French, some Genoese; and we set the rest on shore the next day on a little island on the coast of Brazil, except some wounded men, who were not in a condition to be removed, and whom we were bound to keep on board; but we had an occasion afterwards to dispose of them at the Cape, where, at their own request, we set them on shore.

Captain Sharkey:

How the Governor
of Saint Kitt's Came Home

by
SIR ARTHUR CONAN DOYLE

When the great wars of the Spanish Succession had been brought to an end by the Treaty of Utrecht, the vast number of privateers which had been fitted out by the contending parties found their occupation gone. Some took to the more peaceful but less lucrative ways of ordinary commerce, others were absorbed into the fishing-fleets, and a few of the more reckless hoisted the Jolly Roger at the mizzen and the bloody flag at the main, declaring a private war upon their own account against the whole human race.

With mixed crews, recruited from every nation, they scoured the seas, disappearing occasionally to careen in some lonely inlet, or putting in for a debauch at some outlying port, where they dazzled the inhabitants by their lavishness and horrified them by their brutalities.

On the Coromandel Coast, at Madagascar, in the African waters, and above all in the West Indian and American seas, the pirates were a constant menace. With an insolent luxury they would regulate their depredations by the comfort of the seasons, harrying New England in the summer and dropping south again to the tropical islands in the winter.

They were the more to be dreaded because they had none of that discipline and restraint which made their predecessors, the Buccaneers, both formidable and respectable. These Ishmaels of the sea rendered an account to no man, and treated their prisoners according to the drunken whim of the moment. Flashes of grotesque generosity alternated with longer stretches of inconceivable ferocity, and the skipper who fell into their hands might find himself dismissed with his cargo, after serving as boon companion in some hideous debauch, or might sit at his cabin table with his own nose and his lips served up with pepper and salt in front of him. It took a stout seaman in those days to ply his calling in the Caribbean Gulf.

Such a man was Captain John Scarrow, of the ship *Morning Star*, and yet he breathed a long sigh of relief when he heard the splash of the falling anchor and swung at his moorings within a hundred yards of the guns of the citadel of Basseterre. St Kitt's was his final port of call, and early next morning his bowsprit would be pointed for Old England. He had had enough of those robber-haunted seas. Ever since he had left Maracaibo upon the Main, with his full lading of sugar and red pepper, he had winced at every topsail which glimmered over the violet edge of the tropical sea. He had coasted up the Windward Islands, touching here and there, and assailed continually by stories of villainy and outrage.

Captain Sharkey, of the 20-gun pirate barque, *Happy Delivery*, had passed down the coast, and had littered it with gutted vessels and with murdered men. Dreadful anecdotes were current of his grim pleasantries and of his inflexible ferocity. From the Bahamas to the Main his coal-black barque, with the ambiguous name, had been freighted with death and many things which are worse than death. So nervous was Captain

Scarrow, with his new full-rigged ship and her full and valuable lading, that he struck out to the west as far as Bird's Island to be out of the usual track of commerce. And yet even in those solitary waters he had been unable to shake off sinister traces of Captain Sharkey.

One morning they had raised a single skiff adrift upon the face of the ocean. Its only occupant was a delirious seaman, who yelled hoarsely as they hoisted him aboard, and showed a dried-up tongue like a black and wrinkled fungus at the back of his mouth. Water and nursing soon transformed him into the strongest and smartest sailor on the ship. He was from Marblehead, in New England, it seemed, and was the sole survivor of a schooner which had been scuttled by the dreadful Sharkey.

For a week Hiram Evanson, for that was his name, had been adrift beneath a tropical sun. Sharkey had ordered the mangled remains of his late captain to be thrown into the boat, 'as provisions for the voyage,' but the seaman had at once committed them to the deep, lest the temptation should be more than he could bear. He had lived upon his own huge frame, until, at the last moment, the *Morning Star* had found him in that madness which is the precursor of such a death. It was no bad find for Captain Scarrow, for, with a short-handed crew, such a seaman as this big New Englander was a prize worth having. He vowed that he was the only man whom Captain Sharkey had ever placed under an obligation.

Now that they lay under the guns of Basseterre, all danger from the pirate was at an end, and yet the thought of him lay heavily upon the seaman's mind as he watched the agent's boat shooting out from the custom-house quay.

'I'll lay you a wager, Morgan,' said he to the first mate, 'that the agent will speak of Sharkey in the first hundred words that pass his lips.'

'Well, captain, I'll have you a silver dollar, and chance it,' said the rough old Bristol man beside him.

The negro rowers shot the boat alongside, and the linen-clad steersman sprang up the ladder.

'Welcome, Captain Scarrow!' he cried. 'Have you heard about Sharkey?'

The captain grinned at the mate.

'What devilry has he been up to now?' he asked.

'Devilry! You've not heard, then! Why, we've got him safe under lock and key here at Basseterre. He was tried last Wednesday, and he is to be hanged tomorrow morning.'

Captain and mate gave a shout of joy, which an instant later was taken up by the crew. Discipline was forgotten as they scrambled up through the break of the poop to hear the news. The New Englander was in the front of them with a radiant face turned up to heaven, for he came of the Puritan stock.

'Sharkey to be hanged!' he cried. 'You don't know, Master Agent, if they lack a hangman, do you?'

'Stand back!' cried the mate, whose outraged sense of discipline was even stronger than his interest at the news. 'I'll pay that dollar, Captain Scarrow, with the lightest heart that ever I paid a wager yet. How came the villain to be taken?'

'Why, as to that, he became more than his own comrades could abide, and they took such a horror of him that they would not have him on the ship. So they marooned him upon the Little Mangles to the south of the Mysteriosa Bank, and there he was found by a Portobello trader, who brought him in. There was talk of sending him to Jamaica to be tried, but our good little governor, Sir Charles Ewan, would not hear of it. "He's my meat," said he, "and I claim the cooking of it." If you can stay till tomorrow morning at ten, you'll see the joint swinging.'

'I wish I could,' said the captain, wistfully, 'but I am sadly behind time now. I should start with the evening tide.'

'That you can't do,' said the agent with decision. 'The Governor is going back with you.'

'The Governor!'

'Yes. He's had a dispatch from Government to return without delay. The fly-boat that brought it has gone on to Virginia. So Sir Charles has been waiting for you, as I told him you were due before the rains.'

'Well, well!' cried the captain, in some perplexity, 'I'm a plain seaman, and I don't know much of governors and baronets and their ways. I don't remember that I ever so much as spoke to one. But if it's in King George's service, and he asks a cast in the *Morning Star* as far as London, I'll do what I can for him. There's my own cabin he can have and welcome. As to the cooking, it's lobscouse and salmagundy six days in the week; but he can bring his own cook aboard with him if he thinks our galley too rough for his taste.'

'You need not trouble your mind, Captain Scarrow,' said the agent. 'Sir Charles is in weak health just now, only clear of a quartan ague, and it is likely he will keep his cabin most of the voyage. Dr Larousse said that he would have sunk had the hanging of Sharkey not put fresh life into him. He has a great spirit in him, though, and you must not blame him if he is somewhat short in his speech.'

'He may say what he likes and do what he likes so long as he does not come athwart my hawse when I am working the ship,' said the captain. 'He is Governor of St Kitt's, but I am Governor of the *Morning Star*. And, by his leave, I must weigh with the first tide, for I owe a duty to my employer, just as he does to King George.'

'He can scarce be ready tonight, for he has many things to set in order before he leaves.'

'The early morning tide, then.'

'Very good. I shall send his things aboard tonight, and he will follow them to-morrow early if I can prevail upon him to leave St Kitt's without seeing Sharkey do the rogue's hornpipe. His own orders were instant, so it may be that he will come at once. It is likely that Dr Larousse may attend him upon the journey.'

Left to themselves, the captain and mate made the best preparations which they could for their illustrious passenger. The largest cabin was turned out and adorned in his honour, and orders were given by which barrels of fruit and some cases of wine should be brought off to vary the plain food of an ocean-going trader. In the evening the Governor's baggage began to arrive — great ironbound ant-proof trunks, and official tin packing-cases, with other strange-shaped packages, which suggested the cocked hat or the sword within. And then there came a note, with a heraldic device upon the big red seal, to say that Sir Charles Ewan made his compliments to Captain Scarrow, and that he hoped to be with him in the morning as early as his duties and his infirmities would permit.

He was as good as his word, for the first grey of dawn had hardly begun to deepen into pink when he was brought alongside, and climbed with some difficulty up the ladder. The captain had heard that the Governor was an eccentric, but he was hardly prepared for the curious figure who came limping feebly down his quarterdeck, his steps supported by a thick bamboo cane. He wore a Ramillies wig, all twisted into little tails like a poodle's coat, and cut so low across the brow that the large green glasses which covered his eyes looked as if they were hung from it. A fierce beak of a nose, very long and very thin, cut the air in front of him. His ague had caused him to swathe his throat and chin with a broad linen cravat, and he wore a loose damask powdering-gown secured by a cord round the waist. As he advanced he carried his masterful nose high in the air, but his head turned slowly from side to side in the helpless manner of the purblind, and he called in a high, querulous voice for the captain.

'You have my things?' he asked.

'Yes, Sir Charles,'

'Have you wine aboard?'

'I have ordered five cases, sir?'

'And tobacco?'

'There is a keg of Trinidad.'

'You play a hand at piquet?'

'Passably well, sir.'

'Then up anchor, and to sea!'

There was a fresh westerly wind, so by the time the sun was fairly through the morning haze, the ship was hull down from the islands. The decrepit Governor still limped the deck, with one guiding hand upon the quarter-rail.

'You are on Government service now, captain,' said he. 'They are counting the days till I come to Westminster, I promise you. Have you all that she will carry?'

'Every inch, Sir Charles?'

'Keep her so if you blow the sails out of her. I fear, Captain Scarrow, that you will find a blind and broken man a poor companion for your voyage.'

'I am honoured in enjoying your Excellency's society,' said the captain. 'But I am sorry that your eyes should be so afflicted.'

'Yes, indeed. It is the cursed glare of the sun on the white streets of Basseterre which has gone far to burn them out.'

'I had heard also that you had been plagued by a quartan ague.'

'Yes; I have had a pyrexy, which has reduced me much.'

'We had set aside a cabin for your surgeon.'

'Ah, the rascal! There was no budging him, for he has a snug business amongst the merchants. But hark!'

He raised his ring-covered hand in the air. From far astern there came the low deep thunder of cannon.

'It is from the island!' cried the captain in astonishment. Can it be a signal for us to put back?'

The Governor laughed.

'You have heard that Sharkey, the pirate, is to be hanged this morning. I ordered the batteries to salute when the rascal was kicking his last, so that I might know of it out at sea. There's an end of Sharkey!'

'There's an end of Sharkey!' cried the captain; and the crew took up the cry as they gathered in little knots upon the deck and stared back at the low, purple line of the vanishing land.

It was a cheering omen for their start across the Western Ocean, and the invalid Governor found himself a popular man on board, for it was generally understood that but for his insistence upon an immediate trial and sentence, the villain might have played upon some more venal judge and so escaped. At dinner that day Sir Charles gave many anecdotes of the deceased pirate; and so affable was he, and so skilful in adapting his conversation to men of lower degree, that captain, mate, and Governor smoked their long pipes and drank their claret as three good comrades should.

'And what figure did Sharkey cut in the dock?' asked the captain.

'He is a man of some presence,' said the Governor.

'I had always understood that he was an ugly, sneering devil,' remarked the mate.

'Well, I dare say he could look ugly upon occasions,' said the Governor.

'I have heard a New Bedford whaleman say that he could not forget his eyes,' said Captain Scarrow. 'They were of the lightest filmy blue, with red-rimmed lids. Was that not so, Sir Charles?'

'Alas, my own eyes will not permit me to know much of those of others! But I remember now that the Adjutant-General said that he had such an eye as you describe, and added that the jury were so foolish as to be visibly discomposed when it was turned upon them. It is well for them that he is dead, for he was a man who would never forget an injury, and if he had laid hands upon any one of them he would have stuffed him with straw and hung him for a figure-head.'

The idea seemed to amuse the Governor, for he broke suddenly into a high, neighing laugh, and the two seamen laughed also, but not so heartily, for they remembered that Sharkey was not the last pirate who sailed the western seas, and that as grotesque a fate might come to be their own. Another bottle was broached to drink to a pleasant voyage, and the Governor would drink just one other on the top of it, so that the seamen were glad at last to stagger off — the one to his watch and the other to his bunk. But when after his four hours' spell the mate came down again, he was amazed to see the Governor in his Ramillies wig, his glasses, and his powdering-gown still seated sedately at the lonely table with his reeking pipe and six black bottles by his side.

'I have drunk with the Governor of St Kitt's when he was sick,' said he, 'and God forbid that I should ever try to keep pace with him when he is well.'

The voyage of the *Morning Star* was a successful one, and in about three weeks she was at the mouth of the British Channel. From the first day the infirm Governor had begun to recover his strength, and before they were half-way across the Atlantic he was, save only for his eyes, as well as any man upon the ship. Those who uphold the nourishing qualities of wine might point to him in triumph, for never a night passed that he did not repeat the performance of his first one. And yet he would be out upon deck in the early morning as fresh and brisk as the best of them, peering about with his weak eyes, and asking questions about the sails and the rigging, for he was anxious to learn the ways of the sea. And he made up for the deficiency of his eyes by obtaining leave from the captain that the New

England seaman — he who had been cast away in the boat — should lead him about, and above all that he should sit beside him when he played cards and count the number of the pips, for unaided he could not tell the king from the knave.

It was natural that this Evanson should do the Governor willing service, since the one was the victim of the vile Sharkey, and the other was his avenger. One could see that it was a pleasure to the big American to lend his arm to the invalid, and at night he would stand with all respect behind his chair in the cabin and lay his great stubnailed forefinger upon the card which he should play. Between them there was little in the pockets either of Captain Scarrow or of Morgan, the first mate, by the time they sighted the Lizard.

And it was not long before they found that all they had heard of the high temper of Sir Charles Ewan fell short of the mark. At a sign of opposition or a word of argument his chin would shoot out from his cravat, his masterful nose would be cocked at a higher and more insolent angle, and his bamboo cane would whistle up over his shoulder. He cracked it once over the head of the carpenter when the man had accidentally jostled him upon the deck. Once, too, when there was some grumbling and talk of a mutiny over the state of the provisions, he was of opinion that they should not wait for the dogs to rise, but that they should march forward and set upon them until they had trounced the devilment out of them.

'Give me a knife and a bucket!' he cried with an oath, and could hardly be withheld from setting forth alone to deal with the spokesman of the seamen.

Captain Scarrow had to remind him that though he might be only answerable to himself at St Kitt's, killing became murder upon the high seas. In politics he was, as became his official position, a stout prop of the House of Hanover, and he swore in his cups that he had never met a Jacobite without pistolling him where he stood. Yet for all his vapouring and his violence he was so good a companion, with such a stream of strange anecdote and reminiscence, that Scarrow and Morgan had never known a voyage pass so pleasantly.

And then at length came the last day, when, after passing the island, they had struck land again at the high white cliffs at Beachy Head. As evening fell the ship lay rolling in an oily calm, a league off from Winchelsea, with the long dark snout of Dungeness jutting out in front of her. Next morning they would pick up their pilot at the Foreland, and Sir Charles might meet the king's ministers at Westminster before the evening. The boatswain had the watch, and the three friends were met for a last turn of cards in the cabin, the faithful American still serving as eyes to the Governor. There was a good stake upon the table, for the sailors had tried on this last night to win their losses back from their passenger. Suddenly he threw his cards down, and swept all the money into the pocket of his long-flapped silken waistcoat.

'The game's mine!' said he.

'Heh, Sir Charles, not so fast!' cried Captain Scarrow; 'you have not played out the hand, and we are not the losers.'

'Sink you for a liar!' said the Governor. 'I tell you that I have played out the hand, and that you are a loser.' He whipped off his wig and his glasses as he spoke, and there was a high, bald forehead, and a pair of shifty blue eyes with the red rims of a bull terrier.

'Good God!' cried the mate. 'It's Sharkey!'

The two sailors sprang from their seats, but the big American castaway had put his huge back against the cabin door, and he held a pistol in each of his hands. The passenger had also laid a pistol upon the scattered cards in front of him, and he burst into his high, neighing laugh.

'Captain Sharkey is the name, gentlemen,' said he, 'and this is Roaring Ned Galloway, the quartermaster of the *Happy Delivery*. We made it hot, and so they marooned us: me on

'Heh, Sir Charles, not so fast! You have not played out the hand.'

a dry Tortuga cay, and him in an oarless boat. You dogs — you poor, fond, water-hearted dogs — we hold you at the end of our pistols!'

'You may shoot, or you may not!' cried Scarrow, striking his hand upon the breast of his frieze jacket.

'If it's my last breath, Sharkey, I tell you that you are a bloody rogue and miscreant, with a halter and hell-fire in store for you!'

'There's a man of spirit, and one of my own kidney, and he's going to make a very pretty death of it!' cried Sharkey. 'There's no one aft save the man at the wheel, so you may keep your breath, for you'll need it soon. Is the dinghy astern, Ned?'

'Ay, ay, captain!'

'And the other boats scuttled?'

'I bored them all in three places.'

'Then we shall have to leave you, Captain Scarrow. You look as if you hadn't quite got your bearings yet. Is there anything you'd like to ask me?'

'I believe you're the devil himself!' cried the captain. 'Where is the Governor of St Kitt's?'

'When last I saw him his Excellency was in bed with his throat cut. When I broke prison I learnt from my friends — for Captain Sharkey has those who love him in every port — that the Governor was starting for Europe under a master who had never seen him. I climbed his verandah and I paid him the little debt that I owed him. Then I came aboard you with such of his things as I had need of, and a pair of glasses to hide these tell-tale eyes of mine, and I have ruffled it as a governor should. Now, Ned, you can get to work upon them.'

'Help! Help! Watch ahoy!' yelled the mate; but the butt of the pirate's pistol crashed down on to his head, and he dropped like a pithed ox. Scarrow rushed for the door, but the sentinel clapped his hand over his mouth, and threw his other arm round his waist.

'No use, Master Scarrow,' said Sharkey. 'Let us see you go down on your knees and beg for your life.'

'I'll see you —' cried Scarrow, shaking his mouth clear.

'Twist his arm round, Ned. Now will you?'

'No; not if you twist it off.'

'Put an inch of your knife into him.'

'You may put six inches, and then I won't.'

'Sink me, but I like his spirit!' cried Sharkey.

'Put your knife in your pocket, Ned. You've saved your skin, Scarrow, and it's a pity so stout a man should not take to the only trade where a pretty fellow can pick up a living. You must be born for no common death, Scarrow, since you have lain at my mercy and lived to tell the story. Tie him up, Ned.'

'To the stove, captain?'

'Tut, tut! there's a fire in the stove. None of your rover tricks, Ned Galloway, unless they are called for, or I'll let you know which of us two is captain and which is quartermaster. Make him fast to the table.'

'Nay, I thought you meant to roast him!' said the quartermaster. 'You surely do not mean to let him go?'

'If you and I were marooned on a Bahama cay, Ned Galloway, it is still for me to command and for you to obey. Sink you for a villain, do you dare to question my orders?'

'Nay, nay, Captain Sharkey, not so hot, sir!' said the quartermaster, and, lifting Scarrow like a child, he laid him on the table. With the quick dexterity of a seaman, he tied his spreadeagled hands and feet with a rope which was passed underneath, and gagged him securely with the long cravat which used to adorn the chin of the Governor of St Kitt's.

'Now, Captain Scarrow, we must take our leave of you,' said the pirate. 'If I had half a dozen of my brisk boys at my heels I should have had your cargo and your ship, but Roaring Ned could not find a foremast hand with the spirit of a mouse. I see there are some small craft about, and we shall get one of them. When Captain Sharkey has a boat he can get a smack, when he has a smack he can get a brig, when he has a brig he can get a barque, and when he has a barque he'll soon have a full-rigged ship of his own — so make haste into London town, or I may be coming back, after all, for the *Morning Star*.'

Captain Scarrow heard the key turn in the lock as they left the cabin. Then, as he strained at his bonds, he heard their footsteps pass up the companion and along the quarter-deck to where the dinghy hung in the stern. Then, still struggling and writhing, he heard the creak of the falls and the splash of the boat in the water. In a mad fury he tore and dragged at his ropes, until at last, with flayed wrists and ankles, he rolled from the table, sprang over the dead mate, kicked his way through the closed door, and rushed hatless on to the deck.

'Ahoy! Peterson, Armitage, Wilson!' he screamed. 'Cutlasses and pistols! Clear away the long-boat; Clear away the gig! Sharkey, the pirate, is in yonder dinghy. Whistle up the larboard watch, bo'sun, and tumble into the boats all hands.'

Down splashed the long-boat and down splashed the gig, but in an instant the coxswains and crews were swarming up the falls on to the deck once more.

'The boats are scuttled!' they cried. 'They are leaking like a sieve.'

The captain gave a bitter curse. He had been beaten and outwitted at every point. Above was a cloudless, starlit sky, with neither wind nor the promise of it. The sails flapped idly in the moonlight. Far away lay a fishing-smack, with the men clustering over their net.

Close to them was the little dinghy, dipping and lifting over the shining swell.

110

'They arc dead men!' cried the captain. 'A shout all together, boys, to warn them of their danger.'

But it was too late.

At that very moment the dinghy shot into the shadow of the fishing-boat. There were two rapid pistol-shots, a scream, and then another pistol-shot, followed by silence. The clustering fishermen had disappeared. And then, suddenly, as the first puffs of a land-breeze came out from the Sussex shore, the boom swung out, the mainsail filled, and the little craft crept out with her nose to the Atlantic.

The Man With the Belt of Gold

from Kidnapped

by

ROBERT LOUIS STEVENSON

Kidnapped *tells the story of David Balfour, whose uncle arranged for him to be kidnapped and shipped aboard the brig* Covenant *to prevent him from discovering that he is the rightful heir to the Shaw estate. The year is 1751: the Jacobite rebellion in Scotland has been over for five years, but it is not yet forgotten.*

More than a week went by, in which the ill-luck that had hitherto pursued the *Covenant* upon this voyage grew yet more strongly marked. Some days she made a little way; others, she was driven actually back. As last we were beaten so far to the south that we tossed and tacked to and fro the whole of the ninth day, within sight of Cape Wrath and the wild, rocky coast on either hand of it. There followed on that a council of the officers, and some decision which I did not rightly understand, seeing only the result: that we had made a fair wind of a foul one and were running south.

The tenth afternoon, there was a falling swell and a thick, wet, white fog that hid one end of the brig from the other. All afternoon, when I went on deck, I saw men and officers listening hard over the bulwarks — 'for breakers,' they said; and though I did not so much as understand the word, I felt danger in the air, and was excited.

Maybe about ten at night, I was serving Mr Riach and the captain at their supper, when the ship struck something with a great sound, and we heard voices singing out. My two masters leaped to their feet.

'She's struck,' said Mr Riach.

'No, sir,' said the captain. 'We've only run a boat down.' And they hurried out.

The captain was in the right of it. We had run down a boat in the fog, and she had parted in the midst and gone to the bottom with all her crew, but one. This man (as I heard afterwards) had been sitting in the stern as a passenger, while the rest were on the benches rowing. At the moment of the blow, the stern had been thrown into the air, and the man (having his hands free, and for all he was encumbered with a frieze overcoat that came below his knees) had leaped up and caught hold of the brig's bowsprit. It showed he had luck and much agility and unusual strength, that he should have thus saved himself from such a pass. And yet, when the captain brought him into the round-house, and I set eyes on him for the first time, he looked as cool as I did.

He was smallish in stature, but well set and as nimble as a goat; his face was of a good open expression, but sunburnt very dark, and heavily freckled and pitted with the small-pox; his eyes were unusually light and had a kind of dancing madness in them, that was both engaging and alarming; and when he took off his greatcoat, he laid a pair of fine silver-mounted pistols on the table, and I saw that he was belted with a great sword. His manners, besides, were elegant, and he pledged the captain handsomely. Altogether I thought of him, at the first sight, that here was a man I would rather call my friend than my enemy.

The captain, too, was taking his observations, but rather of the man's clothes than his person. And to be sure, as soon as he had taken off the great coat, he showed forth mighty fine for the round-house of a merchant brig: having a hat with feathers, red waistcoat, breeches of black plush, and a blue coat with silver buttons and handsome silver lace: costly clothes, though somewhat spoiled with the fog and being slept in.

'I'm vexed, sir, about the boat,' says the captain.

'There are some pretty men gone to the bottom,' said the stranger, 'that I would rather see on the dry land again than half a score of boats.'

'Friends of yours?' said Hoseason.

'You have none such friends in your country,' was the reply. 'They would have died for me like dogs.'

'Well, sir,' said the captain, still watching him, 'there are more men in the world than boats to put them in.'

'And that's true too,' cried the other, 'and ye seem to be a gentleman of great penetration.'

'I have been in France, sir,' says the captain, so that it was plain he meant more by the words than showed upon the face of them.

'Well, sir,' says the other, 'and so has many a pretty man, for the matter of that.'

'No doubt, sir,' says the captain; 'and fine coats.'

'Oho!' says the stranger, 'is that how the wind sets?' And he laid his hand quickly on his pistols.

'Don't be hasty,' said the captain. 'Don't do a mischief, before ye see the need for it. Ye've a French soldier's coat upon your back and a Scotch tongue in your head, to be sure; but so has many an honest fellow in these days, and I dare say none the worse of it.'

'So?' said the gentleman in the fine coat: 'are ye of the honest party?' (meaning, Was he a Jacobite? for each side, in these sort of civil broils, takes the name of honesty for its own.)

'Why, sir,' replied the captain, 'I am a true-blue Protestant, and I thank God for it.' (It was the first word of any religion I had ever heard from him, but I learnt afterwards he was a great church-goer while on shore.) 'But, for all that,' says he, 'I can be sorry to see another man with his back to the wall.'

'Can ye so, indeed?' asks the Jacobite. 'Well sir, to be quite plain with ye, I am one of those honest gentlemen that were in trouble about the years forty-five and six; and (to be still quite plain with ye) if I got into the hands of any of the red-coated gentry, it's like it would go hard with me. Now, sir, I was for France; and there was a French ship cruising here to pick me up; but she gave us the go-by in the fog — as I wish from the heart ye had done yoursel'! And the best that I can say is this; If ye can set me ashore where I was going, I have that upon me will reward you highly for your trouble.'

'In France?' says the captain. 'No, sir; that I cannot do. But where ye come from — we might talk of that.'

And then, unhappily, he observed me standing in my corner, and packed me off to the galley to get supper for the gentleman. I lost no time I promise you; and when I came back into the round-house, I found the gentleman had taken a money-belt from about his waist, and poured out a guinea or two upon the table. The captain was looking at the guineas, and then at the belt, and then at the gentleman's face; and I thought he seemed excited.

'Half of it,' he cried, 'and I'm your man!'

The other swept back the guineas into the belt, and put it on again under his waistcoat. 'I have told ye, sir,' said he, 'that not one doit of it belongs to me. It belongs to my chieftain' — and here he touched his hat — 'and while I would be but a silly messenger to grudge some of it that the rest might come safe, I should show myself a hound indeed if I bought my own carcase any too dear. Thirty guineas on the seaside, or sixty if ye set me on the Linnhe loch. Take it, if ye will; if not, ye can do your worst.'

'Ay,' said Hoseason. 'And if I give ye over to the soldiers.'

'Ye would make a fool's bargain,' said the other. 'My chief, let me tell you, sir, is forfeited, like every honest man in Scotland. His estate is in the hands of the man they call King George; and it is his officers that collect the rents, or try to collect them. But for the honour of Scotland, the poor tenant bodies take a thought upon their chief lying in exile; and his money is a part of that very rent for which King George is looking. Now, sir, ye seem to me to be a man that understands things: bring this money within the reach of Government, and how much of it'll come to you?'

'Little enough, to be sure,' said Hoseason; and then, 'If they knew,' he added, dryly. 'But I think, if I was to try, that I could hold my tongue about it.'

'Ah, but I'll begowk* ye there,' cried the gentleman. 'Play me false, and I'll play you cunning. If a hand's laid upon me, they shall ken what money it is.'

'Well,' returned the captain, 'what must be must. Sixty guineas, and done. Here's my hand upon it.'

'And here's mine,' said the other.

And thereupon the captain went out (rather hurriedly, I thought), and left me alone in the round-house with the stranger.

At that period (so soon after the forty-five) there were many exiled gentlemen coming back at the peril of their lives, either to see their friends or to collect a little money; and as for the Highland chiefs that had been forfeited, it was a common matter of talk how their tenants would stint themselves to send them money, and their clansmen outface the soldiery to get it in, and run the gauntlet of our great navy to carry it across. All this I had, of course, heard tell of; and now I had a man under my eyes whose life was forfeit on all these counts and upon one more; for he was not only a rebel and a smuggler of rents, but had taken service with King Louis of France. And as if all this were not enough, he had a belt full of golden guineas round his loins. Whatever my opinions, I could not look on such a man without a lively interest.

'And so you're a Jacobite?' said I, as I set meat before him.

'Ay,' said he, beginning to eat. 'And you, by your long face, should be a Whig.'

'Betwixt and between,' said I, not to annoy him; for indeed I was as good a Whig as Mr Campbell could make me.

'And that's naething,' said he. 'But I'm saying, Mr Betwixt-and-Between,' he added, 'this bottle of yours is dry; and it's hard if I'm to pay sixty guineas and be grudged a dram upon the back of it.'

'I'll go and ask for the key,' said I, and stepped on deck.

The fog was as close as ever, but the swell almost down. They had laid the brig too, not knowing precisely where they were, and the wind (what little there was of it) not serving well for their true course. Some of the hands were still hearkening for breakers; but the captain and the two officers were in the waist with their heads together. It struck me, I don't know why, that they were after no good; and the first word I heard, as I drew softly near, more than confirmed me.

It was Mr Riach, crying out as if upon a sudden thought. 'Couldn't we wile him out of the round-house?'

'He's better where he is,' returned Hoseason; 'He hasn't room to use his sword.'

'Well, that's true,' said Riach; 'but he's hard to come at.'

'Hut!' said Hoseason. 'We can get the man in talk, one upon each side, and pin him by the two arms; or if that'll not hold, sir, we can make a run by both the doors and get him under hand before he has the time to draw.'

At this hearing, I was seized with both fear and anger at

these treacherous, greedy, bloody men that I sailed with. My first mind was to run away; my second was bolder.

'Captain,' said I, 'the gentleman is seeking a dram, and the bottle's out. Will you give me the key?'

They all started and turned about.

'Why, here's our chance to get the firearms!' Riach cried; and then to me: 'Hark ye, David,' he said, 'do ye ken where the pistols are?'

'Ay, ay,' put in Hoseason. 'David kens; David's a good lad. Ye see, David my man, yon wild Hielandman is a danger to the ship, besides being a rank foe to King George, God bless him!'

I had never been so be-Davided since I came aboard; but I said yes, as if all I heard were quite natural.

'The trouble is,' resumed the captain, 'that all our firelocks great and little, are in the round-house under this man's nose; likewise the powder. Now, if I, or one of the officers, was to go in and take them, he would fall to thinking. But a lad like you, David, might snap up a horn and a pistol or two without remark. And if ye can do it cleverly, I'll bear it in mind when it'll be good for you to have friends; and that's when we come to Carolina.'

Here Mr Riach whispered him a little.

'Very right, sir,' said the captain; and then to myself: 'And see here, David, yon man has a beltful of gold, and I give you my word that you shall have your fingers in it.'

I told him I would do as he wished, though indeed I had scarce breath to speak with; and upon that he gave me the key of the spirit-locker, and I began to go slowly back to the round-house. What was I to do? They were dogs and thieves; they had stolen me from my own country; they had killed poor Ransome; and was I to hold the candle to another murder? But then, upon the other hand, there was the fear of death very plain before me; for what could a boy and a man, if they were as brave as lions, against a whole ship's company.

I was still arguing it back and forth, and getting no great clearness, when I came into the round-house and saw the Jacobite eating his supper under the lamp; and at that my mind was made up all in a moment. I have no credit by it; it was by no choice of mine, but as if by compulsion, that I walked right up to the table and put my hand on his shoulder.

'Do ye want to be killed?' said I.

He sprang to his feet, and looked a question at me as clear as if he had spoken.

'Oh!' cried I, 'they're all murderers here; it's a ship full of them! They've murdered a boy already. Now it's you.'

'Ay, ay,' said he; 'but they haven't got me yet.' And then looking at me curiously, 'Will ye stand with me?'

'That will I!' said I. 'I am no thief, nor yet murderer. I'll stand by you.'

'Why then,' said he, 'what's your name?'

'David Balfour,' said I; and then thinking that a man with so fine a coat must like fine people, I added for the first time, 'of Shaws.'

It never occurred to him to doubt me, for a Highlander is used to see great gentlefolk in great poverty; but as he had no estate of his own, my words nettled a very childish vanity he had.

'My name is Stewart,' he said, drawing himself up. 'Alan Breck, they call me. A king's name is good enough for me, though I bear it plain and have the name of no farm-midden to clap to the hind-end of it.'

And having administered this rebuke as though it were something of a chief importance, he turned to examine our defences.

The round-house was built very strong, to support the breaching of the seas. Of its five apertures, only the skylight and the two doors were large enough for the passage of a man.

The doors, besides, could be drawn close; they were of stout oak, and ran in grooves, and were fitted with hooks to keep them either shut or open, as the need arose. The one that was already shut, I secured in this fashion; but when I was proceeding to slide to the other, Alan stopped me.

'David,' said he — 'for I cannae bring to mind the name of your landed estate, and so will make so bold as to call you David — that door, being open, is the best part of my defences.'

'It would be better shut,' says I.

'Not so, David,' says he. 'Ye see, I have but one face; but so long as that door is open and my face to it, the best part of my enemies will be in front of me, where I would aye wish to find them.'

Then he gave me from the rack a cutlass (of which there were a few besides the firearms), choosing it with great care, shaking his head and saying he had never in all his life seen poorer weapons; and next he set me down to the table with a powder-horn, a bag of bullets, and all the pistols, which he bade me charge.

'And that will be better work, let me tell you,' said he, 'for a gentleman of decent birth, than scraping plates and raxing drams to a wheen tarry sailors.'

Thereupon he stood up in the midst with his face to the door, and drawing his great sword, made trial of the room he had to wield it in.

'I must stick to the point,' he said, shaking his head; 'And that's a pity, too. It doesn't set my genius, which is all for the upper guard. And now,' said he, 'do you keep on charging the pistols, and give heed to me.'

I told him I would listen closely. My chest was tight, my mouth dry, the light dark to my eyes; the thought of the numbers that were soon to leap in upon us kept my heart in a flutter; and the sea, which I heard washing round the brig,

120

and where I thought my dead body would be cast ere morning, ran in my mind strangely.

'First of all,' said he, 'how many are against us?'

I reckoned them up; and such was the hurry of my mind, I had to cast the numbers twice. 'Fifteen,' said I.

Alan whistled. 'Well,' said he, 'that can't be cured. And now follow me. It is my part to keep this door, where I look for the main battle. In that, ye have no hand. And mind and dinna fire to this side unless they get me down; for I would rather have ten foes in front of me than one friend like you cracking pistols at my back.'

I told him, indeed, I was no great shot.

'And that's very bravely said,' he cried, in a great admiration of my candour. 'There's many a pretty gentleman that wouldnae dare to say it.'

'But then, sir,' said I, 'there is the door behind you, which they may perhaps break in.'

'Ay,' said he, 'and that is a part of your work. No sooner the pistols charged, than ye must climb up into yon bed where ye're handy at the window; and if they lift hand against the door, ye're to shoot. But that's not all. Let's make a bit of a soldier of ye, David. What else have ye to guard?'

'There's the skylight,' said I. 'But indeed, Mr Stewart, I would need to have eyes upon both sides to keep the two of them; for when my face is at the one, my back is to the other.'

'And that's very true,' said Alan. 'But have ye no ears to your head?'

'To be sure!' cried I. 'I must hear the bursting of the glass!'

'Ye have some rudiments of sense,' said Alan grimly.

But now our time of truce was come to an end. Those on deck had waited for my coming till they grew impatient; and scarce had Alan spoken, when the captain showed face in the open door.

'Stand!' cried Alan, and pointed his sword at him.

The captain stood, indeed; but he neither winced nor drew back a foot.

'A naked sword?' says he. 'This is a strange return for hospitality.'

'Do ye see me?' said Alan. 'I am come of kings; I bear a king's name. My badge is the oak. Do ye see my sword? It has slashed the heads of mair Whigamores than you have toes upon your feet. Call up your vermin to your back, sir, and fall on! The sooner the clash begins, the sooner ye'll taste this steel throughout your vitals.'

The captain said nothing to Alan, but he looked over at me with an ugly look. 'David,' said he, 'I'll mind this'; and the sound of his voice went through me with a jar.

Next moment he was gone.

'And now,' said Alan, 'let your hand keep your head, for the grip is coming.'

Alan drew a dirk, which he held in his left hand in case they should run in under his sword. I, on my part, clambered up into the berth with an armful of pistols, and something of a heavy heart, and set open the window where I was to watch. It was a small part of the deck that I could overlook, but enough for our purpose. The sea had gone down, and the wind was steady and kept the sails quiet; so that, there was a great stillness in the ship, in which I made sure I heard the sound of muttering voices. A little after, and there came a clash of steel upon the deck, by which I knew they were dealing out the cutlasses and one had been let fall; and after that silence again.

I do not know if I was what you call afraid; but my heart beat like a bird's, both quick and little; and there was a dimness came before my eyes which I continually rubbed away, and which continually returned. As for hope, I had none; but only a darkness of despair and a sort of anger against all the world that made me long to sell my life as dear as I was able. I tried to pray, I remember, but that same hurry of my mind, like a man running, would not suffer me to think upon the words; and my chief wish was to have the thing begin and be done with it.

It came all of a sudden when it did, with a rush of feet and a roar, and then a shout from Alan, and a sound of blows and some one crying out as if hurt. I looked back over my shoulder, and saw Mr Shuan in the doorway, crossing blades with Alan.

'That's him that killed the boy!' I cried.

'Look to your window!' said Alan, and as I turned back to my place, I saw him pass his sword through the mate's body.

It was none too soon for me to look to my own part; for my head was scarce back at the window, before five men carrying a spare yard for a battering-ram, ran past me and took post to drive the door in. I had never fired with a pistol in my life, and not often with a gun; far less against a fellow-creature. But it was now or never; and just as they swung the yard, I cried out, 'Take that!' and shot into their midst.

I must have hit one of them, for he sang out and gave back a step, and the rest stopped as if a little disconcerted. Before they had time to recover, I sent another ball over their heads; and at my third shot (which went as wide as the second) the whole party threw down the yard and ran for it.

Then I looked round again into the deck-house. The whole place was full of the smoke of my own firing, just as my ears seemed to be burst with the noise of the shots. But there was Alan, standing as before; only now his sword was running blood to the hilt, and himself so swelled with triumph and fallen into so fine an attitude, that he looked to be invincible. Right before him on the floor was Mr Shuan, on his hands and knees; the blood was pouring from his mouth, and he was sinking slowly lower, with a terrible, white face; and just as I looked, some of those from behind caught hold of him by the heels and dragged him bodily out of the round-house. I believe he died as they were doing it.

'There's one of your Whigs for ye!' cried Alan; and then turning to me, he asked if I had done much execution.

I told him I had winged one, and thought it was the captain.

'And I've settled two,' says he. 'No, there's not enough blood let; they'll be back again. To your watch, David. This was but a dram before meat.'

I settled back to my place, re-charging the three pistols I had fired, and keeping watch with both eye and ear.

Our enemies were disputing not far off upon the deck, and that so loudly that I could hear a word or two above the washing of the seas.

'It was Shuan bauchled it,' I heard one say.

And another answered him with a 'Wheesht, man! He's paid the piper.'

After that the voices fell again into the same muttering as before. Only now, one person spoke most of the time, as though laying down a plan, and first one and then the other answered him briefly, like men taking orders. By this, I made sure they were coming on again, and told Alan.

'It's what we have to pray for,' said he. 'Unless we can give them a good distaste of us, and done with it, there'll be nae sleep for either you or me. But this time, mind, they'll be in earnest.'

By this, my pistols were ready, and there was nothing to do but listen and wait. While the brush lasted, I had not the time to think if I was frighted; but now, when all was still again, my mind ran upon nothing else. The thought of the sharp swords and the cold steel was strong in me; and presently, when I began to hear stealthy steps and a brushing of men's

The skylight was dashed to pieces, and a man leaped through.

clothes against the roundhouse wall, and knew they were taking their places in the dark, I could have found it in my mind to cry out aloud.

All this was upon Alan's side; and I had begun to think my share of the fight was at an end, when I heard some one drop softly on the roof above me.

Then there came a single call on the sea-pipe, and that was the signal. A knot of them made one rush of it, cutlass in hand, against the door; and at the same moment, the glass of the skylight was dashed in a thousand pieces, and a man leaped through and landed on the floor. Before he got to his feet, I had clapped a pistol to his back, and might have shot him, too; only at the touch of him (and him alive) my whole flesh misgave me, and I could no more pull the trigger than I could have flown.

He had dropped his cutlass, as he jumped, and when he felt the pistol, whipped straight round and laid hold of me, roaring out an oath; and at that either my courage came again, or I grew so much afraid as came to the same thing; for I gave a shriek and shot him in the midst of the body. He gave the most horrible ugly groan and fell to the floor. The foot of a second fellow, whose legs were dangling through the skylight, struck me at the same time upon the head; and at that I snatched another pistol and shot this one through the thigh, so that he slipped through and tumbled in a lump on his companion's body. There was no talk of missing, any more than there was time to aim; I clapped the muzzle to the very place and fired.

I might have stood and stared at them for long, but I heard Alan shout as if for help, and that brought me to my senses.

He had kept the door so long; but one of the seamen, while he was engaged with others, had run in under his guard and caught him about the body. Alan was dirking him with his left hand, but the fellow clung like a leech. Another had broken in and had his cutlass raised. The door was thronged with their faces. I thought we were lost, and catching up my cutlass, fell on them in flank.

But I had not time to be of help. The wrestler dropped at last; and Alan, leaping back to get his distance, ran upon the others like a bull, roaring as he went. They broke before him like water, turning, and running, and falling one against another in their haste. The sword in his hand flashed like quicksilver into the huddle of our fleeing enemies; and at every flash there came the scream of a man hurt. I was still thinking we were lost, when lo! they were all gone, and Alan was driving them along the deck as a sheepdog chases sheep.

Yet he was no sooner out than he was back again, being as cautious as he was brave; and meanwhile the seamen continued running and crying out as if he was still behind them; and we heard them tumble one upon the other into the forecastle, and clap-to the hatch upon the top.

The round-house was like a shambles; three were dead inside, another lay in his death agony across the threshold, and there were Alan and I victorious and unhurt.

He came up to me with open arms. 'Come to my arms!' he cried, and embraced and kissed me hard upon both cheeks. 'David,' said he, 'I love you like a brother. And oh, man,' he cried in a kind of ecstasy, 'am I no a bonny fighter?'

Thereupon he turned to the four enemies, passed his sword clean through each of them, and tumbled them out of doors one after the other. As he did so, he kept humming and singing and whistling to himself, like a man trying to recall an air; only what *he* was trying, was to make one. All the while, the flush was in his face, and his eyes were as bright as a five-year-old child's with a new toy. And presently he sat down upon the table, sword in hand; the air that he was making all the time began to run a little clearer, and then clearer still; and then out he burst with a great voice into a Gaelic song.

I have translated it here, not in verse (of which I have no skill) but at least in the king's English. He sang it often afterwards, and the thing became popular; so that I have heard it, and had it explained to me, many's the time.

This is the song of the sword of Alan:
The smith made it,
The fire set it;
Now it shines in the hand of Alan Breck.

Their eyes were many and bright,
Swift were they to behold,
Many the hands they guided:
The sword was alone.

The dun deer troop over the hill,
They are many, the hill is one;
The dun deer vanish,
The hill remains.

Come to me from the hills of heather,
Come from the isles of the sea.
O far-beholding eagles,
Here is your meat.

The Gunner's Fight With the Carronade

from Ninety-Three

by
VICTOR HUGO

One of the carronades of the battery, a twenty-pounder, had got loose.

This is perhaps the most formidable of all ocean accidents. Nothing more terrible can happen to a vessel in open sea and under full sail. A gun that breaks its moorings becomes suddenly some indescribable supernatural beast. It is a machine which transforms itself into a monster. This mass turns upon its wheels, has the rapid movements of a billiard ball; rolls with the rolling; pitches with the pitching; goes, comes, pauses, seems to meditate; resumes its course, rushes along the ship from end to end like an arrow, circles about, springs aside, evades, rears, breaks, kills, exterminates. It is a battering ram which assaults a wall at its own caprice. Moreover, the battering ram is of metal, the wall wood. It is the entrance of matter into space. One might say that this eternal slave avenges itself. It seems as if the power of evil hidden in what we call animate objects finds a vent and bursts suddenly out. It has an air of having lost patience, of seeking some fierce, obscure retribution; nothing more inexorable than this rage of the inanimate. The mad mass has the bounds of a panther, the weight of an elephant, the agility of the mouse, the obstinacy of the axe, the unexpectedness of the surge, the rapidity of lightning, the deafness of the tomb. It weighs ten thousand pounds, and it rebounds like a child's ball. Its flight is a wild whirl abruptly cut at right angles. What is to be done? How to end this? A tempest ceases, a cyclone passes, a wind falls, a broken mast is replaced, a leak is stopped, a fire dies out; but how to control this enormous brute of bronze? In what way can one attack it?

You can make a mastiff hear reason, astound a bull, fascinate a boa, frighten a tiger, soften a lion, but there is no resource with that monster, a cannon let loose. You cannot kill it — it is dead; at the same time it lives. It lives with a sinister life bestowed on it by Infinity.

The planks beneath it give it play. It is moved by the ship, which is moved by the sea, which is moved by the wind. This destroyer is a plaything. The ship, the waves, the blasts, all aid it; hence its frightful vitality. How to assail this fury of complication? How to fetter this monstrous mechanism for wrecking a ship? How foresee its comings and goings, its returns, its stops, its shocks? Any one of these blows upon the sides may stave out the vessel. How divine its awful gyrations? One has to deal with a projectile which thinks, seems to possess ideas, and which changes its direction at each instant. How stop the course of something which must be avoided? The horrible cannon flings itself about, advances, recoils, strikes to the right, strikes to the left, flees, passes, disconcerts, ambushes, breaks down obstacles, crushes men like flies. The great danger of the situation is in the mobility of its base. How combat an inclined plane which has caprices? The ship, so to speak, has lightning imprisoned in its womb which seeks to escape; it is like thunder rolling above an earthquake.

In an instant the whole crew were on foot. The fault was the chief gunner's; he had neglected to fix home the screwnut of the mooring chain, and had so badly shackled the four wheels of the carronade that the play given to the sole and frame had separated the platform and ended by breaking the breeching. The cordage had broken, so that the gun was no longer secure on the carriage. The stationary breeching which prevents recoil was not in use at that period. As a heavy wave struck the port, the carronade, weakly attached, recoiled, burst its chain and began to rush wildly about. Conceive, in order to have an idea of this strange sliding, a drop of water running down a pane of glass.

At the moment when the lashings gave way the gunners were in the battery, some in groups, others standing alone, occupied with such duties as sailors perform in expectation of the command to clear for action. The carronade, hurled forward by the pitching, dashed into this knot of men and crushed four at the first blow; then, flung back and shot out anew by the rolling, it cut in two a fifth poor fellow, glanced off to the larboard side and struck a piece of the battery with such force as to unship it. The men rushed toward the ladder; the gun-deck emptied in the twinkling of an eye. The enormous cannon was left alone. She was given up to herself. She was her own mistress, and mistress of the vessel. She could do what she willed with both. The whole crew, accustomed to laugh in battle, trembled now. To describe the universal terror would be impossible.

Captain Boisberthelot and Lieutenant La Vieuville, although both intrepid men, stopped at the head of the stairs and remained mute, pale, hesitating, looking down on the deck. Someone pushed them aside with his elbow and descended.

It was their passenger — the peasant — the man of whom they had been speaking a moment before.

When he reached the foot of the ladder he stood still.

The cannon came and went along the deck. One might have fancied it the living chariot of the Apocalypse. The marine lantern oscillating from the ceiling added a dizzying whirl of lights and shadows to this vision. The shape of the cannon was indistinguishable from the rapidity of its course; now it looked black in the light, now it cast weird reflections through the gloom.

It kept on its work of destruction. It had already shattered four other pieces, and dug two crevices in the side, fortunately above the water line, though they would leak in case a squall should come on. It dashed itself frantically against the framework. The solid tie-beams resisted, their curved forms giving them great strength; but they creaked ominously under the assaults of this terrible club, which seemed endowed with a sort of appalling ubiquity, striking on every side at once. The strokes of a bullet shaken in a bottle would not be madder or more rapid. The four wheels passed and repassed above the dead men, cut, carved, slashed them till the five corpses were a score of stumps rolling about the deck; the heads seemed to cry out; streams of blood twisted in and out the planks with every pitch of the vessel. The ceiling, damaged in seven places, began to gape. The whole ship was filled with the awful tumult.

The captain promptly recovered his composure, and at his orders the sailors threw down into the deck everything which could deaden or check the mad rush of the gun — mattresses, hammocks, spare sails, coils of rope, extra equipment, and the bales of false assignats of which the corvette carried a whole cargo; an infamous deception which the English considered a fair trick in war.

But what could these rags avail? No one dared descend to arrange them in useful fashion, and in a few instants they were mere heaps of lint. There was just enough sea to render the accident as complete as possible. A tempest would have been desirable; it might have thrown the gun upside down, and the four wheels once in the air, the monster could have been mastered. But the devastation increased. There were gashes and even fractures in the masts, which, embedded in the woodwork of the keel, pierce the decks of ships like great round pillars. The mizzen-mast was cracked, and the mainmast itself was injured under the convulsive blows of the gun. The battery was being destroyed. Ten pieces out of the thirty were disabled; the breaches multiplied in the side, and the corvette began to take in water.

The old passenger who had descended to the gun-deck, looked like a form of stone stationed at the foot of the stairs. He stood motionless, gazing sternly about upon the devastation. Indeed, it seemed impossible to take a single step forward.

Each bound of the liberated carronade menaced the destruction of the vessel. A few minutes more and shipwreck would be inevitable.

They must perish or put a summary end to the disaster — a decision must be made; but how?

What a combatant — this cannon! They must check this mad monster. They must seize this flash of lightning. They must overthrow this thunderbolt.

Boisberthelot said to La Vieuville, 'Do you believe in God, chevalier?'

La Vieuville replied, 'Yes, — no — sometimes.'

'In a tempest?'

'Yes, and in moments like this.'

'Only God can aid us here,' said Boisberthelot.

All were silent — the cannon kept up its horrible fracas.

The waves beat against the ship, their blows from without responded to the strokes of the cannon.

It was like two hammers alternating.

Suddenly into the midst of this sort of inaccessible circus, where the escaped cannon leaped and bounded, there sprang a man with an iron bar in his hand. It was the author of this catastrophe, the gunner whose culpable negligence had caused the accident — the captain of the gun. Having been the means of bringing about the misfortune, he desired to repair it. He

133

The gunner approached to challenge the cannon.

had caught up a handspike in one fist, a tiller-rope with a slipping noose in the other, and jumped down into the gun-deck. Then a strange combat began, a Titanic strife — the struggle of the gun against the gunner; a battle between matter and intelligence; a duel between the inanimate and the human.

The man was posted in an angle, the bar and rope in his two fists; backed against one of the riders, settled firmly on his legs as on two pillars of steel; livid, calm, tragic, rooted as it were in the planks, he waited. He waited for the cannon to pass him.

The gunner knew his piece, and it seemed to him that she must recognise her master. He had lived a long while with her. How many times had he thrust his hand between her jaws! It was his tame monster. He began to address it as he might have done his dog.

'Come!' said he. Perhaps he loved it. He seemed to wish that it would turn towards him. But to come towards him would be to spring upon him. Then he would be lost. How to avoid its crush? There was the question. All stared in terrified silence. Not a breast respired freely, except perchance that of the old man who stood on the deck with the two combatants, a stern second. He himself might be crushed by the piece. He did not stir. Beneath them the blind sea directed the battle.

At the instant when, accepting this awful hand-to-hand contest, the gunner approached to challenge the cannon, some chance fluctuation of the waves kept it for a moment immovable as if suddenly stupified. 'Come on!' the man said to it. It seemed to listen. Suddenly it darted upon him. The gunner avoided the shock.

The struggle began — struggle unheard of — the fragile matching itself against the invulnerable; the thing of flesh attacking the brazen brute; on the one side blind force, on the other a soul. The whole passed in half-light. It was like the indistinct vision of a miracle.

A soul — a strange thing; but you would have said that the cannon had one also — a soul filled with rage and hatred. The blindness appeared to have eyes. The monster had an air of watching the man. There was — one might have fancied so at least — cunning in this mass. It also chose its moment. It became some gigantic insect of metal, having, or seeming to have the will of a demon. Sometimes this colossal grasshopper would strike the low ceiling of the gun-deck, then fall back on its four wheels like a tiger upon its four claws, and dart anew on the man. He, supple, agile, adroit, would glide away like a snake from the reach of these lightning-like movements. He avoided the encounters; but the blows which he escaped fell upon the vessel, and continued the havoc.

An end of broken chain remained attached to the carronade. This chain had twisted itself, one could not tell how, about the screw of the breech-button. One extremity of the chain was fastened to the carriage. The other, hanging loose, whirled madly about the gun, and added to the danger of its blows.

The screw held it like a clenched hand, and the chain, multiplying the strokes of the battering-ram by its strokes of a thong, made a fearful whirlwind about the cannon — a whip of iron in a fist of brass. This chain complicated the battle.

Nevertheless, the man fought. Sometimes, even, it was the man who attacked the cannon. He crept along the side, bar and rope in hand, and the cannon had the air of understand, ing, and fled as if it perceived a snare. The man pursued it, formidable, fearless.

Such a duel could not last long. The gun seemed suddenly to say to itself, 'Come, we must make an end!' and it paused. One felt the approach of the crisis. The cannon, as if in suspense, appeared to have, or had — because it seemed to all a sentient being — a furious premeditation. It sprang unexpectedly upon the gunner. He jumped aside, let it pass, and cried out with a laugh, 'Try again!' The gun, as if in fury, broke a carronade to larboard; then, seized anew by the invisible sling which held it, was flung to starboard towards the man, who escaped.

Three carronades gave way under the blows of the gun; then, as if blind and no longer conscious of what it was doing, it turned its back on the man, rolled from the stern to the bow, bruising the stern and making a breach in the planking of the prow. The gunner had taken refuge at the foot of the stairs, a few steps from the old man, who was watching.

The gunner held his handspike in rest. The cannon seemed to perceive him, and without taking the trouble to turn itself, backed upon him with the quickness of an axe-stroke. The gunner, if driven back against the side, was lost. The crew uttered a simultaneous cry.

But the old passenger, now immovable, made a spring more rapid than all those wild whirls. He seized a bale of the false assignats, and at the risk of being crushed, succeeded in flinging it between the wheels of the carronade. This manoeuvre, decisive and dangerous, could not have been executed with more adroitness and precision by a man trained to all the exercises set down in *Durosel's Manual of Sea Gunnery*.

The bale had the effect of a plug. A pebble may stop a log, a tree branch turn an avalanche. The carronade stumbled. The gunner, in his turn, seizing this terrible chance, plunged his iron bar between the spokes of one of the hind wheels. The cannon was stopped. It staggered. The man, using the bar as a lever, rocked it to and fro. The heavy mass turned over with a clang like a falling bell, and the gunner, dripping with sweat, rushed forward headlong and passed the slipping noose of the tiller-rope about the brazen neck of the overthrown monster.

It was ended. The man had conquered. The ant had subdued the mastodon; the pygmy had taken the thunderbolt prisoner.

The marines and the sailors clapped their hands.

The whole crew hurried down with cables and chains, and in an instant the cannon was securely lashed.

The gunner saluted the passenger.

'Sir,' he said to him, 'you have saved my life.'

How Dantès escaped from the Chateau d'If

from The Count
of Monte Cristo

by
ALEXANDRE DUMAS

On the bed, at full length, and faintly lighted by the pale ray that penetrated the window, was visible a sack of coarse cloth, under the large folds of which were stretched a long and stiffened form; it was Faria's last winding-sheet — a winding-sheet which, as the turnkey said, costs so little. All, then, was completed. A material separation had taken place between Dantès and his old friend; he could no longer see those eyes which had remained open to look even beyond death; he could no longer clasp that hand of industry which had lifted for him the veil that had concealed hidden and obscure things. Faria, the usual and the good companion, with whom he was accustomed to live so intimately, no longer breathed. He seated himself on the edge of that terrible bed, and fell into a melancholy and gloomy reverie.

Alone! — he was alone again! — again relapsed into silence! he found himself once again in the presence of nothingness! Alone! — no longer to see, no longer to hear the voice of the only human being who attached him to life! Was it not better, like Faria, to seek the presence of his Maker, and learn the enigma of life at the risk of passing through the mournful gate of intense suffering? The idea of suicide, driven away by his friend, and forgotten in his presence whilst living, arose like a phantom before him in the presence of his dead body.

'If I could die,' he said, 'I should go where he goes, and should assuredly find him again. But how to die? It is very easy', he continued, with a smile of bitterness; 'I will remain here, rush on the first person that opens the door, will strangle him, and then they will guillotine me.'

But as it happens that in excessive griefs, as in great tempests, the abyss is found between the tops of the loftiest waves, Dantès recoiled from the idea of his infamous death, and passed suddenly from despair to an ardent desire for life and liberty.

'Die! Oh no!' he exclaimed, 'not die now, after having lived and suffered so long and so much! Die! yes, had I died years since; but now it would be, indeed, to give way to my bitter destiny. No, I desire to live; I desire to struggle to the very last; I wish to reconquer the happiness of which I have been deprived. Before I die I must not forget that I have my executioners to punish, and perhaps too, who knows, some friends to reward. Yet they will forget me here, and I shall die in my dungeon like Faria.'

As he said this, he remained motionless, his eyes fixed like a man struck with a sudden idea, but whom this idea fills with amazement. Suddenly he rose, lifted his hand to his brow as if his brain were giddy, paced twice or thrice round his chamber, and then paused abruptly at the bed.

'Ah, ah!' he muttered, 'who inspires me with this thought? Is it thou, gracious God? Since none but the dead pass freely from this dungeon, let me assume the place of the dead.'

Without giving himself time to reconsider his decision, and, indeed, that he might now allow his thoughts to be distracted from his desperate resolution, he bent over the appalling sack, opened it with the knife which Faria had made, drew the corpse from the sack, and transported it along the gallery to his own chamber, laid it on his couch, passed round its head the rag he wore at night round his own, covered it with his counterpane, once again kissed the ice-cold brow, and tried vainly to close the resisting eyes, which glared horribly; turned the head towards the wall, so that the gaoler might, when he brought his evening meal, believe that he was asleep, as was his frequent custom; returned along the gallery, threw the bed against the wall, returned to the other cell, took from the hiding place the needle and thread, flung off his rags, that they might feel naked flesh only beneath the coarse sackcloth, and getting inside the sack, placed himself in the posture in which the dead body had been laid, and sewed up the mouth of the sack withinside.

The beating of his heart might have been heard, if by any mischance the gaolers had entered at that moment. Dantès might have waited until the evening visit was over, but he was afraid that the governor might change his resolution, and order the dead body to be removed earlier. In that case, his last hope would have been destroyed. Now his project was settled under any circumstances, and he hoped thus to carry it into effect. If, during the time he was being conveyed the grave-diggers should discover they were conveying a live instead of a dead body, Dantès did not intend to give them time to recognise him, but with a sudden cutting of the knife he meant to open the sack from top to bottom, and, profiting by their alarm, escape; if they tried to catch him he would use his knife.

If they conducted him to the cemetery and laid him in the grave, he would allow himself to be covered with earth and then, as it was night, the grave-diggers could scarcely have turned their backs, ere he would have worked his way through the soft soil and escape, hoping that the weight would not be too heavy for him to support. If he was deceived in this, and

141

the earth proved too heavy, he would be stifled, and then, so much the better, all would be over. Dantès had not eaten since the previous evening, but he had not thought of hunger or thirst, nor did he now think of it. His position was too precarious to allow him time to reflect on any thought but one.

The first risk that Dantès ran was that the gaoler, when he brought him his supper at seven o'clock, might perceive the substitution he had effected; fortunately, twenty times at least, from misanthropy or fatigue, Dantès had received his gaoler in bed, and then the man placed his bread and soup on the table and went away without saying a word. This time the gaoler might not be silent as usual, but speak to Dantès, and seeing that he received no reply, go to the bed and discover all.

When seven o'clock came, Dantès' agony really commenced. His hand placed upon his heart was unable to repress its throbbings, whilst, with the other, he wiped the perspiration from his temples. From time to time shudderings ran through his whole frame, and collapsed his heart as if it were frozen. Then he thought he was going to die. Yet the hours passed on without any stir in the *château*, and Dantès felt that he had escaped the first danger: it was a good augury. At length, at the hour the governor had appointed, footsteps were heard on the stair. Edmond felt that the moment had arrived, and summoning up all his courage, held his breath, happy if at the same time he could have repressed in like manner the hasty pulsation of his arteries.

They stopped at the door — there were two steps, and Dantès guessed it was the two grave-diggers who came to seek him — this idea was soon converted into certainty when he heard the noise they made in putting down the hand-bier. The door opened, and a dim light reached Dantès' eyes through the coarse sack that covered him; he saw two shadows approach his bed, a third remaining at the door with a torch in his hands. Each of these two men, approaching the ends of the bed, took the sack by its extremities.

'He's heavy though for an old and thin man,' said one, as he raised the head.

'They say every year adds half a pound to the weight of the bones,' said another, lifting the feet.

'Have you tied the knot?' inquired the first speaker.

'What would be the use of carrying so much more weight?' was the reply; 'I can do that when we get there.'

'What's the knot for?' thought Dantès.

They deposited the supposed corpse on the bier. Edmond stiffened himself in order to play the part of a dead man, and then the party, lighted by the man with the torch, who went first, ascended the stairs. Suddenly he felt the fresh and sharp night air, and Dantès recognised the *Mistral*. It was a sudden sensation, at the same time replete with delight and agony. The bearers advanced twenty paces, then stopped, putting their bier down on the ground. One of them went away, and Dantès heard his shoes on the pavement.

'Where am I then?' he asked himself.

'Really, he is by no means a light load!' said the other bearer, sitting on the edge of the hand-barrow. Dantès first impulse was to escape, but fortunately, he did not attempt it.

'Light me you!' said the other bearer, 'or I shall not find what I am looking for.'

The man with the torch complied, although not asked in the most polite terms.

'What can he be looking for?' thought Edmond. 'The spade?'

An exclamation of satisfaction indicated that the grave-digger had found the object of his search.

'At last,' said the other, 'not without some trouble though.'

'Yes,' was the answer, 'but it has lost nothing by waiting.'

As he said this, the man came towards Edmond, who heard a heavy and sounding substance laid down beside him, and

'One!' said the grave-diggers. 'Two! Three!'

at the same moment a cord was fastened round his feet with sudden and painful violence.

'Well, have you tied the knot?' inquired the grave-digger who was looking on.

'Yes, and pretty tight too, I can tell you,' was the answer.

'Move on, then.' And the bier was lifted once more, and they proceeded.

They advanced fifty paces farther, and then stopped to open a door, then went forward again. The noise of waves dashing against the rocks on which the *château* is built, reached Dantès, ears distinctly as they progressed.

'Bad weather!' observed one of the bearers; 'not a pleasant night for a dip in the sea.'

'Why, yes, the abbé runs a chance of being wet,' said the other; and then there was a burst of brutal laughter.

Dantès did not comprehend the jest, but his hair stood er ec on his head.

'Well, here we are at last,' said one of them.

'A little farther — a little farther,' said the other. 'You know very well that the last was stopped on his way, dashed on the rocks, and the governor told us next day that we were careless fellows.'

They ascended five or six more steps, and then Dantès felt that they took him one by the head and the other by the heels, and swung him to and fro.

'One!' said the grave-diggers. 'Two! Three!'

And at the same instant Dantès felt himself flung into the air like a wounded bird falling, falling with a rapidity that made his blood curdle. Although drawn downwards by a heavy weight which was hastening his rapid descent, it seemed to him as if the time were a century. At last, with a terrific dash, he entered the ice-cold water, and as he did so he uttered a shrill cry, stifled in a moment by his immersion beneath the waves.

Dantès had been flung into the sea, into whose depths he was dragged by a thirty-six pound shot tied to his feet. The sea is the cemetery of the Château d'If.

Dantès, although giddy and almost suffocated, had yet sufficient presence of mind to hold his breath; and as his right hand (prepared as he was for every chance) held his knife open, he rapidly ripped up the sack, extricated his arm, then his head; but in spite of all his efforts to free himself from the shot, he felt it dragging him down still lower. He then bent his body, and by a desperate effort severed the cord that bound his legs, at the moment he was suffocating. With a vigorous spring he rose to the surface of the sea, whilst the shot bore to its depths the sack that had so nearly become his shroud.

Dantès merely paused to breathe, and then dived again, in order to avoid being seen. When he arose a second time he was fifty paces from where he had first sunk. He saw overhead a black and tempestuous sky, over which the wind was driving the fleeting vapours that occasionally suffered a twinkling star to appear; before him was the vast expanse of waters, sombre and terrible, whose waves foamed and roared as if before the approach of a storm. Behind him, blacker than the sea, blacker than the sky, rose like a phantom the giant of granite, whose projecting crags seemed like arms extended to seize their prey; and on the highest rock was a torch that lighted two figures. He fancied these two forms were looking at the sea; doubtless these strange grave-diggers had heard his cry. Dantès dived again, and remained a long time beneath the water. This manoeuvre was already familiar to him, and usually attracted a crowd of spectators in the bay before the lighthouse at Marseilles when he swam there, and who, with one accord, pronounced him the best swimmer in the port. When he reappeared the light had disappeared.

It was necessary to strike out to sea. Ratonneau and Pomègue are the nearest isles of all those that surround the Château d'If; but Ratonneau and Pomègue are inhabited, together with the islet of Daume; Tiboulen or Lemaire were the most secure. The isles of Tiboulen and Lemaire are a league from the Château d'If. Dantès, nevertheless, determined to make for them. But how could he find his way in the darkness of the night? At this moment he saw before him, like a brilliant star, the lighthouse of Planier. By leaving this light on the right, he kept the isle of Tiboulen a little on the left; by turning to the left, therefore, he would find it. But, as we have said, it was at least a league from the Château d'If to this island. Often in prison, Faria had said to him, when he saw him idle and inactive, 'Dantès, you must not give way to this listlessness; you will be drowned if you seek to escape, and your strength has not properly been exercised and prepared for exertion.' These words rang in Dantès' ears, even beneath the waves; he hastened to cleave his way through them to see if he had not lost his strength. He found with pleasure that his captivity had taken away nothing of his power, and that he was still master of that element on whose bosom he had so often sported as a boy.

Fear, that relentless pursuer, clogged Dantès' efforts. He listened if any noise was audible; each time that he rose over the waves his looks scanned the horizon, and strove to penetrate the darkness. Every wave seemed a boat in his pursuit, and he redoubled exertions that increased his distance from the *château*, but the repetition of which weakened his strength. He swam on still, and already the terrible *château* had disappeared in the darkness. He could not see it, but he *felt* its presence. An hour passed, during which Dantès, excited by the feeling of freedom, continued to cleave the waves.

'Let us see,' said he, 'I have swum above an hour, but as the wind is against me, that has retarded my speed; however, if I am not mistaken, I must be close to the isle of Tiboulen.

But what if I were mistaken?' A shudder passed over him. He sought to tread water, in order to rest himself; but the sea was too violent, and he felt that he could not make use of this means of repose. 'Well,' said he, 'I will swim on until I am worn out, or the cramp siezes me, and then I shall sink.' And he struck out with the energy of despair.

Suddenly the sky seemed to him to become still darker and more dense, and compact clouds lowered towards him; at the same time he felt a violent pain in his knee. His imagination told him a ball had struck him, and that in a moment he would hear the report; but he heard nothing. Dantès put out his hand, and felt resistance; he then extended his leg, and felt the land, and in an instant guessed the nature of the object he had taken for a cloud. Before him rose a mass of strangely formed rocks, that resembled nothing so much as a vast fire petrified at the moment of its most fervent combustion. It was the isle of Tiboulen. Dantès rose, advanced a few steps, and, with a fervent prayer of gratitude, stretched himself on the granite, which seemed to him softer than down. Then, in spite of the wind and rain, he fell into the deep, sweet sleep of those worn out by fatigue.

At the expiration of an hour Edmond was awakened by the roar of the thunder. The tempest was unchained and let loose in all its fury; from time to time a flash of lightning stretched across the heavens like a fiery serpent, lighting up the clouds that rolled on like the waves of an immense chaos.

Dantès had not been deceived — he had reached the first of the two isles, which was, in reality, Tiboulen. He knew that it was barren and without shelter; but when the sea became more calm, he resolved to plunge into its waves again, and swim to Lemaire, equally arid, but larger, and consequently better adapted for concealment.

An overhanging rock offered him a temporary shelter, and scarcely had he availed himself of it when the tempest burst forth in all its fury. Edmond felt the rock beneath which he lay, tremble, the waves, dashing themselves against the granite rock, wetted him with their spray. In safety as he was, he felt himself become giddy in the midst of this war of the elements and the dazzling brightness of the lightning. It seemed to him that the island trembled to its base, and that it would, like a vessel at anchor, break her moorings and bear him off into the centre of the storm.

He remembered then that he had not eaten or drunk for four and twenty hours. He extended his hands, and drank greedily of the rain-water that had lodged in a hollow of the rock. As he rose, a flash of lightning that seemed as if the whole of the heavens were opened, illumined the darkness. By its light, between the isle of Lemaire and Cape Croiselle, a quarter of a league distant, Dantès saw, like a spectre, a fishing-boat driven rapidly on by the force of the wind and waves. A second after, he saw it again, approaching nearer. Dantès cried out at the top of his voice to warn them of their danger, but they saw it themselves. Another flash showed him four men clinging to the shattered mast and the rigging, while a fifth clung to the broken rudder. The men he beheld doubtless saw him, for their cries were carried to his ears by the wind. Above the splintered mast a sail rent to tatters was waving; suddenly the ropes that held it gave way, and it disappeared in the darkness of the night like a vast sea-bird.

At the same moment a violent crash was heard, and the cries of distress. Perched on the summit of the rock, Dantès saw, by the lightning, the vessel in pieces; and amongst the fragments were visible the agonised features of the unhappy sailors. Then all became dark again.

Dantès ran down the rocks at the risk of himself being dashed to pieces; he listened, he strove to examine, but he heard and saw nothing — all human cries had ceased and the tempest alone continued to rage. By degrees the wind abated, vast, grey clouds rolled towards the west, and the blue firmament appeared studded with bright stars. Soon a red streak became visible in the horizon, the waves whitened, a light played over them and gilded their foaming crests with gold. It was day.

Dantès stood silent and motionless before this vast spectacle, for since his captivity he had forgotten it. He turned towards the fortress and looked both at the sea and the land. The gloomy building rose from the bosom of the ocean with that imposing majesty of inanimate objects that seems at once to watch and command. It was about five o'clock. The sea continued to grow calmer.

'In two or three hours,' thought Dantès, 'the turnkey will enter my chamber, find the body of my poor friend, recognise it, seek for me in vain, and give the alarm. Then the passage will be discovered; the men who cast me into the sea and who must have heard the cry I uttered will be questioned. Then boats filled with armed soldiers will pursue the wretched fugitive. The cannon will warn everyone to refuse shelter to a man wandering about naked and famished. The police of Marseilles will be on alert by the land, whilst the government pursues me by sea. I am cold. I am hungry. I have lost even the knife that saved me. Oh, my God! I have suffered enough surely. Have pity on me, and do for me now what I am unable to do for myself.'

As Dantès (his eyes turned in the direction of the Château d'If) uttered this prayer, he saw appear at the extremity of the isle of Pomègue like a bird skimming over the sea, a small bark, that the eye of a sailor alone could recognise as a Genoese tartane. She was coming out of Marseilles harbour, and was standing out to sea rapidly, her sharp prow cleaving through the waves.

'Oh!' cried Edmond, 'to think that in half an hour I could join her, did I not fear being questioned, detected, and con-

150

veyed back to Marseilles! What can I do? What story can I invent? Under pretext of trading, these men, who are in reality smugglers, will prefer selling me to doing a good action. I must wait. But I cannot — I am starving. In a few hours my strength will be utterly exhausted; besides, perhaps I have not been missed at the fortress. I can pass as one of the sailors wrecked last night. This story will pass current, for there is no one left to contradict me.' As he spoke, Dantès looked towards the spot where the fishing-vessel had been wrecked, and started. The red cap of one of the sailors hung to a point of the rock and some beams that had formed part of the vessel's keep, floated at the foot of the crags.

In an instant Dantès plan was formed. He swam to the cap, placed it on his head, seized one of the beams, and struck out so as to cross the line the vessel was taking. 'I am saved!' murmured he. And this conviction restored his strength.

He soon perceived the vessel, which, having the wind right ahead, was tacking between the Château d'If and the tower of Planier. For an instant he feared less the bark, instead of keeping inshore, should stand out to sea, but he soon saw by her manoeuvres that she wished to pass, like most vessels bound for Italy, between the islands of Jaros and Calaseraigne. However, the vessel and the swimmer insensibly neared one another, and in one of its tacks the bark approached within a quarter of a mile of him. He rose on the waves, making signs of distress; but no one on board perceived him, and the vessel stood on another tack. Dantès would have cried out, but he reflected that the wind would drown his voice.

It was then he rejoiced at his precaution in taking the beam, for without it he would have been unable perhaps, to reach the vessel — certainly to return to shore, should he be unsuccessful in attracting attention.

Dantès, although almost sure as to what course the bark would take, had yet watched it anxiously until it tacked and stood towards him. Then he advanced; before they met however, the vessel again changed her direction.

By a violent effort he rose half out of the water, waving his cap, and uttering a loud shout peculiar to sailors. This time he was both seen and heard, and the tartane instantly steered towards him. At the same time he saw they were about to lower a boat. An instant after, the boat, rowed by two men, advanced rapidly towards him. Dantès abandoned the beam which he now thought useless, and swam vigorously to meet them. But he had reckoned too much upon his strength, and then he felt how serviceable the beam had been to him. His arms grew stiff, his legs had lost their flexibility, and he was almost breathless. He uttered a second cry. The two sailors redoubled their efforts, and one of them cried in Italian, 'Courage'. The word reached his ear as a wave which he no longer had the strength to surmount passed over his head. He rose again to the surface, supporting himself by one of those desperate efforts a drowning man makes, uttered a third cry, and felt himself sink again, as if the fatal shot were again tied to his feet. The water passed over his head, and the sky seemed livid. A violent effort again brought him to the surface. He felt as if something seized him by the hair, but he saw and heard nothing. He had fainted.

When he opened his eyes, Dantès found himself on the deck of the tartane. His first care was to see what direction they were pursuing. They were rapidly leaving the Château d'If behind. Dantès was so exhausted that the exclamation of joy he uttered was mistaken for a sigh.

As we have said, he was lying on the deck. A sailor was rubbing his limbs with a woollen cloth; another, whom he recognised as the one who had cried out 'Courage' held a gourd full of rum to his mouth; while the third, an old sailor, at once the pilot and captain, looked on with that egotistical pity men feel for a misfortune that they have escaped yesterday and which may overtake them tomorrow.

'Who are you?' said the pilot, in bad French.

'I am,' replied Dantès in bad Italian, 'a Maltese sailor. We were coming from Syracuse laden with grain. The storm of last night overtook us at Cape Morgieu, and we were wrecked on these rocks. You have saved my life, and I thank you.'

'Now, what are we to do with you?' said the captain.

'Alas! anything you please. My captain is dead; I have barely escaped; but I am a good sailor. Leave me at the first port you make; I shall be sure to find employment.'

'Do you know the Mediterranean?'

'I have sailed over it since my childhood.'

'You know the best harbours?'

'There are few ports that I could not enter or leave with my eyes shut.'

'I say, Captain,' said the sailor who had cried 'Courage!' to Dantès, 'if what he says is true, what hinders his staying with us?'

'If he says true,' said the captain doubtingly. 'But in his present condition he will promise anything, and take his chance of keeping it afterwards.'

'I will do more than I promise,' said Dantès.

'We shall see,' returned the other, smiling.

'As you will,' said Dantès, getting up. 'Where are you going?'

'To Leghorn.'

'Then why, instead of tacking so frequently, do you not sail nearer the wind?'

'Because we should run straight on to the island of Rion.'

'You shall pass it by twenty fathoms.'

'Take the helm then, and let us see what you know.'

The young man took the helm, ascertaining by a slight pressure if the vessel answered the rudder, and seeing that, without being a first rate sailer, yet she was tolerably obedient:

'To the braces!' said he.

The four seamen who composed the crew, obeyed, whilst the pilot looked on.

'Haul taut!'

They obeyed.

'Belay!'

This order was also executed, and the vessel passed, as Dantès had predicted, twenty fathoms to the right.

'Bravo!' cried the captain.

'Bravo!' repeated the sailors.

And they all regarded with astonishment this man whose eye had recovered an intelligence and his body a vigour they were far from suspecting.

'You see,' said Dantès, quitting the helm, 'I shall be of some use to you at least during the voyage. If you do not want me at Leghorn, you can leave me there, and I will pay you out of the first wages I get, for my food and the clothes you lend me.

'Ah,' said the captain, 'we can agree very well, if you are reasonable.'

'Give me what you give the others,' returned Dantès.

'That's not fair,' said the seaman who had saved Dantès, 'for you know more than we do.'

'What's that to you, Jacopo?' returned the captain. 'Everyone's free to ask what he pleases.'

'That's true,' replied Jacopo, 'I only made a remark.'

'Well, you would do much better to lend him a jacket, and a pair of trousers if you have them.'

'No,' said Jacopo, 'but I have a shirt and a pair of trousers.'

'That is all I want,' interrupted Dantès. 'Thank you, my friend.'

Jacopo dived into the hold and soon returned with what Edmond wanted.

'Now then, do you wish for anything else?' said the captain.

'A piece of bread, and another glass of the capital rum I tasted, for I have not eaten or drunk for a long time.'

He had not in truth, tasted food for forty hours. They brought him a piece of bread, and Jacopo offered him the gourd.

'Larboard your helm!' cried the captain to the helmsman.

Dantès glanced to the same side as he lifted the gourd to his mouth.

'Hulloa! What's the matter at the Château d'If?' said the captain.

A small white cloud, which had attracted Dantès' attention, crowned the summit of the bastion of the Château d'If. A moment later the far off report of a gun was heard. The sailors looked at one another.

'What does it mean?' asked the captain.

'A prisoner has escaped from the Château d'If, and they are firing the alarm gun,' replied Dantès.

The captain glanced at him, but he had lifted the rum to his lips, and was drinking it with so much composure that his suspicions, if he had any, died away.

'At any rate,' murmured he, 'if it be, so much the better, for I have made a rare acquisition.'

Under pretence of being fatigued, Dantès asked to take the helm. The helmsman, enchanted to be relieved, looked at the captain who, by a nod, indicated that he might abandon it to his new comrade. Dantès could thus keep his eye on Marseilles.

'What day of the month?' asked he of Jacopo, who sat down beside him.

'The 28th of February.'

'In what year?' asked Dantès.

'In what year? You ask me what year!'

'Yes,' replied the young man, 'I ask you in what year!'

'You have forgotten?'

'I was so frightened last night,' said Dantès laughing, 'that I have almost lost my memory. I ask you what year it is?'

'1829,' said Jacopo.

It was fourteen years, day for day, since Dantès arrest.

He was nineteen when he entered the Château d'If; he was thirty-three when he escaped. A sorrowful smile passed over his face; he asked himself what had become of Mercédès, who must believe him dead. Then his eyes lighted up with hatred as he thought of the three men who had caused him so long and wretched captivity. He renewed vengeance against, Danglers, Fernand, and Villefort the oath of implacable vengeance he had made in his dungeon. This oath was no longer a vain menace; for the fastest sailor in the Mediterranean would have been unable to overtake the little tartane, that with every stitch of canvas set, was flying before the wind to Leghorn.

Hornblower and the Man Who Felt Queer
from Mr Midshipman Hornblower

by

C. S. FORESTER

This time the wolf was prowling round outside the sheep-fold. H. M. frigate *Indefatigable* had chased the French corvette *Papillon* into the mouth of the Gironde, and was seeking a way of attacking her where she lay anchored in the stream under the protection of the batteries at the mouth. Captain Pellew took his ship into shoal water as far as he dared, until, in fact, the batteries fired warning shots to make him keep his distance, and he stared long and keenly through his glass at the corvette. Then he shut his telescope and turned on his heel to give the order that worked the *Indefatigable* away from the dangerous lee shore — out of sight of land, in fact.

His departure might lull the French into a sense of security which, he hoped, would prove unjustified. For he had no intention of leaving them undisturbed. If the corvette could be captured or sunk, not only would she be unavailable for raids on British commerce but also the French would be forced to increase their coastal defences at this point and lessen the effort that could be put out elsewhere. War is a matter of savage blow and counterblow, and even a forty-gun frigate could strike shrewd blows if shrewdly handled.

Midshipman Hornblower was walking the lee side of the

quarterdeck, as became his lowly station as the junior officer of the watch, in the afternoon, when Midshipman Kennedy approached him. Kennedy took off his hat with a flourish and bowed low, as his dancing master had once taught him, left foot advanced, hat down by the right knee. Hornblower entered into the spirit of the game, laid his hat against his stomach and bent himself in the middle three times in quick succession. Thanks to his physical awkwardness, he could parody ceremonial solemnity almost without trying.

'Most grave and reverend signior,' said Kennedy, 'I bear the compliments of Captain Sir Ed'ard Pellew, who humbly solicits Your Gravity's attendance at dinner at eight bells in the afternoon watch.'

'My respects to Sir Edward,' replied Hornblower, bowing to his knees at the mention of the name, 'and I shall condescend to make a brief appearance.'

'I am sure the captain will be both relieved and delighted,' said Kennedy. 'I will convey him my felicitations along with your most flattering acceptance.'

Both hats flourished with even greater elaboration than before, but at that moment both young men noticed Mr Bolton, the officer of the watch, looking at them from the windward side, and they hurriedly put their hats on and assumed attitudes more consonant with the dignity of officers holding their warrants from King George.

'What's in the captain's mind?' asked Hornblower.

Kennedy laid one finger alongside his nose. 'If I knew that, I should rate a couple of epaulets,' he said. 'Something's brewing, and I suppose one of these days we shall know what it is. Until then, all that we little victims can do is to play, unconscious of our doom. Meanwhile, be careful not to let the ship fall overboard.'

There was no sign of anything brewing while dinner was being eaten in the great cabin of the *Indefatigable*. Pellew was a courtly host at the head of the table. Conversation flowed freely and along indifferent channels among the senior officers present — the two lieutenants, Eccles and Chadd, and the sailing master, Soames. Hornblower and the other junior officer — Mallory, a midshipman of more than two years' seniority — kept silent, as midshipmen should, thereby being able to devote their undivided attention to the food, so vastly superior to what was served in the midshipmen's berth.

'A glass of wine with you, Mr Hornblower,' said Pellew, raising his glass.

Hornblower tried to bow gracefully in his seat while raising his glass. He sipped cautiously, for he had early found that he had a weak head and he disliked feeling drunk.

The table was cleared and there was a brief moment of expectancy as the company awaited Pellew's next move.

'Now, Mr Soames,' said Pellew, 'let us have that chart.'

It was a map of the mouth of the Gironde with the soundings; somebody had pencilled in the positions of the shore batteries.

'The *Papillon*,' said Sir Edward — he did not condescend to pronounce it French-fashion — 'lies just here. Mr Soames took the bearings.' He indicated a pencilled cross on the chart, far up the channel.

'You gentlemen,' went on Pellew, 'are going in with the boats to fetch her out.'

So that was it. A cutting-out expedition.

'Mr Eccles will be in general command. I will ask him to tell you his plan.'

The grey-haired first lieutenant with the surprisingly young blue eyes looked round at the others.

'I shall have the launch,' he said, 'and Mr Soames the cutter. Mr Chadd and Mr Mallory will command the first and second gigs. And Mr Hornblower will command the jolly boat. Each of the boats except Mr Hornblower's will have a junior officer second in command.'

That would not be necessary for the jolly boat with its crew of seven. The launch and cutter would carry from thirty to forty men each, and the gigs twenty each; it was a large force that was being dispatched — nearly half the ship's company.

'She's a ship of war,' explained Eccles, reading their thoughts. 'No merchantman. Ten guns a side, and full of men.'

Nearer two hundred men than a hundred, certainly — plentiful opposition for a hundred and twenty British seamen.

'But we will be attacking her by night and taking her by surprise,' said Eccles, reading their thoughts again.

'Surprise,' put in Pellew, 'is more than half the battle, as you know, gentlemen. Please pardon the interruption, Mr Eccles.'

'At the moment,' went on Eccles, 'we are out of sight of land. We are about to stand in again. We have never hung about this part of the coast, and the Frogs'll think we've gone for good. We'll make the land after nightfall, stand in as far as possible, and then the boats will go in. High water tomorrow morning is at four-fifty; dawn is at five-thirty. The attack will be delivered at four-thirty, so that the watch below will have had time to get to sleep. The launch will attack on the starboard quarter, and the cutter on the larboard quarter. Mr Mallory's gig will attack on the larboard bow, and Mr Chadd's on the starboard bow. Mr Chadd will be responsible for cutting the corvette's cable as soon as he has mastered the forecastle and the other boats' crews have at least reached the quarter-deck.'

Eccles looked round at the three other commanders of the large boats, and they nodded understanding. Then he went on, 'Mr Hornblower with the jolly boat will wait until the attack has gained a foothold on the deck. He will then board at the main chains, either to starboard or larboard, as he sees fit, and he will at once ascend the main rigging, paying no attention to whatever fighting is going on on deck. He will see to it that the main-topsail is loosed, and he will sheet it home on receipt of further orders. I, myself, or Mr Soames in the event of my being killed or wounded, will send two hands to the wheel and will attend to steering the corvette as soon as she is under way. The tide will take us out, and the *Indefatigable* will be awaiting us just out of gunshot from the shore batteries.'

'Any comments, gentlemen?' asked Pellew.

That was the moment when Hornblower should have spoken up — the only moment when he could. Eccles' orders had set in motion sick feelings of apprehension in his stomach. Hornblower was no main-topman, and Hornblower knew it. He hated heights, and he hated going aloft. He knew he had none of the monkey-like agility and self-confidence of the good seaman. He was unsure of himself aloft in the dark even in the *Indefatigable*, and he was utterly appalled at the thought of going aloft in an entirely strange ship and finding his way amid strange rigging. He felt himself quite unfitted for the duty assigned to him, and he should have raised a protest at once, on account of his unfitness. But he let the opportunity pass, for he was overcome by the matter-of-fact way in which the other officers accepted the plan. He looked round at the unmoved faces; nobody was paying any attention to him, and he jibbed at making himself conspicuous. He swallowed; he even got as far as opening his mouth, but still no one looked at him and his protest died.

'Very well, then, gentlemen,' said Pellew. 'I think you had better go into the details, Mr Eccles.'

Then it was too late. Eccles, with the chart before him, was pointing out the course to be taken through the shoals and mudbanks of the Gironde, and expatiating on the position of the shore batteries and on the influence of the lighthouse of Cordouan upon the distance to which the *Indefatigable* could approach in daylight. Hornblower listened, trying to concentrate despite his apprehensions.

Eccles finished his remark and Pellew closed the meeting, 'Since you all know your duties, gentlemen, I think you should start your preparations. The sun is about to set and you will find you have plenty to do.'

The boats' crews had to be told off; it was necessary to see that the men were armed and that the boats were provisioned in case of emergency. Every man had to be instructed in the duties expected of him. And Hornblower had to rehearse himself in ascending the main shrouds and laying out along the main-topsail yard. He did it twice, forcing himself to make the difficult climb up the futtock shrouds, which, projecting outward from the mainmast, made it necessary to climb several feet while hanging back downward, locking fingers and toes into the ratlines.

He could just manage it, moving slowly and carefully, although clumsily. He stood on the foot rope and worked his way out to the yardarm — the foot rope was attached along the yard so as to hang nearly four feet below it. The principle was to set his feet on the rope with his arms over the yard, then, holding the yard in his armpits, to shuffle sideways along the foot rope to cast off the gaskets and loosen the sail.

Twice Hornblower made the whole journey, battling with the disquiet of his stomach at the thought of the hundred-foot drop below him. Finally, gulping with nervousness, he transferred his grip to the brace and forced himself to slide down it to the deck — that would be his best route when the time came to sheet the topsail home. It was a long, perilous descent; Hornblower told himself — as indeed he had said to himself when he had first seen men go aloft — that similar feats in a circus at home would be received with 'Oh's' and 'Ah's' of appreciation.

He was by no means satisfied with himself even when he reached the deck, and at the back of his mind was a vivid picture of his missing his hold, when the time came for him to repeat the performance in the *Papillon*, and falling headlong to the deck — a second or two of frightful fear while rushing through the air, and then a shattering crash. And the success of the attack hinged on him as much as on anyone — if the topsail were not promptly set to give the corvette steerageway, she would run aground on one of the shoals in the river mouth, to be ignominiously recaptured, and half the crew of the *Indefatigable* would be dead or prisoners.

In the waist, the jolly boat's crew was formed up for his inspection. He saw to it that the oars were properly muffled, that each man had pistol and cutlass, and made sure that every pistol was at half cock, so that there was no fear of a premature shot giving warning of the attack. He allocated duties to each man in the loosing of the topsail, laying stress on the possibility that casualties might necessitate unrehearsed changes in the scheme.

'I will mount the rigging first,' said Hornblower.

That had to be the case. He had to lead — it was expected of him. More than that; if he had given any other order, it would have excited comment and contempt.

'Jackson,' went on Hornblower, addressing the coxswain, 'you will quit the boat last and take command if I fall.'

'Aye, aye, sir.'

It was usual to use the poetic expression 'fall' for 'die,' and it was only after Hornblower had uttered the word that he thought about its horrible real meaning in the present circumstances.

'Is that all understood?' asked Hornblower harshly; it was his mental stress that made his voice grate so.

Everyone nodded except one man. 'Begging your pardon, sir,' said Hales, the young man who pulled stroke oar; 'I'm feeling a bit queerlike.'

Hales was a lightly built young fellow of swarthy countenance. He put his hand to his forehead with a vague gesture as he spoke.

'You're not the only one to feel queer,' snapped Hornblower.

The other men chuckled. The thought of running the gauntlet of the shore batteries, of boarding an armed corvette in the teeth of opposition, might well raise apprehension in the breast of any of them. Most of the men detailed for the expedition must have felt qualms to some extent.

'I don't mean that, sir,' said Hales indignantly. 'Course I don't.'

But Hornblower and the others paid him no attention.

'You just keep your mouth shut,' growled Jackson.

There could be nothing but contempt for a man who announced himself sick after being told off on a dangerous duty. Hornblower felt sympathy as well as contempt. He himself had been too much of a coward even to give voice to his apprehension — too much afraid of what people would say about him.

'Dismiss,' said Hornblower. 'I'll pass the word for all of you when you are wanted.'

There were some hours yet to wait while the *Indefatigable* crept inshore, with the lead going steadily and Pellew himself attending to the course of the frigate. Hornblower, despite his nervousness and his miserable apprehensions, yet found time to appreciate the superb seamanship displayed as Pellew brought the big frigate in through these tricky waters on that dark night. His interest was so caught by the procedure that the little tremblings which had been assailing him ceased to manifest themselves; Hornblower was of the type that would continue to observe and to learn on his deathbed.

By the time the *Indefatigable* had reached the point off the mouth of the river where it was desirable to launch the boats, Hornblower had learned a good deal about the practical application of the principle of coastwise navigation and a good deal about the organisation of a cutting-out expedition, and by self-analysis he had learned even more about the psychology of a raiding party before a raid.

He had mastered himself, to all outside appearance, by the time he went down into the jolly boat as she heaved on the inky-black water, and he gave the command to shove off in a quiet, steady voice. Hornblower took the tiller — the feel of that solid bar of wood was reassuring, and it was old habit now to sit in the stern sheets with hand and elbow upon it — and the men began to pull slowly after the dark shapes of the four big boats. There was plenty of time, and the flowing tide would take them up the estuary. That was just as well, for on one side of them lay the batteries of St Dyé, and inside the estuary on the other side was the fortress of Blaye; forty big guns trained to sweep the channel, and none of the five boats could withstand a single shot from one of them.

He kept his eyes attentively on the cutter ahead of him. Soames had the dreadful responsibility of taking the boats up the channel, while all he had to do was to follow in her wake — all, except to loose that main-topsail. Hornblower found himself shivering again.

Hales, the man who had said he felt queer, was pulling stroke oar; Hornblower could just see his dark form moving rhythmically back and forward at each slow stroke. After a single glance, Hornblower paid him no more attention, and was staring after the cutter when a sudden commotion brought his mind back into the boat. Someone had missed his stroke; someone had thrown all six oars into confusion as a result.

'Mind what you're doing, blast you, Hales,' whispered Jackson, the coxswain, with desperate urgency.

For answer there was a sudden cry from Hales, loud, but fortunately not too loud, and Hales pitched forward against Hornblower's and Jackson's legs, kicking and writhing.

'The swine's having a fit,' growled Jackson.

The kicking and writhing went on. Across the water through the darkness came a sharp, scornful whisper. 'Mr Hornblower,' said the voice — it was Eccles putting a word of exasperation into his sotto voce question, 'cannot you keep your men quiet?'

Eccles had brought the launch round almost alongside the jolly boat to say this to him, and the desperate need for silence was dramatically demonstrated by the absence of any of the usual blasphemy. Hornblower opened his mouth to make an explanation, but he fortunately realised that raiders in open boats did not make explanations when under the guns of the fortress of Blaye.

'Aye, aye, sir,' was all he whispered back, and the launch continued on its mission of shepherding the flotilla in the tracks of the cutter.

'Take his oar, Jackson,' he whispered furiously to the coxswain, and he stooped and with his own hands dragged the writhing figure toward him and out of Jackson's way.

'You might try pouring water on 'im sir,' suggested Jackson hoarsely as he moved to the after thwart. 'There's the bailer 'andy.'

Sea water was the seaman's cure for every ill, his panacea. But Hornblower let the sick man lie. His struggles were coming to an end, and Hornblower wished to make no noise with the bailer. The lives of more than a hundred men depended on silence. Now that they were well into the actual estuary they were within easy reach of cannon shot from the shore, and a single cannon shot would rouse the crew of the *Papillon*, ready to man the bulwarks to beat off the attack, ready to drop cannon balls into the boats alongside, ready to shatter approaching boats with a tempest of grape.

Silently the boats glided up the estuary; Soames in the cutter was setting a slow pace, with an occasional stroke at the oars to maintain steerageway. Presumably he knew very well what

166

he was doing; the channel he had selected was an obscure one between mudbanks, impracticable for anything except small boats, and he had a twenty-foot pole with him with which to take the soundings — quicker and much more silent than using the lead. Minutes were passing fast, and yet the night was still utterly dark, with no hint of approaching dawn. Strain his eyes as he would, Hornblower could not be sure that he could see the flat shores on either side of him. It would call for sharp eyes on the land to detect the little boats being carried up by the tide.

Hales at his feet stirred and then stirred again. His hand, feeling around in the darkness, found Hornblower's ankle and apparently examined it with curiosity. He muttered something, the words dragging out into a moan.

'Shut up,' whispered Hornblower, trying, like the saint of old, to make a tongue of his whole body, so that he might express the urgency of the occasion without making a sound audible at any distance. Hales set his elbow on Hornblower's knee and levered himself up into a sitting position, swaying with bent knees and supporting himself against Hornblower.

'Sit down, damn you,' whispered Hornblower, shaking with fury and anxiety.

'Where's Mary?' asked Hales in a conversational tone.

'Shut up!'

'Mary!' said Hales, lurching against him. 'Mary!'

Each successive word was louder. Hornblower felt instinctively that Hales would soon be speaking in a loud voice, that he might even soon be shouting. Old recollections of conversations with his doctor further stirred at the back of his mind; he remembered that persons emerging from epileptic fits were not responsible for their actions, and might be, and often were, dangerous.

'Mary!' said Hales again.

Victory and the lives of a hundred men depended on silencing Hales, and silencing him instantly. Hornblower thought of the pistol in his belt, and of using the butt, but there was another weapon more conveniently to his hand. He unshipped the tiller, a three-foot bar of solid oak, and he swung it with all the venom and fury of despair. The tiller crashed down on Hales' head, and Hales, an unuttered word cut short in his throat, fell silent in the bottom of the boat.

There was no sound from the boat's crew, save for something like a sigh from Jackson, whether approving or disapproving, Hornblower neither knew nor cared. He had done his duty, and he was certain of it. He had struck down a helpless idiot, most probably he had killed him, but the surprise upon which the success of the expedition depended had not been imperilled. He reshipped the tiller and resumed the silent task of keeping in the wake of the gigs.

Far away ahead — in the darkness it was impossible to estimate the distance — there was a nucleus of greater darkness, close on the surface of the black water. It might be the corvette. A dozen more silent strokes, and Hornblower was sure of it. Soames had done a magnificent job of pilotage, leading the boats straight to that objective. The cutter and launch were diverging now from the two gigs. The four boats were separating in readiness to launch their simultaneous converging attack.

'Easy,' whispered Hornblower, and the jolly boat's crew ceased to pull.

Hornblower had his orders. He had to wait until the attack had gained a foothold on the deck. His hand clenched convulsively on the tiller; the excitement of dealing with Hales had driven the thought of having to ascend strange rigging in the darkness clear out of his head, and now it recurred with redoubled urgency. Hornblower was afraid.

Although he could see the corvette, the boats had vanished from his sight, had passed out of his field of vision. The corvette

rode to her anchor, her spars just visible against the night sky —
that was where he had to climb! She seemed to tower up
hugely. Close by the corvette he saw a splash in the dark
water — the boats were closing in fast and someone's stroke
had been a little careless. At that same moment came a shout
from the corvette's deck, and when the shout was repeated,
it was echoed a hundredfold from the boats rushing alongside.
The yelling was lusty and prolonged, of set purpose. A sleeping
enemy would be bewildered by the din, and the progress of
the shouting would tell each boat's crew of the extent of the
success of the others. The British seamen were yelling like
madmen. A flash and a bang from the corvette's deck told of
the firing of the first shot; soon pistols were popping and muskets
banging from several points of the deck.

'Give way!' said Hornblower. He uttered the order as if
it had been torn from him by the rack.

The jolly boat moved forward while Hornblower fought
down his feelings and tried to make out what was going on
on board. He could see no reason for choosing one side of the
corvette in preference to the other, and the larboard side was
the nearer, and so he steered the boat to the larboard main
chains. So interested was he in what he was doing that he
remembered only in the nick of time to give the order, 'In
oars.' He put the tiller over and the boat swirled round and
the bowman hooked on.

From the deck just above came a noise exactly like a tinker
hammering on a cooking pot; Hornblower noted the curious
noise as he stood up in the stern sheets. He felt the cutlass at
his side and the pistol in his belt, and then he sprang for the
chains. With a mad leap he reached them and hauled himself
up. The shrouds came into his hands, his feet found the ratlines
beneath them, and he began to climb. As his head cleared the
bulwark and he could see the deck, the flash of a pistol shot
illuminated the scene momentarily, fixing the struggle on the

deck in a static moment, like a picture. Before and below him a British seaman was fighting a furious cutlass duel with a French officer, and he realised with vague astonishment that the kettle-mending noise he had heard was the sound of cutlass against cutlass — that clash of steel against steel that poets wrote about. So much for romance.

The realisation carried him far up the shrouds. At his elbow he felt the futtock shrouds, and he transferred himself to them, hanging back downward with his toes hooked into the ratlines and his hands clinging like death. That lasted for only two or three desperate seconds, and then he hauled himself onto the topmast shrouds and began the final ascent, his lungs bursting with the effort. Here was the topsail yard, and Hornblower flung himself across it and felt with his feet for the foot rope. Merciful God! There was no foot rope — his feet searching in the darkness met only unresisting air. A hundred feet above the deck he hung, squirming and kicking like a baby held up at arm's length in his father's hands. There was no foot rope; it may have been with this very situation in mind that the Frenchmen had removed it. There was no foot rope, so that he could not make his way out to the yardarm. Yet the gaskets must be cast off and the sail loosed — everything depended on that. Hornblower had seen daredevil seamen run out along the yards, standing upright, as though walking a tight-rope. That was the only way to reach the yardarm now.

For a moment he could not breathe as his weak flesh revolted against the thought of walking along that yard above the black abyss. This was fear, the fear that stripped a man of his manhood, turning his bowels to water and his limbs to paper. Yet his furiously active mind continued to work. He had been resolute enough in dealing with Hales. Where he personally was not involved he had been brave enough; he had not hesitated to strike down the wretched epileptic with all the strength of his arm. That was the poor sort of courage he was capable of displaying. In the simple vulgar matter of physical bravery he was utterly wanting. This was cowardice, the sort of thing that men spoke about behind their hands to other men. He could not bear the thought of that in himself; it was worse — awful though the alternative might be — than the thought of falling through the night to the deck. With a gasp, he brought his knee up onto the yard, heaving himself up until he stood upright. He felt the rounded, canvas-covered timber under his feet, and his instincts told him not to dally there for a moment.

'Come on men!' he yelled, and he dashed out along the yard.

It was twenty feet to the yardarm, and he covered the distance in a few frantic strides. Utterly reckless by now, he put his hands down on the yard, clasped it and laid his body across it again, his hands seeking the gaskets. A thump on the yard told him that Oldroyd, who had been detailed to come after him, had followed him out along the yard — he had six feet less to go. There could be no doubt that the other members of the jolly boat's crew were on the yard, and that Clough had led the way to the starboard yardarm. It was obvious from the rapidity with which the sail came loose. Here was the brace beside him. Without any thought of danger now, for he was delirious with excitement and triumph, he grasped it with both hands and jerked himself off the yard. His waving legs found the rope and twined about it, and he let himself slide down it.

Fool that he was! Would he never learn sense and prudence? Would he never remember that vigilance and precaution must never be relaxed? He had allowed himself to slide so fast that the rope seared his hands, and when he tried to tighten his grip so as to slow down his progress, it caused him such agony that he had to relax it again and slide on down with the rope stripping the skin from his hands as though peeling off a glove. His feet reached the deck and

'Come on men!' he yelled, and he dashed out along the yard

he momentarily forgot the pain as he looked round him.

There was the faintest grey light beginning to show now, and there were no sounds of battle. It had been a well-worked surprise — a hundred men flung suddenly on the deck of the corvette had swept away the anchor watch and mastered the vessel in a single rush before the watch below could come up to offer any resistance.

Chadd's stentorian voice came pealing from the forecastle, 'Cable's cut, sir!'

Then Eccles bellowed from aft, 'Mr Hornblower!'

'Sir!' yelled Hornblower.

'Sheet that topsail home!'

A rush of men came to help — not only his own boat's crew but every man of initiative and spirit. Halyards, sheets and braces; the sail was trimmed round and was drawing full in the light southerly air, and the *Papillon* swung round to go down with the first of the ebb. Dawn was coming up fast, with a trifle of mist on the surface of the water.

Over the starboard quarter came a sullen, bellowing roar, and then the misty air was torn by a series of infernal screams, supernaturally loud. The first cannon balls Hornblower had ever heard were passing him by.

'Mr Chadd! Set the headsails! Loose the fore-tops'l! Get aloft, some of you, and set the mizzen tops'l.'

From the port bow came another salvo — Blaye was firing at them from one side, St Dyé from the other, now that they could guess what had happened on board the *Papillon*. But the corvette was moving fast with wind and tide, and it would be no easy matter to cripple her in the half-light. It had been a very near-run thing; a few seconds' delay could have been fatal. Only one shot from the next salvo passed within hearing, and its passage was marked by a loud snap overhead.

'Mr Mallory, get that forestay spliced!'

'Aye, aye, sir!'

It was light enough to look round the deck now; he could see Eccles at the break of the poop, directing the handling of the corvette, and Soames beside the wheel, conning her down the channel. Two groups of red-coated marines, with bayonets fixed, stood guard over the hatchways. There were four or five men lying on the deck in curiously abandoned attitudes. Dead men; Hornblower could look at them with the callousness of youth. But there was a wounded man, too, crouched groaning over his shattered thigh. Hornblower could not look at him as disinterestedly, and he was glad, maybe only for his own sake, when at that moment a seaman asked for and received permission from Mallory to leave his duties and attend to him.

'Stand by to go about!' shouted Eccles from the poop; the corvette had reached the tip of the middle-ground shoal and was about to make the turn that would carry her into the open sea.

The men came running to the braces, and Hornblower tailed on along with them. But the first contact with the harsh rope gave him such pain that he almost cried out. His hands were like raw meat, and fresh-killed at that, for blood was running from them. Now that his attention was called to them, they smarted unbearably.

The headsail sheets came over, and the corvette went handily about.

'There's the old Indy!' shouted somebody.

The *Indefatigable* was plainly visible now, lying to just out of short from the shore batteries, ready to rendezvous with her prize. Somebody cheered, and the cheering was taken up by everyone, even while the last shots from St Dye, fired at extreme range, pitched sullenly into the water alongside. Hornblower had gingerly extracted his handkerchief from his pocket and was trying to wrap it round his hand.

'Can I help you with that, sir?' asked Jackson.

Jackson shook his head as he looked at the raw surface. 'You was careless, sir. You ought to 'a' gone down 'and over 'and,' he said, when Hornblower explained to him how the injury had been caused. 'Very careless, you was, beggin' your pardon for saying so, sir. But you young gennelmen often is. You don't 'ave no thought for your necks nor your 'ides, sir.'

Hornblower looked up at the main-topsail yard high above his head, and remembered how he had walked along that slender stick of timber out to the yardarm in the dark. At the recollection of it, even here with the solid deck under his feet, he shuddered a little.

'Sorry, sir. Didn't mean to 'urt you,' said Jackson, tying the knot. 'There, that's done, as good as I can do it, sir.'

'Thank you, Jackson,' said Hornblower.

'We got to report the jolly boat as lost, sir,' went on Jackson. 'Lost?'

'She ain't towing alongside, sir. You see, we didn't leave no boat keeper in 'er. Wells, 'e was to be boat keeper, you remember, sir. But I sent 'im up the riggin a'ead o' me, seeing that 'Ales couldn't go. We wasn't too many for the job. So the jolly boat must 'a' come adrift, sir, when the ship went about.'

'What about Hales, then?' asked Hornblower.

''E was still in the boat, sir.'

Hornblower looked back up the estuary of the Gironde. Somewhere up there the jolly boat was drifting about, and lying in it was Hales, probably dead, possibly alive. In either case, the French would find him surely enough, but a cold wave of regret extinguished the warm feeling of triumph in Hornblower's bosom when he thought about Hales back there. If it had not been for Hales, he would never have nerved himself — so, at least, he thought — to run out to the main-topsail yardarm; he would at this moment be ruined and branded as a coward instead of basking in the satisfaction of having capably done his duty.

Jackson saw the bleak look in his face. 'Don't you take on so, sir,' he said. 'They won't 'old the loss of the jolly boat agin you, not the captain and Mr Eccles, they won't.'

'I wasn't thinking about the jolly boat,' said Hornblower. 'I was thinking about Hales.'

'Oh, 'im?' said Jackson. 'Don't you fret about 'im, sir. "E wouldn't never 'ave made no seaman, not no 'ow.'

Jack Easy Aboard the Aurora
from Mr Midshipman Easy
by
CAPTAIN MARRYAT

The first-lieutenant of the *Aurora* was a very good officer in many respects, but, as a midshipman, he had contracted the habit of putting his hands in his pockets, and could never keep them out, even when the ship was in a gale of wind; and hands are of some use in a heavy lurch. He had more than once received serious injury from falling on these occasions, but habit was too powerful; and, although he had once broken his leg by falling down the hatchway, and had moreover a large scar on his forehead, received from being thrown to leeward against one of the guns, he still continued the practice; indeed, it was said that once, when it was necessary for him to go aloft, he had actually taken the two first rounds of the Jacob's ladder without withdrawing them, until, losing his balance, he discovered that it was not quite so easy to go aloft with his hands in his pockets. In fact, there was no getting up his hands, even when all hands were turned up. He had another peculiarity, which was, that he had taken a peculiar fancy to a quack medicine, called Enouy's Universal Medicine for all Mankind; and Mr Pottyfar was convinced in his own mind that the label was no libel, except from the greatness of its truth. In his opinion, it cured everything, and he spent one of his quarterly bills every year in bottles of this stuff; which he not only took himself every time he was unwell, but occasionally when quite well, to prevent his falling sick. He recommended it to everybody in the ship, and nothing pleased him so much as to give a dose of it to everyone who could be persuaded to take it. The officers laughed at him, but it was generally behind his back, for he became very angry if contradicted upon this one point, upon which he certainly might be considered to be a little cracked. He was indefatigable in making proselytes to his creed, and expatiated upon the virtues of the medicine for an hour running, proving the truth of his assertions by a pamphlet which, with his hands, he always carried in his trousers pocket.

Jack reported himself when he came on board, and Mr Pottyfar, who was on the quarter-deck at the time, expressed a hope that Mr Easy would take his share of the duty, now that he had had such a spell on shore; to which Jack very graciously acceded, and then went down below, where he found Gascoigne and his new messmates, with most of whom he was already acquainted.

'Well, Easy,' said Gascoigne, 'have you had enough of the shore?'

'Quite,' replied Jack, recollecting that, after the events of the night before, he was just as well on board; 'I don't intend to ask for any more leave.'

'Perhaps it's quite as well, for Mr Pottyfar is not very liberal on that score, I can tell you; there is but one way of getting leave from him.'

'Indeed,' replied Jack; 'and what is that?'

'You must pretend that you are not well, take some of his quack medicine, and then he will allow you a run on shore to work it off.'

'Oh! that's it, is it? well then, as soon as we anchor in Valetta, I'll go through a regular course, but not till then.'

'It ought to suit you, Jack; it's an equality medicine; cures one disorder just as well as the other.'

'Or kills — which levels all the patients. You're right, Gascoigne, I must patronise that stuff — for more reasons than one. Who was that person on deck in mufti?'

'The mufti, Jack; in other words, the chaplain of the ship; but he's a prime sailor, nevertheless.'

'How's that?'

'Why, he was brought up on the quarter-deck, served his time, was acting-lieutenant for two years, and then, somehow or another, he bore up for the church.'

'Indeed — what were his reasons?'

'No one knows — but they say he has been unhappy since.'

'Why so?'

'Because he did a very foolish thing, which cannot now be remedied. He supposed at the time that he would make a good parson, and now that he has long got over his fit, he finds himself wholly unfit for it — he is still the officer in heart, and is always struggling with his natural bent, which is very contrary to what a parson should feel.'

'Why don't they allow parsons to be broke by a court-martial, and turned out of the service, or to resign their commissions, like other people?'

'It won't do, Jack — they serve Heaven — there's a difference between that and serving his majesty.'

'Well, I don't understand these things. When do we sail?'

'The day after to-morrow.'

'To join the fleet off Toulon?'

'Yes; but I suppose we shall be driven on the Spanish coast going there. I never knew a man-of-war that was not.'

'No; wind always blows from the south, going up the Mediterranean.'

'Perhaps you'll take another prize, Jack — mind you don't go away without the articles of war.'

'I won't go away without Mesty, if I can help it. Oh dear, how abominable a midshipman's berth is after a long run on shore! I positively must go on deck and look at the shore, if I can do nothing else.'

'Why, ten minutes ago you had had enough of it.'

'Yes, but ten minutes here has made me feel quite sick. I shall go to the first-lieutenant for a dose.'

'I say, Easy, we must both be physicked on the same day.'

'To be sure; but stop till we get to Malta.'

Jack went on deck, made acquaintance with the chaplain and some of the officers whom he had not known, then climbed up into the maintop, where he took a seat on the armolest, and, as he looked at the shore, thought over the events that had passed, until Agnes came to his memory, and he thought only of her. When a mid is in love, he always goes aloft to think of the object of his affection; why, I don't know, except that his reverie is not so likely to be disturbed by an order from a superior officer.

The *Aurora* sailed on the second day, and with a fine breeze, stood across, making as much northing as easting; the consequence was, that one fine morning they saw the Spanish coast before they saw the Toulon fleet. Mr Pottyfar took his hands out of his pockets, because he could not examine the coast through a telescope without so doing; but this, it is said, was the first time that he had done so on the quarter-deck from the day that the ship had sailed from Port Mahon. Captain Wilson was also occupied with his telescope, so were many of the officers and midshipmen, and the men at the mastheads used their eyes, but there was nothing but a few small fishing-boats to be seen. So they all went down to breakfast, as the ship was hove-to close in with the land.

'What will Easy bet,' said one of the midshipmen, 'that we don't see a prize to-day?'

'I will not bet that we do not see a vessel — but I'll bet

you what you please, that we do not take one before twelve o'clock at night.'

'No, no, that won't do — just let the teapot travel over this way, for it's my forenoon watch.'

'It's a fine morning,' observed one of the mates, of the name of Martin; 'but I've a notion it won't be a fine evening.'

'Why not?' inquired another.

'I've now been eight years in the Mediterranean, and know something about the weather. There's a watery sky, and the wind is very steady. If we are not under double-reefed topsails to-night, say I'm no conjuror.'

'That you will be, all the same, if we are under bare poles,' said another.

'You're devilish free with your tongue, my youngster. — Easy, pull his ears for me.'

'Pull them easy, Jack, then,' said the boy, laughing.

'All hands make sail!' now resounded at the hatchways.

'There they are, depend upon it,' cried Gascoigne, catching up his hat and bolting out of the berth, followed by all the others except Martin, who had just been relieved, and thought that his presence in the waist might be dispensed with for the short time, at least, which it took him to swallow a cup of tea.

It was very true; a galliot and four lateen vessels had just made their appearance round the easternmost point, and, as soon as they observed the frigate, had hauled their wind. In a minute the *Aurora* was under a press of canvas, and the telescopes were all directed to the vessels.

'All deeply laden, sir,' observed Mr Hawkins, the chaplain; 'how the topsail of the galliot is scored!'

'They have a fresh breeze just now,' observed Captain Wilson to the first-lieutenant.

'Yes, sir, and it's coming down fast.'

'Hands by the royal halyards, there.'

The *Aurora* careened with the canvas to the rapidly increasing breeze.

'Top-gallant sheet and halyards.'

'Luff you may, quarter-master; luff, I tell you. A small pull of that weather maintop-gallant brace — that will do,' said the master.

'Top-men aloft there; — stand by to clew up the royals — and, Captain Wilson, shall we take them in? — I'm afraid of that pole, it bends now like a coach-whip,' said Mr Pottyfar, looking up aloft, with his hands in both pockets.

'In royals — lower away.'

'They are going about, sir,' said the second-lieutenant, Mr Haswell.

'Look out,' observed the chaplain, 'it's coming.'

Again the breeze increases, and the frigate was borne down.

'Hands reef topsails in stays, Mr Pottyfar.'

'Ay, ay, sir — 'bout ship.'

The helm was put down and the topsails lowered and reefed in stays.

'Very well, my lads, very well indeed,' said Captain Wilson.

Again the topsails were hoisted and top-gallant sheets home. It was a strong breeze, although the water was smooth, and the *Aurora* dashed through at the rate of eight miles an hour, with her weather leeches lifting.

'Didn't I tell you so?' said Martin to his messmates on the gangway; 'but there's more yet, my boys.'

'We must take the top-gallant sails off her,' said Captain Wilson, looking aloft — for the frigate now careened to her bearings, and the wind was increasing and squally. 'Try them a little longer'; but another squall came suddenly — the halyards were lowered, and the sails clewed up and furled.

In the meantime the frigate had rapidly gained upon the vessels, which still carried on every stitch of canvas, making short tacks in-shore. The *Aurora* was again put about with her head towards them, and they were not two points on her weather bow. The sky, which had been clear in the morning, was now overcast, the sun was obscured with opaque white clouds, and the sea was rising fast. Another ten minutes, and they then were under double-reefed topsails, and the squalls were accompanied with heavy rain. The frigate now dashed through the waves, foaming in her course and straining under the press of sail. The horizon was so thick that the vessels ahead were no longer to be seen.

'We shall have it, I expect,' said Captain Wilson.

'Didn't I say so?' observed Martin to Gascoigne. 'We take no prizes this day, depend upon it.'

'We must have another hand to the wheel, sir, if you please,' said the quarter-master, who was assisting the helmsman.

Mr Pottyfar, with his hands concealed as usual, stood by the capstern. 'I fear, sir, we cannot carry the mainsail much longer.'

'No,' observed the chaplain, 'I was thinking so.'

'Captain Wilson, if you please, we are very close in,' said the master; 'don't you think we had better go about?'

'Yes, Mr Jones — Hands about ship — and — yes, by heavens, we must! — up mainsail.'

The mainsail was taken off, and the frigate appeared to be immediately relieved. She no longer jerked and plunged as before.

'We're very near the land, Captain Wilson; thick as it is, I think I can make out the loom of it — shall we wear round, sir?' continued the master.

'Yes — hands wear ship — put the helm up.'

It was but just in time, for, as the frigate flew round, describing a circle, as she payed off before the wind, they could perceive the breakers lashing the precipitous coast not two cables' length from them.

'I had no idea we were so near,' observed the captain,

compressing his lips —. 'can they see anything of those vessels?'

'I have not seen them this quarter of an hour, sir,' replied the signalman, protecting his glass from the rain under his jacket.

'How's her head now, quarter-master?'

'South-south-east, sir.'

The sky now assumed a different appearance — the white clouds had been exchanged for others dark and murky, the wind roared at intervals, and the rain came down in torrents. Captain Wilson went down into the cabin to examine the barometer.

'The barometer has risen,' said he on his return on deck. 'Is the wind steady?'

'No sir, she's up and off three points.'

'This will end in a south-wester.'

The wet and heavy sails now flapped from the shifting of the wind.

'Up with the helm, quarter-master.'

'Up it is — she's off to south-by-west.'

The wind lulled, the rain came down in a deluge — for a minute it was quite calm, and the frigate was on an even keel.

'Man the braces. We shall be taken aback directly, depend upon it.'

The braces were hardly stretched along before this was the case. The wind flew round to the south-west with a loud roar, and it was fortunate that they were prepared — the yards were braced round, and the master asked the captain what course they were to steer.

'We must give it up,' observed Captain Wilson, holding on by the belaying pin. 'Shape our course for Cape Sicie, Mr Jones.'

And the *Aurora* flew before the gale, under her foresail and topsails close reefed. The weather was now so thick that nothing could be observed twenty yards from the vessel; the thunder pealed, and the lightning darted in every direction over the dark expanse. The watch was called as soon as the sails were trimmed, and all who could went below, wet, uncomfortable, and disappointed.

'What an old Jonah you are, Martin,' said Gascoigne.

'Yes, I am,' replied he; 'but we have the worst to come yet, in my opinion. I recollect, not two hundred miles from where we are now, we had just such a gale in the *Favourite*, and we as nearly went down, when —'

At this moment a tremendous noise was heard above, a shock was felt throughout the whole ship, which trembled fore and aft as if it were about to fall into pieces; loud shrieks were followed by plaintive cries, the lower deck was filled with smoke, and the frigate was down on her beam ends. Without exchanging a word, the whole of the occupants of the berth flew out, and were up the hatchway, not knowing what to think, but convinced that some dreadful accident had taken place.

On their gaining the deck it was at once explained; the foremast of the frigate had been struck by lightning, had been riven into several pieces, and had fallen over the larboard bow, carrying with it the main topmast and jib-boom. The jagged stump of the foremast was in flames, and burnt brightly, notwithstanding the rain fell in torrents. The ship, as soon as the foremast and main topmast had gone overboard, then broached-to furiously, throwing the men over the wheel and dashing them senseless against the carronades; the forecastle, the fore part of the main deck, and even the lower deck, were spread with men, either killed or seriously wounded, or insensible from the electric shock. The frigate was on her beam ends, and the sea broke furiously over her; all was dark as pitch, except the light from the blazing stump of the foremast, appearing like a torch, held up by the wild demons of the

The ship was on her beam ends, and the sea broke furiously over her.

storm, or when occasionally the gleaming lightning cast a momentary glare, threatening every moment to repeat its attack upon the vessel, while the deafening thunder burst almost on their devoted heads. All was dismay and confusion for a minute or two: at last Captain Wilson, who had himself lost his sight for a short time, called for the carpenter and axes — they climbed up, that is, two or three of them, and he pointed to the mizen-mast; the master was also there, and he cut loose the axes for the seamen to use; in a few minutes the mizen-mast fell over the quarter, and the helm being put hard up, the frigate payed off and slowly righted. But the horror of the scene was not yet over. The boatswain, who had been on the forecastle, had been led below, for his vision was gone for ever. The men who lay scattered about had been examined, and they were assisting them down to the care of the surgeon, when the cry of 'Fire!' issued from the lower deck. The ship had taken fire at the coal-hole and carpenter's store-room, and the smoke that now ascended was intense.

'Call the drummer,' said Captain Wilson, 'and let him beat to quarters — all hands to their stations — let the pumps be rigged and the buckets passed along. Mr Martin, see that the wounded men are taken down below. Where's Mr Haswell? Mr Pottyfar, station the men to pass the water on by hand on the lower deck. I will go there myself. Mr Jones, take charge of the ship.'

Pottyfar, who actually had taken his hands out of his pockets, hastened down to comply with the captain's orders on the main deck, as Captain Wilson descended to the deck below.

'I say, Jack, this is very different from this morning,' observed Gascoigne.

'Yes,' replied Jack, 'so it is; but I say, Gascoigne, what's the best thing to do? — when the chimney's on fire on shore, they put a wet blanket over it.'

'Yes,' replied Gascoigne; 'but when the coal-hole's on fire on board, they will not find that sufficient.'

'At all events, wet blankets must be a good thing, Ned, so let us pull out the hammocks; cut the lanyards and get some out — we can but offer them, you know, and if they do no good, at least it will show our zeal.'

'Yes, Jack, and I think when they turn in again, those whose blankets you take will agree with you, that zeal makes the service very uncomfortable. However, I think you are right.'

The two midshipmen collected three or four hands, and in a very short time they had more blankets than they could carry — there was no trouble in wetting them, for the main deck was afloat — and followed by the men they had collected, Easy and Gascoigne went down with large bundles in their arms to where Captain Wilson was giving directions to the men.

'Excellent, Mr Easy! Excellent, Mr Gascoigne!' said Captain Wilson. Come, my lads, throw them over now, and stamp upon them well; the men's jackets and the captain's coats had already been sacrificed to the same object.

Easy called the other midshipmen, and they went up for a further supply; but there was no occasion, the fire had been smothered: still the danger had been so great that the fore magazine had been floated. During all this, which lasted perhaps a quarter of an hour, the frigate had rolled gunwale under, and many were the accidents which occurred. At last all danger from fire had ceased, and the men were ordered to return to their quarters, when three officers and forty-seven men were found absent — seven of them were dead — most of them were already under the care of the surgeon, but some were still lying in the scuppers.

No one had been more active or more brave during this time of danger than Mr Hawkins the chaplain. He was everywhere, and when Captain Wilson went down to put out the fire he was there, encouraging the men and exerting himself most gallantly. He and Mesty came aft when all was over, one just as black as the other. The chaplain sat down and wrung his hands — 'God forgive me!' said he, 'God forgive me!'

'Why so sir?' said Easy, who stood near. 'I am sure you need not be ashamed of what you have done.'

'No, no, not ashamed of what I've done; but, Mr Easy, I have sworn so, sworn such oaths at the men in my haste — I, the chaplain! God forgive me! — I meant nothing.' It was very true that Mr Hawkins had sworn a great deal during his exertions, but he was at that time the quarter-deck officer and not the chaplain; the example to the men and his gallantry had been most serviceable.

'Indeed, sir,' said Easy, who saw that the chaplain was in great tribulation, and hoped to pacify him, 'I was certainly not there all the time, but I only heard you say, "God bless you, my men! be smart," and so on; surely, that is not swearing.'

'Was it that I said, Mr Easy, are you sure? I really had an idea that I had d----d them all in heaps, as some of them deserved — no, no, not deserved. Did I really bless them — nothing but bless them?'

'Yes, sir,' said Mesty, who perceived what Jack wanted; 'it was nothing, I assure you, but "God bless you Captain Wilson! — Bless your heart, my good men! — Bless the king!" and so on. You do nothing but shower down blessing and wet blanket.'

'I told you so,' said Jack.

'Well, Mr Easy, you've made me very happy,' replied the chaplain: 'I was afraid it was otherwise.'

So indeed it was, for the chaplain had sworn like a boatswain; but as Jack and Mesty had turned all his curses into blessings, the poor man gave himself absolution, and shaking hands with Jack, hoped he would come down into the gunroom and take a glass of grog (nor did he forget Mesty, who received a good allowance at the gunroom door), to which Jack gladly consented, as the rum in the middy's berth had all been exhausted after the rainy morning — but Jack was interrupted in his third glass by somebody telling him the captain wanted to speak with Mr Hawkins and with him.

Jack went up and found the captain on the quarter-deck with the officers.

'Mr Easy,' said Captain Wilson, 'I have sent for you, Mr Hawkins, and Mr Gascoigne to thank you on the quarter-deck for your exertions and presence of mind on this trying occasion.' Mr Hawkins made a bow. Gascoigne said nothing, but he thought of having extra leave when they arrived at Malta. Jack felt inclined to make a speech, and began something about when there was danger that it levelled every one to an equality even on board of a man-of-war.

'By no means, Mr Easy,' replied Captain Wilson, 'it does the very contrary, for it proves which is the best man, and those who are the best raise themselves at once above the rest.'

Jack was very much inclined to argue the point, but he took the compliment and held his tongue, which was the wisest thing he could have done; so he made his bow, and was about to go down into the midshipmen's berth when the frigate was pooped by a tremendous sea, which washed all those who did not hold on down into the waist. Jack was among the number, and naturally catching at the first object which touched him, he caught hold of the chaplain by the leg, who commenced swearing most terribly; but before he could finish the oath, the water which had burst into the cabin through the windows — for the dead lights, in the confusion, had not yet been shipped — burst out the cross bulkheads, sweeping like a torrent the marine, the cabin-door, and everything else in its force, and floating Jack and the chaplain with several others down the main hatchway on to the lower deck. The lower deck being also full of water, men and chests were rolling and tossing about, and Jack was sometimes in company with the chaplain, and at other times separated; at last they both recovered their legs, and gained the midshipmen's berth, which, although afloat, was still a haven of security. Mr Hawkins spluttered and spat, and so did Jack, until he began to laugh.

'This is very trying, Mr Easy,' said the chaplain; 'very trying indeed to the temper. I hope I have not sworn — I hope not.'

'Not a word,' said Jack — 'I was close to you all the time — you onlys aid, "God preserve us!"'

'Only that? I was afraid that I said "God d--n it!"'

'Quite a mistake, Mr Hawkins. Let's go into the gunroom, and try to wash this salt water out of our mouths, and then I will tell you all you said, as far as I could hear it, word for word.'

So Jack by this means got another glass of grog, which was very acceptable in his wet condition, and made himself very comfortable, while those on deck were putting on the dead lights, and very busy setting the goose-wings of the mainsail, to prevent the frigate from being pooped a second time.

The White Whale
from Moby Dick

by
HERMAN MELVILLE

Soon after Ishmael boarded the whaler Pequod, he realised that he was involved in no ordinary whaling cruise. Captain Ahab, obsessed with his purpose to hunt down the white whale Moby Dick, leads his entire crew to fantastic adventure and horrible destruction. Only Ishmael lives to tell the tale.

Sing Out for the Whale

One morning shortly after breakfast, Ahab, as was his wont, ascended the cabin gangway to the deck. There most sea-captains usually walk at that hour, as country gentlemen, after the same meal, take a few turns in the garden.

Soon his steady, ivory stride was heard, as to and fro he paced his old round, upon planks so familiar to his tread, that they were all over dented, like geological stones, with the peculiar marks of his walk. Did you fixedly gaze, too, upon that ribbed and dented brow; there also, you would see still stranger footprints — the footprints of his one unsleeping ever pacing thought.

But on the occasion in question, these dents looked deeper, even as his nervous step that morning left a deeper mark. And, so full of his thought was Ahab, that at every uniform turn that he made, now at the mainmast and now at the binnacle, you could almost see that thought turn in him, indeed, that it all but seemed the inward mould of every outer movement.

'D'ye mark him, Flask?' whispered Stubb; 'the chick that's in him pecks the shell. 'Twill soon be out.'

The hours wore on; — Ahab now shut up within his cabin; anon, pacing the deck, with the same intense bigotry of purpose in his aspect. It drew nearer to the close of day. Suddenly he came to a halt by the bulwarks, and inserting his bone leg into the auger-hole there, and with one hand grasping a shroud, he ordered Starbuck to send everybody aft.

'Sir!' said the mate, astonished at an order seldom or never given on shipboard except in some extraordinary case.

'Send everybody aft', repeated Ahab. 'Mastheads, there! come down!'

When the entire ship's company were assembled, and with curious and not wholly unapprehensive faces, were eyeing him, for he looked not unlike the weather horizon when a storm is coming up, Ahab, after rapidly glancing over the bulwarks, and then darting his eyes among the crew, started from his standpoint; and as though not a soul were nigh him resumed his heavy turns upon the deck. With bent head and half-slouched hat he continued to pace, unmindful of the wondering whispering among the men; till Stubb whispered to Flask, that Ahab must have summoned them there for the purpose of witnessing a pedestrian feat. But this did not last long. Vehemently pausing he cried: —

'What do ye do when ye see a whale, men?'

'Sing out for him!' was the impulsive rejoinder from a score of clubbed voices.

'Good!' cried Ahab, with a wild approval in his tones; observing the hearty animation into which his unexpected question had so magnetically thrown them.

'And what do ye do next, men?'

'Lower away, and after him!'

'And what tune is it ye pull to, men?'

'A dead whale or a stove boat!'

More and more strangely and fiercely glad and approving grew the countenance of the old man at every shout; while the mariners began to gaze curiously at each other, as if marvelling how it was that they themselves became so excited at such seemingly purposeless questions.

But they were all eagerness again, as Ahab, now half revolving in his pivot-hole, with one hand reaching high up a shroud, and tightly, almost convulsively grasping it, addressed them thus —

'All ye mastheaders have before now heard me give orders about a white whale. Look ye! d'ye see this Spanish ounce of gold?' — holding up a broad bright coin to the sun — 'it is a sixteen dollar piece, men. D'ye see it? Mr Starbuck, hand me yon top-maul.'

While the mate was getting the hammer, Ahab, without speaking, was slowly rubbing the gold piece against the skirts of his jacket, as if to heighten its lustre, and without using any words was meanwhile lowly humming to himself, producing a sound so strangely muffled and inarticulate that it seemed the mechanical humming of the wheels of his vitality in him.

Receiving the top-maul from Starbuck, he advanced towards the mainmast with the hammer uplifted in one hand, exhibiting the gold with the other, and with a high-raised voice exclaiming: 'Whosoever of ye raises me a white-headed whale with a wrinkled brow and a crooked jaw; whosoever of ye raises me that white-headed whale, with three holes punctured in his starboard fluke — look ye, whosoever of ye raises me that same white whale, he shall have this gold ounce, my boys!'

'Huzza! huzza!' cried the seamen, as with swinging tarpaulins they hailed the act of nailing the gold to the mast.

'It's a white whale, I say,' resumed Ahab, as he threw down the top-maul; 'a white whale. Skin your eyes for him, men; look sharp for white water; if ye see but a bubble, sing out.'

All this while Tashtego, Daggoo, and Queequeg had looked on with even more intense interest and surprise than the rest, and at the mention of the wrinkled brow and crooked jaw, they had started as if each was separately touched by some specific recollection.

'Captain Ahab,' said Tashtego, 'that white whale must be the same that some call Moby Dick.'

'Moby Dick?' shouted Ahab. 'Do ye know the white whale then, Tash?'

'Does he fan-tail a little curious, sir, before he goes down?' said the Gay-Header deliberately.

'And he has a curious spout too,' said Daggoo, 'very bushy, even for a parmacetty, and mighty quick, Captain Ahab?'

'And he have one, two, tree — oh! good many iron in him hide, too, Captain,' cried Queequeg disjointedly. 'All twisketee be-twisk, like him — him —' faltering hard for a word, and screwing his hand round and round as though uncorking a bottle — 'like him — him —'

'Corkscrew!' cried Ahab; 'ay, Queequeg, the harpoons lie all twisted and wrenched in him; ay, Daggoo, his spout is a big one, like a whole shock of wheat, and white as a pile of our Nantucket wool after the great annual sheep-shearing; aye, Tashtego, and he fan-tails like a split jib in a squall. Death and devils! Men, it is Moby Dick ye have seen — Moby Dick — Moby Dick!'

'Captain Ahab,' said Starbuck, who with Stubb and Flask, had thus far been eyeing his superior with increasing surprise, but at last seemed struck with a thought which somewhat explained all the wonder. 'Captain Ahab, I have heard of Moby Dick — was it not Moby Dick that took off thy leg'?

'Who told thee that?' cried Ahab; then pausing. 'Aye, Starbuck; aye, my hearties all round; it was Moby Dick that dismasted me; Moby Dick that brought me to this dead stump I stand on now. Aye, Aye,' he shouted with a terrific, loud, animal sob, like that of a heart-stricken moose; 'Aye, aye! it was that accursed white whale that razed me; made a poor pegging lubber of me for ever and a day!' Then tossing both arms, with measureless imprecations, he shouted out: 'Aye, Aye! and I'll chase him round Good Hope, and round the Horn, and round the Norway Maelstrom, and round perdition's flames before I give him up. And this is what ye have shipped for, men! to chase that white whale on both sides of land, and over all sides of earth, till he spouts black blood and rolls fin out. What say ye, men, will ye splice hands on it, now? I think ye do look brave.'

'Aye, aye!' shouted the harpooners and seamen, running closer to the excited old man; 'A sharp eye for the White Whale; a sharp lance for Moby Dick!'

'God bless ye,' he seemed to half sob and half shout, 'God bless ye, men. Steward! go draw the great measure of grog. Death to Moby Dick! God hunt us all, if we do not hunt Moby Dick to his death!'

The White Whale

I, Ishmael, was one of that crew; my shouts had gone up with the rest; my oath had been welded with theirs; and stronger I shouted, and more did I hammer and clinch my oath, because of the dread in my soul. A wild, mystical sympathetical feeling was in me; Ahab's quenchless feud seemed mine. With greedy ear I learned the history of that murderous monster against whom I and all the others had taken our oaths of violence and revenge.

For some time past, though at intervals only, the unaccompanied, secluded White Whale had haunted those uncivilised seas most frequented by the Sperm Whale fishermen. But not all of them knew of his existence; only a few of them, comparatively, had knowingly seen him; while the number who as yet had actually and knowingly given battle to him was small indeed. For, owing to the large number of whale cruisers; the disorderly way they were sprinkled over the entire watery circumference, many of them adventurously pushing their quest along solitary latitudes, so as seldom or never for a whole twelvemonth or more on a stretch, to encounter a single news-telling sail of any sort; the inordinate length of each separate voyage; the irregularity of the times of sailing from home; all these, with other circumstances, direct and indirect, long obstructed the spread through the whole world-wide whaling fleet, of the special individualising tidings concerning Moby Dick. It was hardly to be doubted, that several vessels reported to have encountered, at such and such a time, or on such a meridian, a sperm whale of uncommon magnitude and malignity, which whale, after doing great mischief to his assailants, had completely escaped them; to some minds it was not an unfair presumption. I say, that the whale in question must have been no other than Moby Dick. Yet as of late, the sperm whale fishery had been marked by various and not unfrequent instances of great ferocity, cunning and malice in the monster attacked; therefore it was, that those who by accident ignorantly gave battle to Moby Dick; such hunters, perhaps, for the most part, were content to ascribe the peculiar terror he bred, more, as it were, to the perils of the Sperm Whale fishery at large, than to the individual cause. In that way, mostly, the disastrous encounter between

Ahab and the whale had hitherto been popularly regarded.

As for those who, previously hearing of the White Whale, by chance caught sight of him; in the beginning of the thing they had every one of them, almost, as boldly and fearlessly lowered for him, as for any other whale of that species. But at length, such calamities did ensue in these assaults — not restricted to sprained wrists and ankles, broken limbs or devouring amputations — but fatal to the last degree of fatality; those repeated disastrous repulses, all accumulating and piling their terrors upon Moby Dick; those things had gone far to shake the fortitude of many brave hunters, to whom the story of the White Whale had eventually come.

Nor did wild rumours of all sorts fail to exaggerate, and still the more horrify, the true histories of these deadly encounters. For not only do fabulous rumours naturally grow out of the very body of all surprising terrible events — as the smitten tree gives birth to its fungi; but, in maritime life, far more than in that of *terra firma*, wild rumours abound, wherever there is any adequate reality for them to cling to. And as the sea surpasses the land in this matter, so the whale fishery surpasses every other sort of maritime life, in the wonderfulness and fearfulness of the rumours which sometimes circulate there.

No wonder, then, that ever gathering volume from the mere transit over the widest watery spaces, the outblown rumours of the White Whale did in the end incorporate with themselves all manner of morbid hints, the half-formed foetal suggestions of supernatural agencies, which eventually invested Moby Dick with new terrors unborrowed from anything that visibly appears. So that in many cases, such a panic did he finally strike, that few who by those rumours, at least, had heard of the White Whale, few of those hunters were willing to encounter the perils of his jaws.

One of the wild suggestions referred to, as at last coming to be linked with the White Whale in the minds of the superstitiously inclined, was the unearthly conceit that Moby Dick was ubiquitous; that he had actually been encountered in opposite latitudes at one and the same instant of time.

Nor, credulous as such minds must have been, was this conceit altogether without some faint show of superstitious probability. For as the secrets of the currents in the seas have never yet been divulged even to the most erudite research, so the hidden ways of the Sperm Whale when beneath the surface remain, in great part, unaccountable to his pursuers; and from time to time have originated the most curious and contradictory speculations regarding them, especially concerning the mystic modes whereby, after sounding to a great depth, he transports himself with such vast swiftness to the most widely distant points.

It is a thing well known to both American and English whaleships, and as well a thing placed upon authoritative record years ago by Scoresby, that some whales have been captured far north in the Pacific in whose bodies have been found the barbs of harpoons darted in the Greenland seas. Nor is it to be gainsaid, that in some of these instances it has been declared that the interval of time between the two assaults could not have exceeded very many days. Hence, by inference, it has been believed by some whalemen, that the Nor'-West Passage, so long a problem to man, was never a problem to the whale. So that here, in the real living experience of living men, the prodigies related in old times of the inland Strello mountain in Portugal (near whose top there was said to be a lake in which the wrecks of ships floated up to the surface); and that still more wonderful story of the Arethusa fountain near Syracuse (whose waters were believed to come from the Holy Land by an underground passage); these fabulous narrations are almost fully equalled by the realities of the whaleman.

Forced into familiarity, then, with such prodigies as these, and knowing that after repeated, intrepid assaults, the White Whale had escaped alive, it cannot be much matter of surprise that some whalemen should go still further in their superstitions; declaring Moby Dick not only ubiquitous, but immortal. (For immortality is but ubiquity in time); and though groves of spears should be planted in his flanks, he would still swim away unharmed; or if indeed he should ever be made to spout thick blood, such a sight would be but a ghastly deception; for again in unensanguined billows hundreds of leagues away, his unsullied jet would once more be seen.

But even stripped of these supernatural surmisings, there was enough in the earthly make and incontestable character of the monster to strike the imagination with unwonted power. For, it was not so much his uncommon bulk that so much distinguished him from other sperm whales, but, as was elsewhere thrown out — a peculiar snow-white wrinkled forehead, and a high, pyramidal white hump. These were his prominent features; the tokens whereby, even in the limitless, uncharted seas, he revealed his identity, at a long distance, to those who knew him.

The rest of his body was so streaked, and spotted, and marbled with the same shrouded hue, that, in the end, he had gained his distinctive appelation of the White Whale; a name indeed, literally justified by his vivid aspect, when seen gliding at high noon through a dark blue sea, leaving a milky-way wake of creamy foam, all spangled with golden gleamings. Nor was it his unwonted magnitude, nor his remarkable hue, nor yet his deformed lower jaw, that so much invested the whale with natural terror, as that unexampled, intelligent malignity which, according to specific accounts, he had over and over again evinced in his assaults. More than all, his treacherous retreats struck more of dismay than perhaps else. For, when swimming before his exulting pursuers, with every symptom of alarm, he had several times been known to turn round suddenly, and, bearing down upon them, either stave their boats to splinters, or drive them back in consternation to their ship.

Already several fatalities had attended his chase. But though similar disasters however little bruited ashore, were by no means unusual in the fishery; yet, in most instances, such seemed the White Whale's internal forethought of ferocity, that every dismembering or death he caused, was not wholly regarded as having been inflicted by an unintelligent agent.

Judge, then, to what pitches of inflamed, distracted fury the minds of his more desperate hunters were impelled, when amid the chips of chewed boats, and the sinking limbs of torn comrades, they swam out of the white curds of the whale's direful wrath into the serene, exasperating sunlight, that smiled on, as if at a birth or a bridal.

His three boats stove around him, and oars and men both, whirling in the eddies; one captain, seizing the line-knife from his broken prow, had dashed at the whale, as an Arkansas duellist at his foe, blindly seeking with a six-inch blade, to reach the fathom-deep life of the whale. That captain was Ahab. And then it was, that suddenly sweeping his sickle-shaped lower jaw beneath him, Moby Dick had reaped away Ahab's leg, as a mower a blade of grass in the field. No turbaned Turk, no hired Venetian or Malay, could have smote him with more seeming malice. Small reason was there, to doubt then, that ever since that almost fatal encounter, Ahab had cherished a wild vindictiveness against the whale, all the more fell, that for his frantic morbidness he at last came to identify with him, not only all his bodily woes, but all his intellectual and spiritual exasperations. The White Whale swam before him as the monomaniac incarnation of all those malicious agencies which some deep men feel eating in them, till they are left living on with half a heart and half a lung. That intangible malignity which has been found from the beginning; which

the ancient Ophites of the east reverenced in their statue devil;
— Ahab did not fall down and worship it like them; but
deliriously transferring its idea to the abhorred white whale,
he pitted himself, all mutilated, against it. All that most
maddens and torments; all that stirs up the lees of things; all
truth with malice in it; all that cracks the sinews and cakes
the brain; the subtle demonisms of life and thought; all evil,
to crazy Ahab, were visibly personified, and made practically
assailable in Moby Dick. He piled upon the whale's white
hump the sum of all the general rage and hate felt by his
whole race from Adam down.

Moby Dick's Last Fight

That night, in the mid-watch, when the old man- as his
wont at intervals — stepped forth from the scuttle in which
he leaned, and went to his pivot-hole, he suddenly thrust out
his face fiercely, snuffing up the sea air as a sagacious ship's
dog will, in drawing nigh to some barbarous isle. He declared
that a whale must be near. Soon that peculiar odour, sometimes
to a great distance given forth by the living Sperm Whale,
was palpable to all the watch; nor was any mariner surprised
when, after inspecting the compass, and then the dog-vane,
and then ascertaining the precise bearing of the odour as
nearly as possible, Ahab rapidly ordered the ship's course to
be slightly altered, and the sail to be shortened. The acute
policy dictating these movements was sufficiently vindicated
at daybreak by the sight of a long sleek on the sea directly
and lengthwise ahead, smooth as oil, and resembling in the
pleated watery wrinkles bordering it, the polished metallic-like

marks of some swift tide-rip, at the mouth of a deep, rapid stream.

'Man the mastheads! Call all hands!'

Thundering with the butts of three clubbed handspikes on the forecastle deck, Daggoo roused the sleepers with such judgement claps that they seemed to exhale from the scuttle, so instantaneously did they appear with their clothes in their hands.

'What d'ye see?' cried Ahab, flattening his face to the sky.

'Nothing, nothing, sir!' was the sound hailing down in reply.

'T'gallant-sails! stunsails alow and aloft on both sides!'

All sail being set, he now cast loose the life-line, reserved for swaying him to the mainroyal masthead; and in a few moments they were hoisting him thither, when, while but two-thirds of the way aloft, and while peering ahead through the horizontal vacancy between the maintopsail and top-gallant sail, he raised a gull-like cry in the air, 'There she blows! — there she blows! A hump like a snow-hill! It is Moby Dick!'

Fired by the cry which seemed simultaneously taken up by the three look-outs, the men on deck rushed to the rigging to behold the famous whale they had so long been pursuing. Ahab, now had gained his final perch, some feet above the other look-outs, Tashtego, standing just beneath him on the cap of the top-gallant mast, so that the Indian's head was almost on a level with Ahab's heel. From this height the whale was seen some mile or so ahead, at every roll of the sea revealing his high sparkling hump, and regularly jetting his silent spout into the air. To the credulous mariners, it seemed the same silent spout they had so long ago beheld in the moonlit Atlantic and Indian Oceans.

'And did none of yet see it before?' cried Ahab, hailing the perched men all around him.

'I saw him almost the same instant, sir, that Captain Ahab did, and I cried out,' said Tashtego.

'Not the same instant; not the same — no, the doubloon is mine, Fate reserved the doubloon for me. I only; none of ye could have raised the White Whale first. There she blows! there she blows! There she blows! There again! — there again!' he cried, in long-drawn lingering methodic tones, attuned to the gradual prolongings of the whale's visible jets. 'He's going to sound! In stunsails! Down top-gallant sails! Stand by the three boats. Mr Starbuck, remember, stay on board, and keep the ship. Helm there! Luff, luff a point! So; steady, man, steady! There go flukes. No, no; only black water! All ready the boats there? Stand by, stand by! Lower me, Mr Starbuck; lower, lower, — quick, quicker!' and he slid through the air to the deck.

'He is heading straight to leeward, sir,' cried Stubb; 'right away from us; cannot have seen the ship yet.'

'Be dumb, man! Stand by the braces! Hard down the helm! — brace up! Shiver her! — shiver her! So; well that! Boats, boats!'

Soon all the boats but Starbuck's were dropped; the boat-sails set; all the paddles plying; with rippling swiftness, shooting to leeward; and Ahab heading the onset. A pale, death-glimmer lit up Fedallah's sunken eyes; a hideous motion gnawed his mouth.

Like noiseless nautilus shells, their light prows sped through the sea; but only slowly they neared the foe. As they neared him, the ocean grew still more smooth; seemed drawing a carpet over its waves; seemed a noon-meadow, so serenely it spread. At length, the breathless hunter came so nigh his seemingly unsuspecting prey, that his entire dazzling hump was distinctly visible, sliding along the sea as if an isolated thing, and continually set in a revolving ring of finest, fleecy, greenish foam. He saw the vast involved wrinkles of the slightly projecting head beyond. Before it, far out on the soft Turkish-rugged waters, went the glistening white shadows from his broad milky forehead, a musical rippling playfully accompanying the shade; and behind, the blue waters interchangeably flowed over into the moving valley of his steady wake; and on either hand bright bubbles arose and danced by his side. But these were broken again by the light toes of hundreds of gay fowl softly feathering the sea, alternate with their fitful flight; and like to some flagstaff rising from the painted hull of an argosy, the tall but shattered pole of a recent lance projected from the white whale's back; and at intervals one of the cloud of soft-toed fowls hovering, and to and fro skimming like a canopy over the fish, silently perched and rocked on this pole, the long tail feathers streaming like pennons.

A gentle joyousness — a mighty mildness of repose in swiftness, invested the gliding whale. Not the white bull Jupiter swimming away with ravished Europa clinging to his graceful horns; his lovely leering eyes sideways intent upon the maid; with smooth bewitching fleetness rippling straight for the nuptual bower in Crete; not Jove did surpass the glorified White Whale as he so divinely swam.

On each soft side — coincident with the parted swell, that but once leaving him, then flowed so wide away — on each bright side, the whale shed off enticings. No wonder there had been some among the hunters who namelessly transported and allured by all this serenity had ventured to assail it; but had fatally found that quietude but the vesture of tornadoes. Yet, calm, enticing calm, oh whale; thou glidest on, to all who for the first time eye thee, no matter how many in that same way thou may'st have bejuggled and destroyed before.

And thus, through the serene tranquillities of the tropical sea, among waves whose hand-clappings were suspended by exceeding rapture, Moby Dick moved on, still withholding from sight the full terrors of his submerged trunk, entirely hiding the wretched hideousness of his jaws. But soon the fore part of him slowly rose from the water; for an instant his whole marbleised body formed a high arch, like Virginia's Natural Bridge, and warningly waving his bannered flukes in the air. The grand god revealed himself, sounded and went out of sight. Hoveringly halting, and dipping on the wing, the white sea-fowls longingly lingered over the agitated pool that he left.

With oars apeak, and paddles down, the sheets of their sails adrift, the three boats now stilly floated, awaiting Moby Dick's appearance.

'An hour,' said Ahab, standing rooted in his boat's stern, and he gazed beyond the whale's place, towards the dim blue spaces and wide wooing vacancies to leeward. It was only an instant, for again his eyes seemed whirling in his head as he swept the watery circle. The breeze now freshened; the sea began to swell.

'The birds! — the birds!' cried Tashtego.

In long Indian file, as when herons take wing, the white birds were now all flying towards Ahab's boat; and when within a few yards began fluttering over the water there, wheeling round and round, with joyous expectant cries. Their vision was keener than man's; Ahab could discover no sign in the sea. But suddenly as he peered down and into its depths, he profoundly saw a white living spot no bigger than a white weasel, with a wonderful celerity uprising and magnifying as it rose, till it turned and then there were plainly revealed two long crooked rows of white, glistening teeth, floating up from the undiscoverable bottom. It was Moby Dick's open mouth and scrolled jaw; his vast shadowed bulk but still half blending with the blue of the sea. The glittering mouth yawned beneath the boat like an open-doored marble tomb; and giving one sidelong sweep with his steering oar, Ahab whirled the craft aside from this tremendous apparition. Then, calling upon Fedellah to change placeds with him, went forward to the bows, and seizing Perth's harpoon, commanded his crew to grasp their oars and stand by to stern.

Both jaws like an enormous shears bit the craft completely in twain.

Now, by reason of this timely spinning round the boat upon its axis, its bow, by anticipation, was made to face the whale's head while yet under water. But as if perceiving this stratagem, Moby Dick with that malicious intelligence ascribed to him, sidelingly transplanted himself, as it were, in an instant, shooting his plaited head lengthwise beneath the boat.

Through and through; through every plank and each rib, it thrilled for an instant, the whale obliquely lying on his back, in the manner of a biting shark, slowly and feelingly taking its bows full within his mouth, so that the long, narrow, scrolled lower jaw curled high up into the open air, and one of the teeth caught in a rowlock. The bluish pearl-white of the inside of the jaw was within six inches of Ahab's head, and reached higher than that. In this altitude the White Whale now shook the slight cedar as a mildly cruel cat her mouse. With unastonished eyes Fedallah gazed, and crossed his arms; but the tiger-yellow crew were tumbling over each other's heads to gain the uttermost stern.

And now, while both elastic gunwales were springing in and out, as the whale dallied with the doomed craft in this devilish way; and from his body being submerged beneath the boat, he could not be darted at from the bows, for the bows were almost inside of him, as it were; and while the other boats involuntarily paused, as before a quick crisis impossible to withstand, then it was that monomaniac Ahab, furious with this tantalising vicinity of his foe, which placed him all alive and helpless in the very jaws he hated; frenzied with all this, he seized the long bone with his naked hands, and wildly strove to wrench it from its grip. As he now thus vainly strove, the jaw slipped from him; the frail gunwales bent in, collapsed and snapped, as both jaws like an enormous shears, sliding further aft, bit the craft completely in twain, and locked themselves fast again in the sea, midway between the two floating wrecks. These floated aside, the broken ends drooping, the crew at the sternwreck clinging to the gunwales, and striving to hold fast to the oars to lash them across.

At that preluding moment, ere the boat was yet snapped, Ahab, the first to perceive the whale's intent, by the crafty upraising of his head, a movement that loosed his hold for the first time; at that moment his hand had made one final attempt to push the boat out of the bite. But only slipping further into the whale's mouth, and tilting over sideways as it slipped, the boat had shaken off his hold on the jaw; spilled him out of it, as he leaned to the push, and so he fell flat-faced upon the sea.

Ripplingly withdrawing from his prey, Moby Dick now lay at a little distance, vertically thrusting his oblong white head up and down in the billows; and at the same time slowly revolving his whole splendid body; so that when his vast wrinkled forehead rose — some twenty or more feet out of the water — the now rising swells, with all their confluent waves, dazzling broke against it; vindictively tossing their shivered spray still higher into the air. So, in a gale, the but half baffled Channel billows only recoil from the base of Eddystone, triumphantly to overlap its summit with their scud.

But soon resuming his horizontal attitude, Moby Dick swam swiftly round and round the wrecked crew; sideways churning up the water in his vengeful wake, as if lashing himself up to still another and more deadly assault. The sight of the splintered boat seemed to madden him, as the blood of grapes and mulberries cast before Antiochus's elephant in the book of Maccabees. Meanwhile Ahab half smothered in the foam of the whale's insolent tail, and too much of a cripple to swim, — though he could still keep afloat, even in the heart of such a whirlpool as that; helpless Ahab's head was seen, like a tossed bubble which the least chance shock might burst. From the boat's fragmentary stern, Fedallah incuriously and mildly eyed him; the clinging crew, at the other drifting end, could not succour him; more than enough it was for them to look to themselves. For so revolvingly appalling was the White Whale's aspect, and so planetarily swift the ever-contracting circles he made, that he seemed horizontally swooping upon them. And though the other boats, unharmed, still hovered hard by, still they dared not pull into the eddy to strike, lest that should be the signal for the instant destruction of the jeopardised castaways, Ahab, and all; nor in that case could they themselves hope to escape. With straining eyes, then, they remained on the outer edge of the direful zone, whose centre had now become the old man's head.

Meantime, from the beginning all this had been descried from the ship's mastheads; and squaring her yards, she had borne down upon the scene; and was now so nigh, that Ahab, in the water hailed her; — 'Sail on the' — but that moment a breaking sea dashed on him from Moby Dick, and whelmed him for the time. But struggling out of it again, and chancing to rise on a towering crest, he shouted, — 'Sail on the whale! — Drive him off!'

The *Pequod's* prows were pointed; and breaking up the charmed circle, she effectually parted the White Whale from his victim. As he sullenly swam off, the boats flew to the rescue.

Dragged into Stubb's boat with bloodshot blinding eyes, the white brine caking in his wrinkles; the long tension of Ahab's bodily strength did crack, and helplessly he yielded to his body's doom: for a time, lying all crushed in the bottom of Stubb's boat, like one trodden under foot of a herd of elephants. Far inland, nameless wails came from him, as desolate sounds from our ravines.

But the intensity of his physical prostration did but so much the more abbreviate it. In an instant's compass, great hearts sometimes condense to one deep pang, the sum-total of those shallow pains kindly diffused through feebler men's whole lives. And so, such hearts, though summary in each one suffering; still, if the gods decree it, in their lifetime aggregate a whole age of woe, wholly made up of instantaneous intensities; for even in their pointless centres those noble natures contain the entire circumferences of inferior souls.

'The harpoon,' said Ahab, half-way rising and draggingly leaning on one bended arm — 'is it safe?'

'Aye, sir, for it was not darted; this is it,' said Stubb, showing .

'Say it before me; — any missing men?'

'One, two, three, four, five; — there were five oars, sir, and here are five men.'

'That's good. — Help me, man; I wish to stand. So, so I see him! there! there! going to leeward still; what a leaping spout! — Hands off from me! The eternal sap runs in Ahab's bones again! Set the sail; out oars; the helm!'

It is often the case that when a boat is stove, its crew, being picked up by another boat, help to work that second boat; and the chase is thus continued with what is called double-banked oars. It was thus now. But the added power of the boat did not equal the added power of the whale, for he seemed to have treble-banked his every fin; swimming with a velocity which plainly showed that, if now, under these circumstances, pushed on, the chase would prove an indefinitely prolonged, if not a hopeless one; nor could any crew endure for so long a period, such an unintermitted, intense, straining at the oar; a thing barely tolerable only in some one brief vicissitude. The ship itself, then, as it sometimes happens, offered the most promising intermediate means of overtaking the chase. Accordingly, the boats now made for her, and were soon swayed up to their cranes — the two parts of the wrecked boat having been previously secured by her — and then hoisting everything to her side, and stacking the canvas high up, and sideways outstretching it with stunsails, like the double-jointed wings of an albatross; the *Pequod* bore down in the leeward wake of Moby Dick. At the well-known, methodical intervals, the whale's glittering spout was regularly announced from the manned mastheads; and when he would be reported as just gone down, Ahab would take the time, and then pacing the deck, binnacle-watch in hand, so soon as the last sound of the allotted hour expire, his voice was heard — 'Whose is the doubloon now? D'ye see him?' and if the reply was 'No, sir!' straightway he commanded them to lift him to his perch. In this way the day wore on; Ahab, now aloft and motionless; anon, unrestingly pacing the planks.

As he was thus walking, uttering no sound, except to hail the men aloft, or to bid them hoist a sail still higher, or to spread one to a still greater breadth — thus to and fro pacing, beneath his slouched hat, at every turn he passed his own wrecked boat, which had been dropped upon the quarter-deck, and lay there reversed, broken bow to shattered stern. At last, he paused before it; and as in an already over-clouded sky fresh troops of clouds will sometimes sail across, so over the old man's face there now stole some such added gloom as this.

Stubb saw him pause; and perhaps intending, not vainly, though, to evince his own unabated fortitude, and thus keep up a valiant place in his Captain's mind, he advanced, and eyeing the wreck exclaimed — 'The thistle the ass refused — it pricked his mouth too keenly, sir; ha! ha!'

'What soulless thing is this that laughs before a wreck? Man, man! did I not know thee brave as fearless fire (and as mechanical) I could swear thou wert a poltroon. Groan nor laugh should be heard before a wreck.'

'Aye, sir,' said Starbuck, drawing near, 'tis a solemn sight; an omen, and an ill one.'

'Omen? omen? — the dictionary! If the gods think to speak outright to a man, they will honourably speak outright; not shake their heads and give an old wife's darkling hint. —

Begone! Ye two are the opposite poles of one thing; Starbuck is Stubb reversed, and Stubb is Starbuck; and ye two are all mankind; and Ahab stands alone among the millions of the peopled earth, nor gods nor men his neighbours! Cold, cold — I shiver! — How now? Aloft there? D'ye see him? Sing out for every spout, though he spout ten times a second!'

The day was nearly done; only the hem of his golden robe was rustling. Soon, it was almost dark, but the look-out men still remained unset.

'Can't see the spout now, sir; — too dark' — cried a voice from the air.

'How heading when last seen?'

'As before, sir — straight to leeward'

'Good! he will travel slower now 'tis night. Down royals and top—gallant stunsails, Mr Starbuck. We must not run over him before morn. He's making a passage now, and may heave-to a while. Helm there! — keep her full before the wind! — Aloft! come down! — Mr Stubb, send a fresh hand to the foremast head, and see it manned till morning.' — Then advancing towards the doubloon in the mainmast — 'Men, this gold is mine, for I earned it; but I shall let it abide here till the White Whale is dead; and then, whosoever of ye first raises him, upon the day he shall be killed, this gold is that man's; and if on that day I shall again raise him, then, ten times its sum shall be divided among all of ye! Away now! — the deck is thine, Sir.'

And so saying, he placed himself half-way within the scuttle, and slouching his hat, stood there till dawn, except when at intervals rousing himself to see how the night wore on.

At daybreak the three mastheads were punctually manned afresh.

'D'ye see him?' cried Ahab after allowing a little space for the light to spread.

'See nothing, sir.'

'Turn up all hands and make sail! he travels faster than I thought for — the top-gallant sails! — aye, they should have been kept on her all night. But no matter — 'tis but resting for the rush.'

The ship tore on, leaving such a furrow in the sea as when a cannon-ball, missent, becomes a ploughshare and turns up the level field.

'By salt and hemp!' cried Stubb, 'but this swift motion of the deck creeps up one's legs and tingles at the heart. This ship and I are two grave fellows! Ha! ha! Some one take me up, and launch me, spine-wise, on the sea, for by live-oaks! my spine's a keel. Ha, ha! we go the gait that leaves no dust behind!'.

'There she blows — she blows! — she blows! — right ahead!' was now the masthead cry.

'Aye, aye!' cried Stubb, 'I knew it — ye can't escape — blow on and split your spout, O Whale! the mad fiend himself is after ye! Blow your trump — blister your lungs! Ahab will dam off your blood, as a miller shuts his gater-gate upon the stream.'

And Stubb did but speak out for well-nigh all that crew. The frenzies of the chase had by this time worked them bubblingly up, like old wine worked anew. Whatever pale fears and forebodings some of them might have felt before; these were not only now kept out of sight through the growing awe of Ahab, but they were broken up, and on all sides routed, as timid prairie hares that scatter before the bounding bison. The hand of Fate had snatched all their souls; and, by the stirring perils of the previous day; the rack of the past night's suspense; the fixed unfearing, blind, reckless way in which their wild craft went plunging towards its flying mark; by all these things, their hearts were bowled along. The wind that made great bellies of their sails, and rushed the vessel on by arms invisible as irresistible; this seemed the symbol of that unseen agency which so enslaved them to the race.

There were one man, not thirty. For as the one ship that held them all, though it was put together of all contrasting things — oak, and maple, and pine wood; iron and pitch, and hemp — yet all these ran into each other in the one concrete hull, which shot on its way, both balanced and directed by the long central keel; even so, all the individualities of the crew. This man's valour, that man's fear; guilt and guiltiness, all varieties were welded into oneness, and were all directed to that fatal goal which Ahab their one lord and keel did point to.

The rigging lived. The mastheads, like the tops of tall palms, were out-spreadingly tufted with arms and legs. Clinging to a spar with one hand, some reached forth the other with impatient wavings; others, shading their eyes from the vivid sunlight, sat far out on the rocking yards; all the spars in full bearing of mortals, ready and ripe for their fate. Ah! how they still strove through that infinite blueness to seek out the thing that might destroy them!

'Why sing ye not out for him, if ye see him?' cried Ahab, when, after the lapse of some minutes since the first cry, no more had been heard. 'Sway me up, men; ye have been deceived; not Moby Dick casts one odd jet that way, and then disappears.'

It was even so; in their headlong eagerness, the men had mistaken some other thing for the whale-spout, as the event itself soon proved; for hardly had Ahab reached his perch; hardly was the rope belayed to its pin on deck, when he struck the key-note to an orchestra, that made the air vibrate as with the combined discharges of rifles. The triumphant halloo of thirty buckskin lungs was heard, as — much nearer to the ship than the place of the imaginary jet, less than a mile ahead — Moby Dick bodily burst into view. For not by any calm and indolent spoutings; not by the peaceable gush of that mystic fountain in his head, did the White Whale now reveal his vicinity; but by the far more wondrous phenomenon of breaching. Rising with his utmost velocity from the furthest depths, the Sperm Whale thus booms his entire bulk into the pure element of air, and piling up a mountain of dazzling foam, shows his place to the distance of seven miles and more. In those moments, the torn, enraged waves he shakes off seem his mane; in some cases this breaching is his act of defiance.

'There she breaches! there she breaches!' was the cry, as in his immeasurable bravadoes the White Whale tossed himself salmon-like to Heaven. So suddenly seen in the blue plain of the sea, and relieved against the still bluer margin of the sky, the spray that he raised, for the moment, intolerably glittered and glared like a glacier; and stood there gradually fading away from its first sparkling intensity, to the dim and fading mistiness of an advancing shower in a vale.

'Aye, breach your last to the sun, Moby Dick!' cried Ahab, 'thy hour and thy harpoon are at hand! Down! down all of ye, but one man at the fore. The boats! — stand by!'

Undmindful of the tedious rope-ladders of the shrouds, the men, like shooting stars, slid to the deck, by the isolated backstays and halyards; while Ahab, less dartingly but still rapidly, was dropped from his perch.

'Lower away,' he cried, so soon as he had reached his boat — a spare one, rigged the afternoon previous. 'Mr Starbuck, the ship is thine — keep away from the boats, but keep near them. Lower all!'

As if to strike a quick terror into them, by this time being the first assailant himself, Moby Dick had turned, and was now coming for the three crews. Ahab's boat was central; and cheering his men, he told them he would take the whale head-and-head — that is, pull straight up to his forehead — not an uncommon thing; for when within a certain limit, such a course excludes the coming onset from the whale's sidelong vision. But ere that close limit was gained, and while yet all three boats were plain as the ship's three masts to his eye; the White Whale, churning himself into furious speed, almost in an instant as it were, rushing among the boats with open jaws, and lashing tail, offered appalling battle on every side; and heedless of the irons darted at him from every boat, seemed only intent on annihilating each separate plank of which those boats were made. But skilfully manoeuvred, incessantly wheeling like trained chargers in the field; the boats for a while eluded him; though, at times, but by a plank's breadth; while all the time, Ahab's unearthly slogan tore every other cry but his to shreds.

But at last in his untraceable volutions, the White Whale so crossed and recrossed, and in a thousand ways entangled the slack of the three lines now fast to him, that they foreshortened, and, of themselves, warped the devoted boats towards the planted irons in him; though now for a moment the whale drew aside a little, as if to rally for a more tremendous charge. Seizing that opportunity, Ahab first paid out more line; and then was rapidly hauling and jerking in upon it again — hoping that way to disencumber it of some snarls — when lo! — a sight more savage than the embattled teeth of sharks!

Caught and twisted — corkscrewed in the mazes of the line — loose harpoons and lances, with all their bristling barbs and points, came flashing and dripping up to the chocks in the bows of Ahab's boat. Only one thing could be done. Seizing the boat-knife, he critically reached within — through — and then, without — the rays of steel; dragged in the line beyond, passed it, inboard, to the bowsman, and then, twice sundering the rope near the chocks — dropped the intercepted fagot of steel into the sea; and was all fast again. That instant, the White Whale made a sudden rush among the remaining tangles of the other lines; by doing so, irresistibly dragged the more involved boats of Stubb and Flask towards his flukes; dashed them together like two rolling husks on a surf-beaten beach, and then, diving down into the sea, disappeared in a coiling maelstrom, in which, for a space, the odorous cedar chips of the wrecks danced round and round, like the grated nutmeg in a swiftly stirred bowl of punch.

While the two crews were yet circling in the waters, reaching out after the revolving line-tubs, oars, and other floating furniture, while aslope little Flask bobbed up and down like an empty vial, twitching his legs upwards to escape the dreaded jaws of sharks; and Stubb was lustily singing out for some one to ladle him up; and while the old man's line — now parting — admitted of his pulling into the creamy pool to rescue whom he could — in that wild simultaneousness of a thousand concreted perils — Ahab's yet unstricken boat seemed drawn up towards Heaven by invisible wires — as, arrow-like, shooting perpendicularly from the sea, the White Whale dashed his broad forehead against its bottom, and sent it, turning over and over, into the air; till it fell again — gunwale downwards — and Ahab and his men struggled out from under it, like seals from a seaside cave.

The first uprising momentum of the whale — modifying its direction as he struck the surface — involuntarily launched him along it, to a little distance from the centre of the destruction he had made; and with his back to it, he now lay for a moment slowly feeling with his flukes from side to side; and whenever a stray oar, bit of plank, the least chip or crumb of the boats touched his skin, his tail swiftly drew back, and came sideways, smiting the sea. But soon, as if satisfied that his work for that time was done, he pushed his plaited forehead through the ocean, and trailing after him the intertangled lines, continued his leeward way at a traveller's methodic pace.

As before, the attentive ship having descried the whole fight, again came bearing down to the rescue, and dropping a boat,

'Aye, aye, Starbuck, 'tis sweet to lean sometimes.'

picked up the floating mariners, tubs, oars, and whatever else could be caught at, and safely landed them upon her decks. Some sprained shoulders, wrists and ankles; livid contusions; wrenched harpoons and lances; inextricable intricacies of rope, shattered oars and planks; all these were there; but no fatal or even serious ill seemed to have befallen anyone. As with Fedallah the day before, so Ahab was now found grimly clinging to his boat's broken half, which offered a comparatively easy float; nor did it exhaust him as the previous day's mishap.

But when he was helped to the deck, all eyes were fastened upon him; as instead of standing by himself he still half-hung upon the shoulder of Starbuck, who had thus far been the foremost to assist him. His ivory leg had been snapped off, leaving but one short sharp splinter.

'Aye, aye, Starbuck, 'tis sweet to lean sometimes, be the leaner who he will; and would old Ahab had leaned oftener than he has.'

'The ferrule has not stood, sir,' said the carpenter, now coming up; 'I put good work into that leg.'

'But no bones broken, sir, I hope,' said Stubb with true concern.

'Aye! and all splintered to pieces, Stubb! d'ye see it? But even with a broken bone, old Ahab is untouched; and I account no living bone of mine one jot more me than this dead one that's lost. Nor white whale, nor man, nor fiend, can so much as graze old Ahab in his own proper and inaccessible being. Can any lead touch yonder floor, any mast scrape yonder roof? Aloft there! which way?'

'Dead to leeward, sir.'

'Up helm, then; pile on the sail again, shipkeepers; down the rest of the spare boats and rig them — Mr Starbuck, away, and muster the boats and crews.'

'Let me first help thee towards the bulwarks, sir.'

'Oh, oh, oh! how this splinter gores me now! Accursed fate! that the unconquerable captain in the soul should have had such a craven mate!'

'Sir?'

'My body, man, not thee. Give me something for a cane — there, that shivered lance will do. Muster the men. Surely I have not seen him yet. By heaven, it cannot be! — missing? quick! call them all.'

The old man's hinted thought was true. Upon mustering the company, the Parsee was not there.

'The Parsee!' cried Stubb, 'he must have been caught in —'

'The black vomit wrench thee! Run all of ye above, alow cabin, forecastle — find him — not gone — not gone!'

But they returned to him with the tidings that the Parsee was nowhere to be found.

'Aye, sir,' said Stubb — 'caught among the tangles of your line. I thought I saw him dragged under.'

'*My* line? *My* line? Gone? Gone? What means that little word? What death-knell rings in it, that old Ahab shakes as if he were the belfry. The harpoon, too! Toss over the litter there, d'ye see it? — the forged iron, men, the white whale's — no, no, no, blistered fool! this hand did dart it! 'Tis in the fish! Aloft there! Keep him nailed. Quick! all hands to the rigging of the boats — collect the oars — harpooners! the irons, the irons! Hoist the royals higher — a pull on all the sheets! Helm there! steady, steady, for your life! I'll ten times girdle the unmeasured globe; yea and dive straight through it, but I'll slay him yet!'

'Great God! but for one single instant show thyself,' cried Starbuck. 'Never, never wilt thou capture him, old man. In Jesus' name, no more of this, that's worse than devil's madness. Two days chased; twice stove to splinters; thy very leg once more snatched from under thee; thy evil shadow gone — all good angels mobbing thee with warnings; what more wouldst thou have? Shall we be dragged by him to the bottom of the sea? Shall we be towed by him to the infernal world? Oh, oh! Impiety and blasphemy to hunt him more!'

'Starbuck, of late I've felt strangely moved to thee; ever since that hour we both saw — thou know'st what, in one another's eyes. But in this matter of the whale, be the front of thy face to me as the palm of this hand — a lipless, unfeatured blank. Ahab is for ever Ahab, man. This whole act's immutably decreed. 'Twas rehearsed by thee and me a billion years before this ocean rolled. Fool! I am the Fates' lieutenant; I act under orders. Look thou, underling! that thou obeyest mine. Stand round me, men. Ye see an old man cut down to the stump; leaning on a shivered lance; propped up on a lonely foot. 'Tis Ahab — his body's part; but Ahab's soul's a centipede, that moves upon a hundred legs. I feel strained, half stranded, as ropes that tow dismasted frigates in a gale; and I may look so. But ere I break, ye'll hear me crack; and till ye hear *that*, know that Ahab's hawser tows his purpose yet. Believe ye, men, in the things called omens? Then laugh aloud, and cry encore! For ere they drown, drowning things will twice rise to the surface; then rise again, to sink for evermore. So with Moby Dick — two days he's floated — tomorrow will be the third. Aye, men, he'll rise once more — but only to spout his last.'

The morning of the third day dawned fair and fresh, and once more the solitary night-man at the fore-masthead was relieved by crowds of the daylight look-outs, who dotted every mast and almost every spar.

'D'ye see him?' cried Ahab. 'Aloft there. What d'ye see?'

'Nothing, sir.'

'Nothing! The doubloon goes a-begging! See the sun! Aye, aye, it must be so. I've over-sailed him. How, got the start? Aye, he's chasing *me*, now; not I, *him* — that's bad. I might have known it, too. Fool! the lines — the harpoons he's towing. Aye, aye, I have run him by last night. About! About! Come down, all of ye, but the regular look-outs! Man the braces!'

Steering as she had done, the wind had been somewhat on the *Pequod's* quarter, so that now being pointed in the reverse direction, the braced ship sailed hard upon the breeze as she rechurned the cream in her own white wake.

'Against the wind he now steers for the open jaw,' murmured Starbuck to himself, as he coiled the new-hauled main-brace upon the rail. 'God keep us, but already my bones feel damp within me, and from the inside wet my flesh. I misdoubt me that I disobeyed my God in obeying him!'

'Stand by to sway me up!' cried Ahab, advancing to the hempen basket. 'We should meet him soon.'

'Aye, aye, sir,' and straightway Starbuck did Ahab's bidding, and once more Ahab swung on high.

A whole hour now passed; golden-beaten out to ages. Time itself now held long breaths with keen suspense. But at last, some three points off the weather-bow, Ahab descried the spout again, and instantly from the three mastheads three shrieks went up as if the tongues of fire had voiced it.

'Forehead to forehead I meet thee, this third time, Moby Dick! On deck there! Brace sharper up; crowd her into the wind's eye. He's too far off to lower yet, Mr Starbuck. The sails shake! Stand over that helmsman with a topmaul! So, so he travels fast, and I must down.'

He gave the word, and still gazing round him, was steadily lowered through the cloven blue air to the deck.

In due time the boats were lowered; but as standing in his shallop's stern, Ahab just hovered upon the point of the descent, he waved to the mate, who held one of the tackle-ropes on deck, and bade him pause.

'Starbuck!'

'Sir?'

'For the third time my soul's ship starts upon this voyage, Starbuck.'

'Aye, sir, thou wilt have it so.'

'Some ships sail from their ports, and ever afterwards are missing, Starbuck! Some men die at ebb tide; some at low water; some at the full of the flood; and I feel now like a billow that's all one crested comb, Starbuck. Lower away! Stand by the crew!'

In an instant the boat was pulling round close under the stern.

'The sharks! the sharks!' cried a voice from the low cabin-window there. 'O master, my master, come back!'

But Ahab heard nothing; for his own voice was high-lifted then; and the boat leaped on.

Yet the voice spake true; for scarce had he pushed from the ship, when numbers of sharks, seemingly rising from out of the dark waters, beneath the hull, maliciously snapped at the blades of the oars, every time they dipped in the water; and in this way accompanied the boat with their bites. It is a thing not uncommonly happening to the whale-boats in those swarming seas; the sharks at times apparently following them in the same prescient way that vultures hover over the banners of marching regiments in the east. But these were the first sharks that had been observed by the *Pequod* since the White Whale had been first descried; and whether it was that Ahab's crew were all such tiger-yellow barbarians, and there-fore their flesh more musky to the senses of sharks — a matter sometimes well known to affect them — however it was, they seemed to follow that one boat without molesting the others.

'Heart of wrought steel,' murmured Starbuck, gazing over the side, and following with his eyes the receding boat, 'canst thou yet ring boldly to that sight? lowering thy keel among ravening sharks, and followed by them, open-mouthed, to the chase; and this the critical third day? For when three days flow together in one continuous intense pursuit, be sure the first in the morning, the second the noon, and the third the evening and the end of that thing — be that the end what it may.'

The boats had not gone very far, when by a signal from the mastheads — a downward pointed arm, Ahab knew that the whale had sounded; but intending to be near him at the next rising, he held on his way a little sideways from the vessel; the becharmed crew maintaining the profoundest silence, as the head-beat waves hammered and hammered against the opposing bow.

Suddenly the waters around them slowly swelled in broad circles, then quickly upheaved, as if sideways sliding from a submerged berg of ice, swiftly rising to the surface. A low rumbling sound was heard; a subterraneous hum; and then all held their breaths; as bedraggled with trailing ropes, and harpoons, and lances, a vast form shot lengthwise, but obliquely from the sea. Shrouded in a thin drooping veil of mist, it hovered for a moment in the rainbowed air; and then fell swamping back into the deep. Crushed thirty feet upwards, the waters flashed for an instant like heaps of fountains, then brokenly sank in a shower of lakes, leaving the circling surface creamed like new milk round the marble trunk of the whale.

'Give way!' cried Ahab to the oarsmen and the boats darted forward to the attack; but maddened by yesterdays fresh irons that corroded in him, Moby Dick seemed combinedly possessed by all the angels that fell from heaven. The wide tiers of welded tendons overspreading his broad white forehead, beneath the transparent skin, looked knitted together; as head on, he came churning his tail among the boats; and once more flailed them apart; spilling out the irons and lances from the two mates' boats, and dashing in one side of the upper part of their bows, but leaving Ahab's almost without a scar.

While Daggoo and Queequeg were stopping the strained

planks; and as the whale swimming out from them, turned, and showed one entire flank as he shot by them again; at that moment a quick cry went up. Lashed round and round to the fish's back; pinioned in the turns upon turns in which, during the past night, the whale had reeled the involutions of the lines around him, the half-torn body of the Parsee was seen; his sable raiment frayed to shreds, his distended eyes turned full upon old Ahab.

The harpoon dropped from his hand.

'Befooled, befooled!' — drawing in a long lean breath — 'Aye, Parsee! I see thee again. Aye, and thou goest before; and this, *this* then is the hearse that thou didst promise. But I hold thee to the last letter of thy word. Where is the second hearse? Away, mates, to the ship! Those boats are useless now; repair them if ye can in time, and return to me; if not, Ahab is enough to die. Down, men! The first thing that but offers to jump from this boat I stand in, that thing I harpoon. Ye are not other men, but my arms and legs; so obey me. Where's the whale? gone down again?'

But he looked too nigh the boat; for as if bent upon escaping with the corpse he bore, and as if the particular place of the last encounter had been but a stage in his leeward voyage, Moby Dick was now again steadily swimming forward; and had almost passed the ship, which thus far had been sailing in the contrary direction to him, though for the present her headway had been stopped. He seemed swimming with his utmost velocity, and now only intent upon pursuing his own straight path in the sea.

'Oh! Ahab,' cried Starbuck, 'not too late is it even now, the third day, to desist. See! Moby Dick seeks thee not. It is thou, thou, that madly seekest him!'

Setting sail to the rising wind, the lonely boat was swiftly impelled to leeward by both oars and canvas. And at last when Ahab was sliding by the vessel, so near as plainly to distinguish Starbuck's face as he leaned over the rail, he hailed him to turn the vessel about, and follow him, not too swiftly, at a judicious interval. Glancing upwards, he saw Tashtego, Queequeg, and Daggoo, eagerly mounting to the three mastheads; while the oarsmen were rocking in the two staved boats which had just been hoisted to the side, and were busily at work in repairing them. One after the other, through the port holes, as he sped, he also caught flying glimpses of Stubb and Flask, busying themselves on deck among bundles of new irons and lances. As he saw all this; as he heard the hammers in the broken boats; far other hammers seemed driving a nail into his heart. But he rallied. And now marking that the vane of flag was gone from the main masthead, he shouted to Tashtego, who had just gained that perch, to descend again for another flag, and a hammer and nails, and so nail it to the mast.

Whether fagged by the three days' running chase, and the resistance to his swimming in the knotted hamper he bore; or whether it was some latent deceitfulness and malice in him; whichever was true, the White Whale's way now began to abate, as it seemed, from the boat so rapidly nearing him once more; though indeed the whale's last start had not been so long a one as before. And still as Ahab glided over the waves the unpitying sharks accompanied him; and so pertinaciously stuck to the boat; and so continually bit at the plying oars, that the blades became jagged and crunched, and left small splinters in the sea, at almost every dip.

'Heed them not! those teeth but give new rowlocks to your oars. Pull on! 'tis the better rest, the shark's jaws than the yielding water.'

'But at every bite, sir, the thin blades grow smaller and smaller!'

'They will last long enough! Pull on! But who can tell' — he muttered — 'whether these sharks swim to feast on a whale or on Ahab? But pull on! Aye, all alive now — we near him. The helm! take the helm; let me pass,' — and so saying, two of the oarsmen helped him forward to the bows of the still flying boat.

At length as the craft was cast to one side, and ran ranging along with the White Whale's flank, he seemed strangely oblivious of its advance — as the whale sometimes will — and Ahab was fairly within the smoky mountain mist, which, thrown off from the whale's spout, curled round his great Monadnock hump. He was even thus close to him; when, with body arched back, and both arms lengthwise high-lifted to the poise, he darted his fierce iron, and his far fiercer curse into the hated whale. As both steel and curse sank to the socket, as if sucked into a morass, Moby Dick sideways writhed; spasmodically rolled his nigh flank against the bow, and, without staving a hole in it, so suddenly canted the boat over, that had it not been for the elevated part of the gunwale to which he then clung, Ahab would have once more been tossed into the sea. As it was, three of the oarsmen — who foreknew not the precise instant of the dart, and were therefore unprepared for its effects — these were flung out; but so fell, that, in an instant two of them clutched the gunwale again, and rising to its level on a combing wave, hurled themselves bodily inboard again; the third man helplessly drooping astern, but still afloat and swimming.

Almost simultaneously, with a mighty volition of ungraduated instantaneous swiftness, the White Whale darted through the weltering sea. But when Ahab cried out to the steersman to take new turns with the line, and hold it so; and commanded the crew to turn round on their seats, and tow the boat up to the mark; the moment the treacherous line felt that double strain and tug, it snapped in the empty air!

'What breaks in me? Some sinew cracks! — 'tis whole again; oars! oars! Burst in upon him!'

Hearing the tremendous rush of the sea-crashing boat, the whale wheeled round to present his blank forehead at bay; but in that evolution, catching sight of the nearing black hull of the ship; seemingly seeing in it the source of all his persecutions; bethinking it — it may be — a larger and nobler foe; of a sudden he bore down upon its advancing prow, smiting his jaws amid fiery showers of foam.

Ahab staggered; his hand smote his forehead. 'I grow blind; hands! stretch out before me that I may yet grope my way. Is't night?'

'The whale! The ship!' cried the clinging oarsmen.

'Oars! oars! Slope downwards to thy depths, O sea, that ere it be for ever too late, Ahab may slide this last, last time upon his mark! I see: the ship! the ship! Dash on, my men! Will ye not save my ship?'

But as the oarsmen violently forced their boat through the sledge-hammering seas, the before whale-smitten bow-ends of two planks burst through, and in an instant almost, the temporarily disabled boat lay nearly level with the waves; its half-wading, splashing crew, trying hard to stop the gap and bale out the pouring water.

Meantime, for that one holding instant, Tashtego's masthead hammer remained suspended in his hand; and the red flag, half-wrapping him as with a plaid, then streamed itself straight out from him, as his own forward-flowing heart; while Starbuck and Stubb, standing upon the bowsprit beneath, caught sight of the downcoming monster just as soon as he.

'The whale! the whale! Up helm, up helm! Oh, all ye sweet powers of air, now hug me close! Let not Starbuck die, if die he must, in a woman's fainting fit. Up helm, I say — ye fools, the jaw! the jaw! Is this the end of all my bursting prayers? all my life-long fidelities? Oh, Ahab, Ahab, lo, thy work. Steady! helmsman, steady! Nay, nay! Up helm again!

He turns to meet us! Oh, his unappeasable brow drives on towards one, whose duty tells him he cannot depart. My God, stand by me now!'

'Stand not by me, but stand under me, whoever you are that will now help Stubb; for Stubb, too, sticks here. I grin at thee, thou grinning whale! Whoever helped Stubb, or kept Stubb awake, but Stubb's own unwinking eye? And now poor Stubb goes to bed upon a mattress that is all too soft; would it were stuffed with brushwood. I grin at thee, thou grinning whale! Look ye, moon and stars! I call ye assassins of as good a fellow as ever spouted up his ghost. For all that, I would yet ring glasses with ye, would ye but hand the cup! Oh, oh, oh, oh! thou grinning whale, but there'll be plenty of gulping soon! Why fly ye not, O Ahab? For me, off shoes and jacket to it; let Stubb die in his drawers! A most mouldy and over-salted death, though; — cherries! cherries! Oh, Flask, for one red cherry ere we die!'

'Cherries? I only wish that we were where they grow. Oh, Stubb, I hope my poor mother's drawn my part-pay ere this; if not, few coppers will come to her now, for the voyage is up.'

From the ship's bows, nearly all the seamen now hung inactive, hammers, bits of plank, lances, and harpoons, mechanically retained in their hands, just as they had darted from their various employments; all their enchanted eyes intent upon the whale, which from side to side strangely vibrating his predestinating head, sent a broad band of overspreading semi-circular foam before him as he rushed. Retribution, swift vengeance, eternal malice were in his whole aspect, and spite of all that mortal man could do, the solid white buttress of his forehead smote the ship's starboard bow, till men and timbers reeled. Some fell flat upon their faces. Like dislodged trucks, the heads of the harpooners aloft shook on their hull-like necks. Through the breach, they heard the waters pour, as mountain torrents down a flume.

'The ship! The hearse! — the second hearse!' cried Ahab from the boat; 'its wood could only be American!'

Diving beneath the settling ship, the Whale ran quivering along its keel, but turning under water, swiftly shot to the surface again, far off the other bow, but within a few yards of Ahab's boat, where, for a time, he lay quiescent.

'I turn my body from the sun. What ho, Tashtego! let me hear thy hammer. Oh! ye three unsurrendered spires of mine; thou uncracked keel; and only god-bullied hull; thou firm deck, and haughty helm, and Pole-pointed prow — death-glorious ship! must ye then perish, and without me? Am I cut off from the last fond pride of meanest shipwrecked captains? Oh, lonely death on lonely life! Oh, now I feel my topmost greatness lies in my topmost grief. Ho, ho! from all your furthest bounds, pour ye now in, ye bold billows of my whole foregone life, and top this one piled comber of my death! Towards thee I roll, thou all-destroying but unconquering whale; to the last I grapple with thee; from hell's heart I stab at thee; for hate's sake I spit my last breath at thee. Sink all coffins and all hearses to one common pool! and since neither can be mine let me then tow to pieces, while still chasing thee, though tied to thee, thou damned whale! *Thus*, I give up the spear.'

The harpoon was darted; the stricken whale flew forward; with igniting velocity the line ran through the groove; ran foul. Ahab stooped to clear it, he did clear it; but the flying turn caught him round the neck, and voicelessly as Turkish mutes bow-string their victims, he was shot out of the boat, ere the crew knew he was gone. Next instant, the heavy eye-splice in the rope's final end flew out of the stark-empty tub, knocked down an oarsman, and smoting the sea, disappeared in its depth.

For an instant, the tranced boat's crew stood still then turned.

'The ship! Great God, where is the ship?'

Soon they through dim, bewildering mediums saw her sidelong fading phantom, as in the gaseous Fata Morgana; only the uppermost masts out of water; while fixed by infatuation or fidelity, or fate, to their once lofty perches, the pagan harpooners still maintained their sinking lookouts on the sea. And now concentric circles seized the lone boat itself, and all its crew, and each floating oar, and every lance-pole and spinning, animate and inanimate, all round and round in one vortex, carried the smallest chip of the *Pequod* out of sight.

But as the last whelmings intermixingly poured themselves over the sunken head of the Indian at the mainmast, leaving a few inches of the erect spar yet visible, together with long streaming yards of the flag, which calmly undulated, with ironical coincidings, over the destroying billows they almost touched; — at that instant, a red arm and a hammer hovered backwardly uplifted in the open air, in the act of nailing the flag faster and yet faster to the subsiding spar. A sky-hawk that tauntingly had followed the main-truck downwards from its natural home among the stars, pecking at the flag, and incommoding Tashtego there; this bird now chanced to intercept its broad fluttering wing between the hammer and the wood; and simultaneously feeling that ethereal thrill, the submerged savage beneath, in his death-grasp, kept his hammer frozen there; and so the bird of heaven, with unearthly shrieks, and his imperial beak thrust upwards, and his whole captive form folded in the flag of Ahab, went down with his ship, which, like Satan, would not sink to hell till she had dragged a living part of heaven along with her, and helmeted herself with it.

Now small fowls flew screaming over the yet yawning gulf; a sullen white surf beat against its steep sides; then all collapsed, and the great shroud of the sea rolled on as it rolled five thousand years ago.

Two Adventures
of Baron Munchhausen
from Gulliver Revived

by
RUDOLF ERICH RASPE

I

I embarked at Portsmouth in a first-rate English man-of-war, of one hundred guns, and fourteen hundred men, for North America; nothing worth relating happened till we arrived within three hundred leagues of the river Saint Lawrence, when the ship struck with amazing force against (as we supposed) a rock; however, upon heaving the lead, we could find no bottom, even with three hundred fathom. What made this circumstance the more wonderful, and indeed beyond all comprehension, was, that the violence of the shock was such that we lost our rudder, broke our bowsprit in the middle, and split all our masts from top to bottom, two of which went by the board; a poor fellow, who was aloft, furling the main-sheet, was flung at least three leagues from the ship; but he fortunately saved his life, by laying hold of the tail of a very large sea-gull, who brought him back, and lodged him on the very spot whence he was thrown. Another proof of the violence of the shock was the force with which the people between decks were driven against the floors above them; my head particularly was pressed into my stomach, where it continued for some months, before it recovered its natural situation. Whilst we were all in a state of astonishment at the general and unaccountable confusion in which we were involved, the whole was suddenly explained by the appearance of a large whale, who had been basking asleep within sixteen feet of the surface of the water. This animal was so much displeased with the disturbance which our ship had given him (for in our passage we had with our rudder scratched his nose), that he beat in all the gallery and part of the quarter-deck with his tail, and almost at the same instant, took the main sheet-anchor, which was suspended, as it usually is, from the head, between his teeth, and ran away with the ship, for at least sixty leagues, at the rate of twelve leagues an hour, when fortunately the cable broke, and we lost both the whale and the anchor. However, upon our return to Europe some months after, we found the same whale, within a few leagues of the same spot, floating dead upon the water; it measured above half-a-mile in length. As we could but take a small quantity of such a monstrous animal on board, we got our boats out, and, with much difficulty, cut off his head, where, to our great joy, we found the anchor, and above 40 fathoms of the cable concealed on the left side of his mouth, just under his tongue. Perhaps this was the cause of his death, as that side of his tongue was much swelled, with a great degree of inflammation. This was the only extraordinary circumstance that happened on this voyage.

II

In a voyage which I made to the East Indies with Captain Hamilton I took a favourite pointer with me; he was, to use a common phrase, worth his weight in gold, for he never deceived me. One day, when we were by the best observations we could make, at least three hundred leagues from the land, my dog pointed; I observed him for near an hour with astonishment, and mentioned the circumstance to the Captain,

I bet one hundred guineas that we should find game within half an hour.

and every officer on board, asserting that we must be near land, for my dog smelt game; this occasioned a general laugh; but that did not alter in the least the good opinion I had of my dog. After much conversation pro and con, I boldly told the Captain, I placed more confidence in Tray's nose, than I did in the eyes of every seaman on board, and therefore boldly proposed laying the sum I had agreed to pay for my passage (viz., one hundred guineas) that we should find game within half an hour; the Captain (a good hearty fellow) laughed again, desired Mr Crawford, the surgeon who was present, to feel my pulse; he did so, reported me in good health; the following dialogue between them took place; I overheard it, though spoken low and at some distance.

CAPTAIN   His brain is turned; I cannot with honour accept his wager.

SURGEON   I am of a different opinion; he is quite sane, and depends more upon the scent of his dog, than he will upon the judgment of all the officers on board; he will certainly lose, and he richly merits it.

CAPTAIN   Such a wager cannot be fair on my side; but I'll take him up, if I can return his money later.

During the above conversation, Tray continued in the same situation, and confirmed me still more in my former opinion. I proposed the wager a second time; it was then accepted.

Done and Done were scarcely said on both sides, when some sailors who were fishing in the long-boat, which was made fast to the stern of the ship, harpooned an exceedingly large shark, which they brought on board, and began to cut up for the purposes of barrelling the oil, when behold, they found no less than *six brace of live partridges* in this animal's stomach! They had been so long in that situation, that one of the hens was sitting upon four eggs, and a fifth was hatching when the shark was opened!!!

236

This young bird we brought up, by placing it with a litter of kittens that came into the world a few minutes before! The old cat was as fond of it as any of her own four-legged progeny, and made herself very unhappy when it flew out of her reach till it returned again; as to the other partridges, there were four hens amongst them; one or more were, during the voyage, constantly sitting, and consequently we had plenty of game at the Captain's table; and in gratitude to poor Tray (for being the means of winning one hundred guineas) I ordered him the bones daily, and sometimes a whole bird.

A Descent
into the Maelstrom

by

EDGAR ALLAN POE

We had now reached the summit of the loftiest crag. For some minutes the old man seemed too much exhausted to speak.

'Not long ago,' said he at length, 'and I could have guided you on this route as well as the youngest of my sons; but, about three years past, there happened to me an event such as never before happened to mortal man — or at least such as no man ever survived to tell of — and the six hours of deadly terror which I then endured have broken me up body and soul. You suppose me a *very* old man — but I am not. It took less than a single day to change these hairs from a jetty black to white, to weaken my limbs, and to unstring my nerves, so that I tremble at the least exertion, and am frightened at a shadow. Do you know that I can scarcely look over this little cliff without getting giddy?'

The 'little cliff' upon whose edge he had so carelessly thrown himself down to rest that the weightier portion of his body hung over it, while he was only kept from falling by the tenure of his elbow on its extreme and slippery edge — this 'little cliff' arose, a sheer unobstructed precipice of black shining rock, some fifteen or sixteen hundred feet from the world of crags beneath us. Nothing would have tempted me within half a dozen yards of its brink. In truth so deeply was I excited by the perilous position of my companion, that I fell at full length on the ground, clung to the shrubs around me, and dared not even glance upward at the sky — while I struggled in vain to divest myself of the idea that the very foundations of the mountain were in danger from the fury of the winds. It was long before I could reason myself into sufficient courage to sit up and look out into the distance.

'You must get over these fancies,' said the guide, for 'I have brought you here that you might have the best possible view of the scene of that event I mentioned — and to tell you the whole story with the spot just under your eye.'

'We are now,' he continued, in that particularising manner which distinguished him — 'we are now close upon the Norwegian coast — in the sixty-eighth degree of latitude — in the great province of Nordland — and in the dreary district of Lofoden. The mountain upon whose top we sit is Helseggen, the Cloudy. Now raise yourself up a little higher — hold on to the grass if you feel giddy — so — look out, beyond the belt of vapour beneath us, into the sea.'

I looked dizzily, and beheld a wide expanse of ocean, whose waters were so inky a hue as to bring at once to my mind the Nubian geographer's account of the *Mare Tenebrarum*. A panorama more deplorably desolate no human imagination can conceive. To the right and left, as far as the eye could reach, there lay outstretched, like ramparts of the world, lines of horridly black and beetling cliff, whose character of gloom was but the more forcibly illustrated by the surf which reared high up against it, its white and ghastly crest, howling and shrieking for ever. Just opposite the promontory upon whose apex we were placed, and at a distance of some five or six miles out at sea, there was visible a small, bleak-looking island; or, more properly, its position was discernible through the wilderness of surge in which it was enveloped. About two miles nearer the land, arose another of smaller size, hideously craggy and barren, and encompassed at various intervals by a cluster of dark rocks.

The appearance of the ocean, in the space between the more distant island and the shore, had something very unusual about it. Although, at the time, so strong a gale was blowing landward that a brig in the remote offing lay-to under a double-reefed trysail, and constantly plunged her whole hull out of sight, still there was here nothing like a regular swell, but only a short, quick, angry cross dashing of water in every direction — as well in the teeth of the wind as otherwise. Of foam there was little except in the immediate vicinity of the rocks.

'The island in the distance,' resumed the old man, 'is Moskoe. That a mile to the northward is Ambaaren. Yonder are Islesen, Hotholm, Keildhelm, Suarven, and Buckholm. Farther off — between Moskoe and Vurrgh — are Otterholm, Flimen, Sandflesen, and Stockholm. These are the true names of the places — but why it has been thought necessary to name them at all, is more than either you or I can understand. Do you hear anything? Do you see any change in the water?'

We had now been about ten minutes upon the top of Helseggen, to which we had ascended from the interior of Lofoden, so that we had caught no glimpse of the sea until it had burst upon us from the summit. As the old man spoke I became aware of a loud and gradually increasing sound, like the moaning of a vast herd of buffaloes upon an American prairie; and at the same moment I perceived that what seamen term the 'chopping' character of the ocean beneath us, was rapidly changing into a current which set to the eastward. Even while I gazed, this current acquired a monstrous velocity. Each moment added to its speed — to its headlong impetuosity. In five minutes the whole sea, as far as Vurrgh, was lashed into ungovernable fury; but it was between Moskoe and the coast that the main uproar held its sway. Here the vast bed of the waters, seamed and scarred into a thousand conflicting channels, burst suddenly into frenzied convulsion — heaving, boiling, hissing — gyrating in gigantic and innumerable vortices, and all whirling and plunging on to the eastward with a rapidity which water never elsewhere assumes, except in precipitous descents.

In a few minutes more, there came over the scene another radical alteration. The general surface grew somewhat more smooth, and the whirlpools, one by one, disappeared, while prodigious streaks of foam became apparent where none had been seen before. These streaks, at length, spreading out to a great distance, and entering into combination, took unto themselves the gyratory motion of the subsided vortices, and seemed to form the germ of another more vast. Suddenly — very suddenly — this assumed a distinct and definite existence, in a circle of more than a mile in diameter. The edge of the whirl was represented by a broad belt of gleaming spray; but no particle of this slipped into the mouth of the terrific funnel, whose interior, as far as the eye could fathom it, was a smooth, shining, and jet-black wall of water, inclined to the horizon at an angle of some forty-five degrees, speeding dizzily round and round with a swaying and sweltering motion, and sending forth to the winds an appalling voice, half shriek, half roar, such as not even the mighty cataract of Niagara ever lifts up in its agony to Heaven.

The mountain trembled to its very base, and the rock rocked. I threw myself upon my face, and clung to the scant herbage in an excess of nervous agitation.

'This,' said I at length, to the old man — 'this *can* be nothing else but the great whirlpool of the Maelstrom.'

'So it is sometimes termed,' said he. 'We Norwegians call it the Moskoe-strom, from the island of Moskoe in the midway.

The ordinary account of this vortex had by no means prepared me for what I saw. That of Jonas Ramus, which is perhaps the most circumstantial of any, cannot impart the faintest conception either of the magnificence or of the horror of the scene — or of the wild bewildering sense of *the novel* which confounds the beholder. I am not sure from what point of view the writer in question surveyed it, nor at what time, but it could neither have been from the summit of Helseggen, nor during a storm. There are some passages of his description nevertheless, which may be quoted for their details, although their effect is exceedingly feeble in conveying an impression of the spectacle.

'Between Lofoden and Moskoe,' he says, 'the depth of the water is between thirty-six and forty fathoms; but on the other side, toward Ver (Vurrgh) this depth decreases so as not to afford a convenient passage for a vessel, without the risk of splitting on the rocks, which happens even in the calmest weather. When it is flood, the stream runs up the country between Lofoden and Moskoe with a boisterous rapidity; but the roar of its impetuous ebb to the sea is scarce equalled by the loudest and most dreadful cataracts; the noise being heard several leagues off, and the vortices or pits are of such an extent and depth, that if a ship comes within its attraction, it is inevitably absorbed and carried down to the bottom, and there beat to pieces against the rocks; and when the water relaxes, the fragments thereof are thrown up again. But these intervals of tranquillity are only at the turn of the ebb and flood, and in calm weather, and last but a quarter of an hour, its violence gradually returning. When the stream is most boisterous, and its fury heightened by a storm, it is dangerous to come within a Norway mile of it. Boats, yachts, and ships have been carried away by not guarding against it before they were carried within its reach. It likewise happens frequently, that whales come too near the stream, and are overpowered by its violence; and then it is impossible to describe their howlings and bellowings in their fruitless struggles to disengage themselves. A bear once, in attempting to swim from Lofoden to Moskoe, was caught by the stream and borne down, while he roared terribly, so as to be heard on shore. Large stocks of firs and pine-trees, after being absorbed by the current, rise again broken and torn to such a degree as if bristles grew upon them. This plainly shows the bottom to consist of craggy rocks, among which they are whirled to and fro. This stream is regulated by the flux and reflux of the sea — it being constantly high and low water every six hours. In the year 1645, early in the morning of Sexagesima Sunday, it raged with such a noise and impetuosity that the very stones of the houses on the coast fell to the ground.'

In regard to the depth of the water, I could not see how this could have been ascertained at all in the immediate vicinity of the vortex. The 'forty fathoms' must have reference only to portions of the channel close upon the shore of either Moskoe or Lofoden. The depth in the middle of the Moskoe-strom must be immeasurably greater; and no better proof of this fact is necessary than can be obtained from even the sidelong glance into the abyss of the whirl which may be had from the highest crag of Helseggen. Looking down from this pinnacle upon the howling Phlegethon below, I could not help smiling at the simplicity with which the honest Jonas Ramus records, as a matter difficult of belief, the anecdotes of the whales and the bears, for it appeared to me, in fact, a self-evident thing, that the largest ships of the line in existence, coming within the influence of that deadly attraction, could resist it as little as a feather the hurricane, and must disappear bodily at once.

The attempts to account for the phenomenon — some of which I remember, seemed to me sufficiently plausible on perusal — now wore a very different and unsatisfactory aspect. The idea generally received is that this, as well as three smaller vortices among the Ferroe Islands, 'have no other cause than the collision of waves rising and falling, at flux and reflux, against a ridge of rocks and shelves, which confines the water so that it precipitates itself like a cataract; and thus the higher the flood rises, the deeper the fall must be, and the natural result of all is a whirlpool or vortex, the prodigious suction of which is sufficiently known by lesser experiments. —'

These are the words of the *Encyclopaedia Britannica*. Kircher and others imagine that in the centre of the channel of the Maelstrom is an abyss penetrating the globe, and issuing in some very remote part — the Gulf of Bothnia being somewhat decidedly named in one instance. This opinion, idle in itself, was the one to which, as I gazed, my imagination most readily assented; and, mentioning it to the guide, I was rather surprised to hear him say that, although it was the view almost universally entertained of the subject by the Norwegians, it nevertheless was not his own. As to the former notion, he confessed his inability to comprehend it; and here I agreed with him — for, however conclusive on paper, it becomes altogether unintelligible, and even absurd, amid the thunder of the abyss.

'You have had a good look at the whirl now,' said the old man, 'and if you will creep round this crag, so as to get in its lee, and deaden the roar of the water, I will tell you a story that will convince you I ought to know something of the Moskoe-strom.'

I placed myself as desired, and he proceeded.

'Myself and my two brothers once owned a schooner-rigged smack of about seventy tons burthen, with which we were in the habit of fishing among the islands beyond Moskoe, nearly to Vurrgh. In all violent eddies at sea there is good fishing at proper opportunities, if one has only the courage to attempt it; but among the whole of the Lofoden coastmen, we three were the only ones who made a regular business of going out to the islands, as I tell you. The usual grounds are a great way down to the southward. There fish can be got at all hours, without much risk, and therefore these places were preferred. The choice spots over here among the rocks, however, not only yield the finest variety, but in greater abundance; so that we often got in a single day, what the more timid of the craft could not scrape together in a week. In fact, we made it a matter of desperate speculation — the risk of life standing instead of labour, and courage answering for capital.'

'We kept the smack in a cove about five miles higher up the coast than this; and it was our practice, in fine weather, to take advantage of the fifteen minutes' slack to push across the main channel of the Moskoe-strom, far above the pool, and then drop down upon anchorage somewhere near Otterholm, or Sandflesen, where the eddies are not so violent as elsewhere. Here we used to remain until nearly time for slack-water again, when we weighed and made for home. We never set out upon this expedition without a steady side wind for coming and going, one that we felt sure would not fail us before our return, and we seldom made a miscalculation upon this point. Twice, during six years, we were forced to stay all night at anchor on account of a dead calm, which is a rare thing indeed just about here; and once we had to remain on the grounds nearly a week, starving to death, owing to a gale which blew up shortly after our arrival, and made the channel too boisterous to be thought of. Upon this occasion we should have been driven out to sea in spite of everything (for the whirlpools threw us round and round so violently, that, at length, we fouled our anchor and dragged it), if it had not been that we drifted into one of the innumerable cross-currents — here to-day and gone to-morrow — which drove us under the lee of Flimen, where, by good luck, we brought up.

'I could not tell you the twentieth part of the difficulties we encountered "on the ground" — it is a bad spot to be in even in good weather — but we made shift always to run the gauntlet of the Moskoe-strom itself without accident; although at times my heart has been in my mouth when we happened to be a minute or so behind or before the slack. The wind sometimes was not as strong as we thought it at starting, and then we made rather less way than we could wish, while the current rendered the smack unmanageable. My eldest brother had a son eighteen years old, and I had two stout boys of my own. These would have been of great assistance at such times, in using the sweeps as well as afterward in fishing — but, somehow, although we ran the risk ourselves, we had not the heart to let the young ones get into danger — for, after all said and done, it *was* a horrible danger, and that is the truth.

'It is now within a few days of three years since what I am going to tell you occurred. It was on the 10th July, 18 —, a day which the people of this part of the world will never forget — for it was one in which blew the most terrible hurricane that ever came out of the heavens. And yet all the morning, and indeed until late in the afternoon, there was a gentle and steady breeze from the south-west, while the sun shone brightly, so that the oldest seaman among us could not have foreseen what was to follow.

'The three of us — my two brothers and myself — had crossed over to the islands, about two o'clock p. m., and soon nearly loaded the smack with fine fish, which we all remarked were more plenty that day than we had ever known them. It was just seven, *by my watch*, when we weighed and started for home, so as to make the worst of the Strom at slack water, which we knew would be at eight.

'We set out with a fresh wind on our starboard quarter, and for some time spanked along at a great rate, never dreaming of danger, for indeed we saw not the slightest reason to apprehend it. All at once we were taken aback by a breeze from over Helseggen. This was most unusual — something that had never happened to us before — and I began to feel a little uneasy, without exactly knowing why. We put the boat on the wind, but could make no headway at all for the eddies, and I was upon the point of proposing to return to the anchorage when, looking astern, we saw the whole horizon covered with a singular copper-coloured cloud that rose with the most amazing velocity.

'In the meantime the breeze that had headed us off fell away and we were dead becalmed, drifting about in every direction. This state of things, however, did not last long enough to give us time to think about it. In less than a minute the storm was upon us — in less than two the sky was entirely overcast — and what with this and the driving spray, it became suddenly so dark that we could not see each other in the smack.

'Such a hurricane as then blew it is folly to attempt describing. The oldest seaman in Norway never experienced anything like it. We had to let our sails go by the run before it cleverly took us; but, at the first puff, both our masts went by the board as if they had been sawed off — the mainmast taking with it my youngest brother who had lashed himself to it for safety.

'Our boat was the lightest feather of a thing that ever sat upon water. It had a complete flush deck, with only a small hatch near the bow, and this hatch it had always been our custom to batten down when about to cross the Strom, by way of precaution against the chopping seas. But for this circumstance we should have foundered at once — for we lay entirely buried for some moments. How my eldest brother escaped destruction I cannot say, for I never had an opportunity of ascertaining. For my part, as soon as I had let the foresail run, I threw myself flat on deck, with my feet against the narrow gunwale of the bow, and with my hands grasping a ring-bolt near the foot of the foremast. It was mere instinct that prompted me to do this — which was undoubtedly the best thing I could have done — for I was much too flurried to think.

'For some moments we were completely deluged, as I say, and all this time I held my breath, and clung to the bolt. When I could stand it no longer, I raised myself upon my knees, still keeping hold with my hands and thus got my head clear. Presently our little boat gave herself a shake just as a dog does in coming out of the water, and thus rid herself, in some measure, of the seas. I was now trying to get the better of the stupor that had come over me, and to collect my senses so as to see what was to be done, when I felt somebody grasp my arm. It was my eldest brother, and my heart leaped for joy, for I had made sure that he was overboard — but the next moment all this joy was turned to horror — for he put his mouth close to my ear, and screamed out the word "*Moskoe-strom!*"

'No one will ever know what my feelings were at that moment. I shook from head to foot as if I had had the most violent fit of ague. I knew what he meant by that one word well enough — I knew what he wished to make me understand. With the wind that now drove us on, we were bound for the whirl of the Strom, and nothing could save us.

'You perceive that in crossing the Strom *channel*, we always went a long way up above the whirl, even in the calmest weather, and then had to wait and watch carefully for the slack — but now we were driving right upon the pool itself, and in such a hurricane as this! "To be sure," I thought, "we shall get there just about the slack — there is some little hope in that" — but in the next moment I cursed myself for being so great a fool as to dream of hope at all. I knew very well that we were doomed, had we been ten times a ninety-gun ship.

'By this time the first fury of the tempest had spent itself, or perhaps we did not feel it so much, as we scudded before it, but at all events the seas, which at first had been kept down by the wind, and lay flat and frothing, now got up into absolute mountains. A singular change, too, had come over the heavens. Around in every direction it was still as black as pitch, but nearly overhead there burst out, all at once, a circular rift of clear sky — as clear as I ever saw — and of a deep bright blue — and through it there blazed forth the full moon with a lustre that I never before knew her to wear. She lit up everything about us with the greatest distinctness — but oh God, what a scene it was to light up!

'I now made one or two attempts to speak to my brother — but in some manner which I could not understand, the din had so increased that I could not make him hear a single word, although I screamed at the top of my voice in his ear. Presently he shook his head, looking as pale as death, and held up one of his fingers, as if to say *"listen!"*

'At first I could not make out what he meant — but soon a hideous thought flashed upon me. I dragged my watch from its fob. It was not going. I glanced at its face in the moonlight and then burst into tears as I flung it far away into the ocean. *It had run down at seven o'clock! We were behind the time of the slack and the whirl of the Strom was in full fury!*

'When a boat is well built, properly trimmed, and not deep laden, the waves in a strong gale, when she is going large, seem always to slip from beneath her — which appears strange to a landsman, and this is what is called *"riding"*, in sea phrase.

'Well, so far we had ridden the waves very cleverly; but presently a gigantic sea happened to take us right under the counter, and bore us with it as it rose — up — up — as if into the sky. I would not have believed that any wave could rise so high. And then down we came with a sweep, a slide, and a plunge that made me feel sick and dizzy, as if I was falling from some lofty mountain-top in a dream. But while we were up I had thrown a quick glance around — and that one glance was all-sufficient. I saw our exact position in an instant. The Moskoe-strom whirlpool was about a quarter of a mile dead ahead — but no more like the every-day Moskoe-strom than the whirl, as you now see it, is like a mill race. If I had now known where we were, and what we had to expect, I should not have recognised the place at all. As it was, I involuntarily closed my eyes in horror. The lids clenched themselves together as if in a spasm.

It could not have been more than two minutes afterwards until we suddenly felt the waves subside, and were enveloped in foam. The boat made a sharp half-turn to larboard, and then shot off in its new direction like a thunderbolt. At the same moment the roaring noise of the water was completely drowned in a kind of shrill shriek — such a sound as you might imagine given out by the water-pipes of many thousand steam-vessels letting off their steam all together. We were now in the belt of surf that always surrounds the whirl; and I thought, of course, that another moment would plunge us into the abyss, down which we could only see indistinctly on account of the amazing velocity with which we were borne along. The boat did not seem to sink into the water at all, but to skim like an air-bubble upon the surface of the surge. Her starboard side was next the whirl, and on the larboard arose the world of ocean we had left. It stood like a huge writhing wall between us and the horizon.

'It may appear strange, but now, when we were in the very jaws of the gulf, I felt more composed than when we were only approaching it. Having made up my mind to hope no more, I got rid of a great deal of that terror which unmanned me at first. I suppose it was despair that strung my nerves.

'It may look like boasting — but what I tell you is the truth — I began to reflect how magnificent a thing it was to die in such a manner, and how foolish it was in me to think of so paltry a consideration as my own individual life, in view of so wonderful a manifestation of God's power. I do believe that I blushed with shame when this idea crossed my mind. After a little while I became possessed with the keenest curiosity about the whirl itself. I positively felt a *wish* to explore its depths, even at the sacrifice I was going to make; and my principal grief was that I should never be able to tell my old companions on shore about the mysteries I should see. These, no doubt, were singular fancies to occupy a man's mind in such extremity — and I have often thought since, that the revolutions of the boat around the pool might have rendered me a little light-headed.

'There was another circumstance which tended to restore my self-possession; and this was the cessation of the wind, which could not reach us in our present position — for, as you saw for yourself, the belt of the surf is considerably lower than the general bed of the ocean, and this latter now towered above us, a high, black, mountainous ridge. If you have never been at sea in a heavy gale, you can form no idea of the confusion of mind occasioned by the wind and spray together. They blind, deafen, and strangle you, and take away all power of action or reflection. But we were now, in a great measure, rid of these annoyances — just as death-condemned felons in prison are allowed petty indulgences, forbidden them while their doom is yet uncertain.

'How often we made the circuit of the belt it is impossible to say. We careered round and round for perhaps an hour, flying rather than floating, getting gradually more and more into the middle of the surge, and then nearer and nearer to its horrible inner edge. All this time I had never let go of the ring-bolt. My brother was at the stern, holding on to a small empty water-cask which had been securely lashed under the coop of the counter, and was the only thing on deck that had not been swept overboard when the gale first took us. As we approached the brink of the pit he let go his hold upon this, and made for the ring, from which, in the agony of his terror, he endeavoured to force my hands, as it was not large enough to afford us both a secure grasp. I never felt deeper grief than when I saw him attempt this act — although I knew he was a madman when he did it — a raving maniac through sheer fright. I did not care, however, to contest the point with him. I knew it could make no difference whether either of us held on at all; so I let him have the bolt, and went astern to the cask. This there was no great difficulty in doing; for the smack flew round steadily enough, and upon an even keel — only swaying to and fro with the immense sweeps and swelters of the whirl. Scarcely had I secured myself in my new position, when we gave a wild lurch to starboard, and rushed headlong into the abyss. I muttered a hurried prayer to God and thought all was over.

'As I felt the sickening sweep of the descent, I had instinctively tightened my hold upon the barrel, and closed my eyes. For some seconds I dared not open them — while I expected instant destruction, and wondered that I was not already in my death-struggles with the water. But moment after moment elapsed. I still lived. The sense of falling had ceased; and the motion of the vessel seemed much as it had been before, while in the belt of foam, with the exception that she now lay more along. I took courage and looked once again upon the scene.

'Never shall I forget the sensation of awe, horror and admiration with which I gazed about me. The boat appeared to be hanging, as if by magic, midway down, upon the interior surface of a funnel vast in circumference, prodigious in depth, and whose perfectly smooth sides might have been mistaken for ebony, but for the bewildering rapidity with which they spun round, and for the gleaming and ghastly radiance they shot forth, as the rays of the full moon, from that circular rift amid the clouds which I have already described, streamed in a flood of golden glory along the black walls, and far away down into the inmost recesses of the abyss.

At first I was too much confused to observe anything accurately. The general burst of terrific grandeur was all that I beheld. When I recovered myself a little, however, my gaze

The boat appeared to be hanging upon the interior surface of a vast
funnel.

fell instinctively downward. In this direction I was able to obtain an unobstructed view, from the manner in which the smack hung on the inclined surface of the pool. She was quite upon an even keel — that is to say, her deck lay in a plane parallel with that of the water — but this latter sloped at an angle of more than forty-five degrees, so that we seemed to be lying upon our beam-ends. I could not help observing, nevertheless, that I had scarcely more difficulty in maintaining my hold and footing in this situation, than if we had been upon a dead level; and this I suppose was owing to the speed at which we revolved.

'The rays of the moon seemed to search to the very bottom of the profound gulf; but still I could make out nothing distinctly on account of a thick mist in which everything there was enveloped, and over which there hung a magnificent rainbow, like that narrow and tottering bridge which Mussulmans say is the only pathway between Time and Eternity. This mist, or spray, was no doubt occasioned by the clashing of the great walls of the funnel, as they all met together at the bottom — but the yell that went up to the Heavens from out of that mist I dare not attempt to describe.'

'Our first slide into the abyss itself, from the belt of foam above, had carried us a great distance down the slope; but our further descent was by no means proportionate. Round and round we swept — not with any uniform movement — but in dizzying swings and jerks, that sent us sometimes only a few hundred yards — sometimes nearly the complete circuit of the whirl. Our progress downward, at each revolution, was slow, but very perceptible!'

'Looking about me upon the wide waste of liquid ebony on which we were thus born, I perceived that our boat was not the only object in the embrace of the whirl. Both above and below us were visible fragments of vessels, large masses of building-timber and trunks of trees, with many smaller articles, such as pieces of house furniture, broken boxes, barrels and staves. I have already described the unnatural curiosity which had taken the place of my original terrors. It appeared to grow upon me as I drew nearer and nearer to my dreadful doom. I now began to watch, with a strange interest, the numerous things that floated in our company. I *must* have been delirious, for I even sought *amusement* speculating upon the relative velocities of their several descents toward the foam below. "This fir-tree", I found myself at one time saying, "will certainly be the next thing that takes the awful plunge and disappears," — and then I was disappointed to find that the wreck of a Dutch merchant ship overtook it and went down before. At length, after making several guesses of this nature, and being deceived in all — this fact — the fact of my invariable miscalculation, set me upon a train of reflection that made my limbs again tremble, and my heart beat heavily once more.'

'It was not a new terror that thus affected me, but the dawn of a more exciting *hope*. This hope arose partly from memory, and partly from present observation. I called to mind the great variety of buoyant matter that strewd the coast of Lofoden, having been absorbed and then thrown forth by the Moskoe-strom. By far the great number of the articles were shattered in the most extraordinary way — so chafed and roughened as to have the appearance of being stuck full of splinters — but then I distinctly recollected that there were *some* of them which were not disfigured at all. Now I could not account for this difference except by supposing that the roughened fragments were the only ones which had been *completely absorbed* — that the others had entered into the whirl at so late a period of the tide, or, from some reason, had descended so slowly after entering, that they did not reach the bottom before the turn of the flood came, or of the ebb, as the case might be. I conceived it possible, in either instance, that they might thus be whirled up again to the level of the ocean, without undergoing the fate of those which had been drawn in more early or absorbed more rapidly. I made, also, three important observations. The first was, that as a general rule, the larger the bodies were, the more rapid their descent — the second, that, between two masses of equal extent, the one spherical, and the other *of any other shape* the superiority in speed of descent was with the sphere — the third, that, between two masses of equal size, the one cylindrical, and the other of any other shape, the cylinder was absorbed more slowly. Since my escape, I have had several conversations on this subject with an old schoolmaster in the district; and it was from him that I learned the use of the words "cylinder" and "sphere". He explained to me — although I have forgotten the explanation — how what I observed was, in fact, the natural consequence of the forms of the floating fragments — and showed me how it happened that a cylinder, swimming in a vortex, offered more resistance to its suction, and was drawn in with greater difficulty than an equally bulky body, of any form whatever.'

'There was one startling circumstance which went a great way in enforcing these observations, and rendering me anxious to turn them to account, and this was that, at every revolution we passed something like a barrel, or else the yard or the mast of a vessel, while many of these things, which had been on our level when I first opened my eyes upon the wonders of the whirlpool, were now high up above us, and seemed to have moved but little from their original station.

'I no longer hesitated what to do. I resolved to lash myself securely to the water-cask upon which I now held, to cut it loose from the counter, and to throw myself with it into the water. I attracted my brother's attention by signs, pointed to the floating barrels that came near us, and did everything in my power to make him understand what I was about to do. I thought at length that he comprehended my design — but, whether this was the case or not, he shook his head despairingly, and refused to move from his station by the ring-bolt. It was impossible to reach him; the emergency admitted of no delay; and so, with a bitter struggle, I resigned him to his fate, fastened myself upon the cask by means of the lashings which secured it to the counter, and precipitated myself with it into the sea, without another moment's hesitation.'

'The result was precisely what I had hoped it might be. As it is myself who now tells you this tale — and you see that I *did* escape — and as you are already in possession of the mode in which this escape was effected, and must therefore anticipate all that I have further to say — I will bring my story quickly to conclusion. It might have been an hour, or thereabout, after my quitting the smack, when, having descended to a vast distance beneath me, it made three or four wild gyrations in rapid succession, and, bearing my beloved brother with it, plunged headlong, at once and forever, into the chaos of foam below. The barrel to which I was attached sunk very little farther than half the distance between the bottom of the gulf and the spot at which I leaped overboard, before a great change took place in the character of the whirlpool. The slope of the sides of the vast funnel became momently less and less steep. The gyrations of the whirl grew, gradually, less and less violent. By degrees, the froth and the rainbow disappeared, and the bottom of the gulf seemed slowly to uprise. The sky was clear, the winds had gone down and the full moon was setting radiantly in the west, when I found myself on the surface of the ocean, in full view of the shores of Lofoden, and above the spot where the pool of the Moskoe-strom *had been*. It was the hour of the slack — but the sea still heaved in mountainous waves from the effects of the hurricane. I was borne violently into the channel of the Strom, and in a few minutes was hurried down the coast into the "grounds" of the fishermen. A boat picked me up — exhausted from fatigue — and (now that the danger was removed) speechless from the memory of its horror. Those who drew me on board were my old mates and daily companions — but they knew me no more than they would have known a traveller from the spirit-land. My hair which had been raven black the day before, was white as you see it now. They say too that the whole expression of my countenance had changed. I told them my story — they did not believe it. I now tell it to *you* — and I can scarcely expect you to put more faith in it than did the merry fishermen of Lofoden.'

The Bottom of the Sea

From 20,000 Leagues
Under the Sea

by
JULES VERNE

The submarine made an appearance in science fiction long before it became a reality. P. Arronax, the narrator of 20,000 Leagues Under the Sea *(written in 1869) is a scientist who joins an expedition in search of a mysterious sea monster which has been reported to roam the seas. The 'monster' is discovered to be the electrically-propelled subma-rine* Nautilus. *Its captain, Nemo, takes Arronax, his servant Conseil and the harpooner Ned Land as prisoners. They are treated as honoured guests, however, and Captain Nemo shows them the wonders of his underwater world.*

This cell was, to speak correctly, the arsenal and wardrobe of the Nautilus. A dozen diving apparatuses hung from the partition waiting our use.

Ned Land, on seeing them, showed evident repugnance to dress himself in one.

'But, my worthy Ned, the forests of the Island of Crespo are nothing but submarine forests.'

'Good!' said the disappointed harpooner, who saw his dreams of fresh meat fade away. 'And you, M. Arronax, are you going to dress yourself in those clothes?'

'There is no alternative, Master Ned.'

'As you please, sir,' replied the harpooner, shrugging his shoulders; 'but as for me, unless I am forced, I will never get into one.'

'No one will force you, Master Ned,' said Captain Nemo.

'Is Conseil going to risk it?' asked Ned.

'I follow my master wherever he goes,' replied Conseil.

At the Captain's call two of the ship's crew came to help us to dress in these heavy and impervious clothes, made of india-rubber without seam, and constructed expressly to resist considerable pressure. One would have thought it a suit of armour, both supple and resisting. This suit formed trousers and waistcoat. The trousers were finished off with thick boots, weighted with heavy leaden soles. The texture of the waistcoat was held together by bands of copper, which crossed the chest, protecting it from the great pressure of the water, and leaving the lungs free to act; the sleeves ended in gloves, which in no way restrained the movement of the hands. There was a vast difference noticeable between these consummate apparatuses and the old cork breastplates, jackets, and other contrivances in vogue during the eighteenth century.

Captain Nemo and one of his companions (a sort of Hercules, who must have possessed great strength), Conseil, and myself, were soon enveloped in the dresses. There remained nothing more to be done but to enclose our heads in the metal box. But before proceeding to this operation, I asked the Captain's permission to examine the guns we were to carry.

One of the Nautilus men gave me a simple gun, the butt end of which, made of steel, hollow in the centre, was rather large. It served as a reservoir for compressed air, which a valve, worked by a spring, allowed to escape into a metal tube. A box of projectiles, in a groove in the thickness of the butt end, contained about twenty of these electric balls, which, by means of a spring, were forced into the barrel of the gun. As soon as one shot was fired, another was ready.

'Captain Nemo,' said I, 'this arm is perfect, and easily handled; I only ask to be allowed to try it. But how shall we gain the bottom of the sea?'

'At this moment, Professor, the Nautilus is stranded in five fathoms, and we have nothing to do but to start.'

'But how shall we get off?'

'You shall see.'

Captain Nemo thrust his head into the helmet, Conseil and I did the same, not without hearing an ironical 'Good sport!' from the Canadian. The upper part of our dress terminated in a copper collar, upon which was screwed the metal helmet. Three holes, protected by thick glass, allowed us to see in all directions, by simply turning our head in the interior of the headdress. As soon as it was in position, the Rouquayrol apparatus on our backs began to act; and, for my part, I could breathe with ease.

With the Ruhmkorff lamp hanging from my belt, and the gun in my hand, I was ready to set out. But to speak the truth, imprisoned in these heavy garments, and glued to the deck by my leaden soles, it was impossible for me to take a step.

But this state of things was provided for. I felt myself being pushed into a little room contiguous to the wardrobe-room. My companions followed, towed along in the same way. I heard a water-tight door, furnished with stopper-plates, close upon us, and we were wrapped in profound darkness.

After some minutes, a loud hissing was heard. I felt the cold mount from my feet to my chest. Evidently from some part of the vessel they had, by means of a tap, given entrance to the water, which was invading us, and with which the room was soon filled. A second door cut in the side of the Nautilus then opened. We saw a faint light. In another instant our feet trod the bottom of the sea.

And now, how can I retrace the impression left upon me by that walk under the waters? Words are impotent to relate such wonders! Captain Nemo walked in front, his companion followed some steps behind. Conseil and I remained near each other, as if an exchange of words had been possible through our metallic cases. I no longer felt the weight of my clothing, or of my shoes, of my reservoir of air, or my thick helmet, in the midst of which my head rattled like an almond in its shell.

The light, which lit the soil thirty feet below the surface of the ocean, astonished me by its power. The solar rays shone through the watery mass easily, and dissipated all colour, and I clearly distinguished objects at a distance of a hundred and fifty yards. Beyond that the tints darkened into fine gradations of ultramarine, and faded into vague obscurity. Truly this water which surrounded me was but another air denser than the terrestrial atmosphere, but almost as transparent. Above me was the calm surface of the sea. We were walking on fine even sand, not wrinkled, as on a flat shore, which retains the impression of the billows. This dazzling carpet, really a reflector, repelled the rays of the sun with wonderful intensity, which accounted for the vibration which penetrated every atom of liquid. Shall I be believed when I say that, at the depth of thirty feet, I could see as if I was in broad daylight?

For a quarter of an hour I trod on this sand, sown with the impalpable dust of shells. The hull of the Nautilus, resembling a long shoal, disappeared by degrees; but its lantern, when darkness should overtake us in the waters, would help to guide us on board by its distinct rays.

Soon forms of objects outlined in the distance were discernible. I recognised magnificent rocks, hung with a tapestry of zoophites of the most beautiful kind, and I was at first struck by the peculiar effect of this medium.

It was then ten in the morning; the rays of the sun struck the surface of the waves at rather an oblique angle, and at the touch of their light, decomposed by refraction as through a prism, flowers, rocks, plants, shells, and polypi were shaded at the edges by the seven solar colours. It was marvellous, a feast for the eyes, this complication of coloured tints, a perfect kaleidoscope of green, yellow, orange, violet, indigo, and blue; in one word, the whole palette of an enthusiastic colourist! Why could I not communicate to Conseil the lively sensations which were mounting to my brain, and rival him in expressions of admiration? For aught I knew, Captain Nemo and his companion might be able to exchange thoughts by means of signs previously agreed upon. So, for want of better, I talked to myself; I declaimed in the copper box which covered my head, thereby expending more air in vain words than was perhaps expedient.

Various kinds of isis, clusters of pure tuft-coral, prickly fungi, and anemones, formed a brilliant garden of flowers, enamelled with porphitae, decked with their collarettes of blue tentacles, sea-stars studding the sandy bottom, together with asterophytons like fine lace embroidered by the hands of naiads, whose festoons were waved by the gentle undulations caused by our walk. It was a real grief to me to crush under my feet the brilliant specimens of molluscs which strewed the ground by thousands, of hammerheads, donaciae (veritable bounding shells), of staircases, and red helmet shells, angel-wings, and many others produced by this inexhaustible ocean. But we were bound to walk, so we went on, whilst above our heads waved shoals of physalides leaving their tentacles to float in their train, medusae whose umbrellas of opal or rose-pink, escalloped with a band of blue, sheltered us from the rays of the sun and fiery pelagiae, which, in the darkness, would have strewn our path with phosphorescent light.

All these wonders I saw in the space of a quarter of a mile, scarcely stopping, and following Captain Nemo, who beckoned me on by signs. Soon the nature of the soil changed; to the sandy plain succeeded an extent of slimy mud, which the Americans call 'ooze,' composed of equal parts of silicious and calcareous shells. We then travelled over a plain of sea-weed of wild and luxuriant vegetation. This sward was of close texture, and soft to the feet, and rivalled the softest carpet woven by the hand of man. But whilst verdure was spread at our feet, it did not abandon our heads. A light network of marine plants, of that inexhaustible family of sea-weeds of which more than two thousand kinds are known, grew on the surface of the water. I saw long ribbons of fucus floating, some globular, others tuberous; laurenciae and cladostephi of most delicate foliage, and some rhodomeniae palmatae, resembling the fan of a cactus. I noticed that the green plants kept nearer the top of the sea, whilst the red were at a greater depth, leaving to the black or brown hydrophytes the care of forming gardens and parterres in the remote beds of the ocean.

We had quitted the Nautilus about an hour and a half. It was near noon; I knew by the perpendicularity of the sun's rays, which were no longer refracted. The magical colours disappeared by degrees, and the shades of emerald and sapphire were effaced. We walked with a regular step, which rang upon the ground with astonishing intensity; the slightest noise was transmitted with a quickness to which the ear is unaccustomed on the earth; indeed, water is a better conductor of sound than air, in the ratio of four to one. At this period the earth sloped downwards; the light took a uniform tint. We were at a depth of a hundred and five yards and twenty inches, under-going a pressure of six atmospheres.

At this depth I could still see the rays of the sun, though feebly; to their intense brilliancy had succeeded a reddish twilight, the lowest state between day and night; but we could still see well enough; it was not necessary to resort to the Ruhmkorff apparatus as yet. At this moment Captain Nemo stopped; he waited till I joined him, and then pointed to an obscure mass, looming in the shadow, at a short distance.

'It is the forest of the Island of Crespo,' thought I — and I was not mistaken.

A Submarine Forest

We had at last arrived on the borders of this forest, doubtless one of the finest of Captain Nemo's immense domains. He looked upon it as his own, and considered he had the same right over it that the first men had in the first days of the world. And, indeed, who would have disputed with him the possession of this submarine property? What other hardier pioneer would come, hatchet in hand, to cut down the dark copses?

This forest was composed of large tree-plants; and the moment we penetrated under its vast arcades, I was struck by the singular position of their branches — a position I had not yet observed.

Not a herb which carpeted the ground, not a branch which clothed the trees, was either broken or bent, nor did they extend horizontally; all stretched up to the surface of the ocean. Not a filament, not a ribbon, however thin they might be, but kept as straight as a rod of iron. The fuci and llianas grew in rigid perpendicular lines, due to the density of the element which had produced them. Motionless, yet, when bent to one side by the hand, they directly resumed their former position. Truly it was the region of perpendicularity!

I soon accustomed myself to this fantastic position, as well as to the comparative darkness which surrounded us. The soil of the forest seemed covered with sharp blocks, difficult to avoid. The submarine flora struck me as being very perfect, and richer even than it would have been in the arctic or tropical zones, where these productions are not so plentiful. But for some minutes I involuntarily confounded the genera, taking zoophytes for hydrophytes, animals for plants; and who would not have been mistaken? The fauna and the flora are too closely allied in this submarine world.

These plants are self-propagated, and the principle of their existence is in the water, which upholds and nourishes them. The greater number, instead of leaves, shoot forth blades of capricious shapes, comprised within a scale of colours — pink, carmine, green, olive, fawn, and brown. I saw there (but not dried up, as our specimens of the Nautilus are) pavonari spread like a fan, as if to catch the breeze; scarlet ceramies, whose laminaries extended their edible shoots of fern-shaped nereocysti, which grow to a height of fifteen feet; clusters of acetabuli, whose stems increase in size upwards; and numbers of other marine plants, all devoid of flowers!

'Curious anomaly, fantastic element!' said an ingenious naturalist, 'in which the animal kingdom blossoms, and the vegetable does not!'

Under these numerous shrubs (as large as trees of the temperate zone), and under their damp shadow, were massed together real bushes of living flowers, hedges of zoophytes, on which blossomed some zebrameandrines, with crooked grooves, some yellow caryophylliae; and, to complete the illusion, the fish-flies flew from branch to branch like a swarm of humming-birds, whilst yellow lepisacomthi, with bristling jaws, dactyl-opteri, and monocentrides rose at our feet like a flight of snipes.

In about an hour Captain Nemo gave the signal to halt. I, for my part, was not sorry, and we stretched ourselves under an arbour of alariae, the long thin blades of which stood up like arrows.

This short rest seemed delicious to me; there was nothing wanting but the charm of conversation; but, impossible to speak, impossible to answer, I only put my great copper head to Conseil's. I saw the worthy fellow's eyes glistening with delight, and to show his satisfaction, he shook himself in his breastplate of air, in the most comical way in the world.

After four hours of this walking I was surprised not to find myself dreadfully hungry. How to account for this state of the stomach I could not tell. But instead I felt an insurmountable desire to sleep, which happens to all divers. And my eyes soon closed behind the thick glasses, and I fell into a heavy slumber, which the movement alone had prevented before. Captain Nemo and his robust companion, stretched in the clear crystal, set us the example.

How long I remained buried in this drowsiness, I cannot judge; but when I woke, the sun seemed sinking towards the horizon. Captain Nemo had already risen, and I was beginning to stretch my limbs, when an unexpected apparition brought me briskly to my feet.

A few steps off, a monstrous sea-spider, about thirty-eight inches high, was watching me with squinting eyes, ready to spring upon me. Though my diver's dress was thick enough to defend me from the bite of this animal, I could not help shuddering with horror. Conseil and the sailor of the Nautilus awoke at this moment. Captain Nemo pointed out the hideous crustacean, which a blow from the butt end of the gun knocked over, and I saw the horrible claws of the monster writhe in terrible convulsions. This accident reminded me that other animals more to be feared might haunt these obscure depths, against whose attacks my diving-dress would not protect me. I had never thought of it before, but I now resolved to be upon my guard. Indeed, I thought that this halt would mark the termination of our walk; but I was mistaken, for, instead of returning to the Nautilus, Captain Nemo continued his bold excursion. The ground was still on the incline, its declivity seemed to be getting greater, and to be leading us to greater depths. It must have been about three o'clock when we reached a narrow valley, between high perpendicular walls, situated about seventy-five fathoms deep. Thanks to the perfection of our apparatus, we were forty-five fathoms below the limit which nature seems to have imposed on man as to his submarine excursions.

I say seventy-five fathoms, though I had no instrument by which to judge the distance. But I knew that even in the clearest waters the solar rays could not penetrate further. And accordingly the darkness deepened. At ten paces not an object was visible. I was groping my way, when I suddenly saw a brilliant white light. Captain Nemo had just put his electric apparatus into use; his companion did the same, and Conseil and I followed their example. By turning a screw I established a communication between the wire and the spiral glass, and the sea, lit by our four lanterns, was illuminated for a circle of thirty-six yards.

Captain Nemo was still plunging into the dark depths of the forest, whose trees were getting scarcer at every step. I noticed that vegetable life disappeared sooner than animal life. The medusae had already abandoned the arid soil, from which a great number of animals, zoophytes, articulata, molluscs, and fishes, still obtained sustenance.

As we walked, I thought the light of our Ruhmkorff apparatus could not fail to draw some inhabitant from its dark couch. But if they did approach us, they at least kept at a respectful distance from the hunters. Several times I saw Captain Nemo stop, put his gun to his shoulder, and after some moments drop it and walk on. At last, after about four hours, this marvellous excursion came to an end. A wall of superb rocks, in an imposing mass, rose before us, a heap of gigantic blocks, an enormous steep granite shore, forming dark grottos, but which presented no practicable slope; it was the prop of the Island of Crespo. It was the earth! Captain Nemo stopped suddenly. A gesture of his brought us all to a halt; and however desirous I might be to scale the wall, I was obliged to stop. Here ended Captain Nemo's domains.

And he would not go beyond them. Further on was a portion of the globe he might not trample upon.

The return began. Captain Nemo hed returned to the head of his little band, directing their course without hesitation. I thought we were not following the same road to return to the Nautilus. The new road was very steep, and consequently very painful. We approached the surface of the sea rapidly. But this return to the upper strata was not so sudden as to cause relief from the pressure too rapidly, which might have produced serious disorder in our organisation, and brought on internal lesions, so fatal to divers. Very soon light reappeared and grew, and the sun being low on the horizon, the refraction edged the different objects with a spectral ring. At ten yards and a half deep, we walked amidst a shoal of little fishes of all kinds, more numerous than the birds of the air, and also more agile; but no aquatic game worthy of a shot had as yet met our gaze, when at that moment I saw the Captain shoulder his gun quickly, and follow a moving object into the shrubs. He fired; — I heard a slight hissing, and a creature fell stunned at some distance from us. It was a magnificent sea-otter, an enhydrus, the only exclusively marine quadruped. This otter was five feet long, and must have been very valuable. Its skin, chestnut-brown above, and silvery underneath, would have made one of those beautiful furs so sought after in the Russian and Chinese markets; the fineness and the lustre of its coat would certainly fetch £ 80. I admired this curious mammal, with its rounded head ornamented with short ears, its round eyes, and white whiskers like those of a cat, with webbed feet and nails, and tufted tail. This precious animal, hunted and tracked by fishermen, has now become very rare, and taken refuge chiefly in the northern parts of the Pacific, or probably its race would soon become extinct.

Captain Nemo's companion took the beast, threw it over his shoulder, and we continued our journey. For one hour a plain of sand lay stretched before us. Sometimes it rose to within two yards and some inches of the surface of the water. I then saw our image clearly reflected, drawn inversely, and above us appeared an identical group reflecting our movements and our actions; in a word, like us in every point, except that they walked with their heads downward and their feet in the air.

Another effect I noticed, which was the passage of thick clouds which formed and vanished rapidly; but on reflection I understood that these seeming clouds were due to the varying thickness of the reeds at the bottom, and I could even see the fleecy foam which their broken tops multiplied on the water, and the shadows of large birds passing above our heads, whose rapid flight I could discern on the surface of the sea.

On this occasion, I was witness to one of the finest gunshots which ever made the nerves of a hunter thrill. A large bird of great breadth of wing, clearly visible, approached, hovering over us. Captain Nemo's companion shouldered his gun and fired, when it was only a few yards above the waves. The creature fell stunned, and the force of its fall brought it within the reach of the dexterous hunter's grasp. It was an albatross of the finest kind.

Our march had not been interrupted by this incident. For two hours we followed these sandy plains, then fields of algae very disagreeable to cross. Candidly, I could do no more when I saw a glimmer of light, which, for a half mile, broke the darkness of the waters. It was the lantern of the Nautilus. Before twenty minutes were over we should be on board, and I should be able to breathe with ease, for it seemed that my reservoir supplied air very deficient in oxygen. But I did not reckon on an accidental meeting, which delayed our arrival for some time.

I had remained some steps behind, when I presently saw Captain Nemo coming hurriedly towards me. With his strong

270

hand he bent me to the ground, his companion doing the same to Conseil. At first I knew not what to think of this sudden attack, but I was soon reassured by seeing the Captain lie down beside me, and remain immovable.

I was stretched on the ground, just under shelter of a bush of algae, when raising my head, I saw some enormous mass, casting phosphorescent gleams, pass blusteringly by.

My blood froze in my veins as I recognised two formidable sharks which threatened us. It was a couple of tintoreas, terrible creatures, with enormous tails and a dull glassy stare, the phosphorescent matter ejected from holes pierced around the muzzle. Monstrous brutes! which would crush a whole man in their iron jaws. I did not know whether Conseil stopped to classify them; for my part, I noticed their silver bellies, and their huge mouths bristling with teeth, from a very unscientific point of view, and more as a possible victim than as a naturalist.

Happily the voracious creatures do not see well. They passed without seeing us, brushing us with their brownish fins, and we escaped by a miracle from a danger certainly greater than meeting a tiger full-face in the forest. Half an hour after, guided by the electric light, we reached the *Nautilus*. The outside door had been left open, and Captain Nemo closed it as soon as we had entered the first cell. He then pressed a knob. I heard the pumps working in the midst of the vessel, I felt the water sinking from around me, and in a few moments the cell was entirely empty. The inside door then opened, and we entered the vestry.

There our diving-dress was taken off, not without some trouble; and, fairly worn out from want of food and sleep, I returned to my room, in great wonder at this surprising excursion at the bottom of the sea.

A Vanished Continent

That night, about eleven o'clock, I received a most unexpected visit from Captain Nemo. He asked me very graciously if I felt fatigued from my watch of the preceding night. I answered in the negative.

'Then, M. Aronnax, I propose a curious excursion.'

'Propose, Captain?'

'You have hitherto only visited the submarine depths by daylight, under the brightness of the sun. Would it suit you to see them in the darkness of the night?'

'Most willingly.'

'I warn you, the way will be tiring. We shall have far to walk, and must climb a mountain. The roads are not well kept.'

'What you say, Captain, only heightens my curiosity; I am ready to follow you.'

'Come then, sir, we will put on our diving dresses.'

Arrived at the robing-room, I saw that neither of my companions nor any of the ship's crew were to follow us on this excursion. Captain Nemo had not even proposed my taking with me either Ned or Conseil.

In a few moments we had put on our diving dresses; they placed on our backs the reservoirs, abundantly filled with air, but no electric lamps were prepared. I called the Captain's attention to the fact.

'They will be useless,' he replied.

I thought I had not heard aright, but I could not repeat my observation, for the Captain's head had already disappeared in its metal case. I finished harnessing myself, I felt them put an ironpointed stick into my hand, and some minutes later, after going through the usual form, we set foot on the bottom of the Atlantic, at a depth of 150 fathoms. Midnight was near. The waters were profoundly dark, but Captain Nemo pointed out in the distance a reddish spot, a sort of large light shining brilliantly, about two miles from the *Nautilus*. What this fire might be, what could feed it, why and how it lit up the liquid mass, I could not say. In any case, it did light our way, vaguely, it is true, but I soon accustomed myself to the peculiar darkness, and I understood, under such circumstances, the uselessness of the Ruhmkorff apparatus.

As we advanced, I heard a kind of pattering above my head. The noise redoubling, sometimes producing a continual shower, I soon understood the cause. It was rain falling violently, and crisping the surface of the waves. Instinctively the thought flashed across my mind that I should be wet through! By the water! in the midst of the water! I could not help laughing at the odd idea. But indeed, in the thick diving dress, the liquid element is no longer felt, and one only seems to be in an atmosphere somewhat denser than the terrestrial atmosphere. Nothing more.

After half an hour's walk the soil became stony. Medusae, microscopic crustacea, and pennatules lit it slightly with their phosphorescent gleam. I caught a glimpse of pieces of stone covered with millions of zoophytes, and masses of sea-weed. My feet often slipped upon this viscous carpet of seaweed, and without my iron-tipped stick I should have fallen more than once. In turning round, I could still see the whitish lantern of the *Nautilus* beginning to pale in the distance.

But the rosy light which guided us increased and lit up the horizon. The presence of this fire under water puzzled me in the highest degree. Was it some electric effulgence? Was I going towards a natural phenomenon as yet unknown to the savants of the earth? Or even (for this thought crossed my brain) had the hand of man aught to do with this conflagration? Had he fanned this flame? Was I to meet in these depths companions and friends of Captain Nemo whom he was going to visit, and who, like him, led this strange existence? Should I find down there a whole colony of exiles, who, weary of the miseries of this earth, had sought and found independence in the deep ocean? All these foolish and unreasonable ideas pursued me. And in this condition of mind, over-excited by the succession of wonders continually passing before my eyes, I should not have been surprised to meet at the bottom of the sea one of those submarine towns of which Captain Nemo dreamed.

Our road grew lighter and lighter. The white glimmer came in rays from the summit of a mountain about 800 feet high. But what I saw was simply a reflection, developed by the clearness of the waters. The source of this inexplicable light was a fire on the opposite side of the mountain.

In the midst of this stony maze, furrowing the bottom of the Atlantic, Captain Nemo advanced without hesitation. He knew this dreary road. Doubtless he had often travelled over it, and could not lose himself. I followed him with unshaken confidence. He seemed to me like a genie of the sea; and, as he walked before me, I could not help admiring his stature, which was outlined in black on the luminous horizon.

It was one in the morning when we arrived at the first slopes of the mountain; but to gain access to them we must venture through the difficult paths of a vast copse.

Yes; a copse of dead trees, without leaves, without sap, trees petrified by the action of the water, and here and there overtopped by gigantic pines. It was like a coal pit, still standing, holding by the roots to the broken soil, and whose branches, like fine black paper cuttings, showed distinctly on the watery ceiling. Picture to yourself a forest in the Hartz, hanging on to the sides of the mountain, but a forest swallowed up. The paths were encumbered with seaweed and fucus, between which grovelled a whole world of crustacea. I went along, climbing the rocks, striding over extended trunks, breaking the sea bind-weed, which hung from one tree to the other; and frightening the fishes, which flew from branch to branch. Pressing onward, I felt no fatigue. I followed my guide, who was never tired. What a spectacle! how can I express it? how paint the aspect of those woods and rocks in this medium, — their under parts dark and wild, the upper coloured with red tints, by that light which the reflecting powers of the waters doubled? We climbed rocks, which fell directly after with gigantic bounds, and the low growling of an avalanche. To right and left ran long, dark galleries, where sight was lost. Here opened vast glades which the hand of man seemed to have worked; and I sometimes asked myself if some inhabitant of these submarine regions would not suddenly appear to me.

But Captain Nemo was still mounting. I could not stay behind. I followed boldly. My stick gave me good help. A false step would have been dangerous on the narrow passes sloping down to the sides of the gulfs; but I walked with firm step, without feeling any giddiness. Now I jumped a crevice the depth of which would have made me hesitate had it been among the glaciers on the land; now I ventured on the unsteady trunk of a tree, thrown across from one abyss to the other, without looking under my feet, having only eyes to admire the wild sights of this region.

There, monumental rocks, leaning on their regularly cut bases, seemed to defy all laws of equilibrium. From between their stony knees, trees sprang, like a jet under heavy pressure, and upheld others which upheld them. Natural towers, large scarps, cut perpendicularly, like a 'curtain,' inclined at an angle which the laws of gravitation could never have tolerated in terrestrial regions.

Two hours after quitting the Nautilus, we had crossed the line of trees, and a hundred feet above our heads rose the top of the mountain, which cast a shadow on the brilliant irradiation of the opposite slope. Some petrified shrubs ran fantastically here and there. Fishes got up under our feet like birds in the long grass. The massive rocks were rent with impenetrable fractures, deep grottos, and unfathomable holes, at the bottom of which formidable creatures might be heard moving. My blood curdled when I saw enormous antennae blocking my road, or some frightful claw closing with a noise in the shadow of some cavity. Millions of luminous spots shone brightly in the midst of the darkness. They were the eyes of giant crustacea crouched in their holes; giant lobsters setting themselves up like halberdiers, and moving their claws with the clicking sound of pincers; titanic crabs, pointed like a gun on its carriage; and frightful looking poulps, interweaving their tentacles like a living nest of serpents.

We had now arrived on the first platform, where other surprises awaited me. Before us lay some picturesque ruins, which betrayed the hand of man, and not that of the Creator. There were vast heaps of stone, amongst which might be traced the vague and shadowy forms of castles and temples, clothed with a world of blossoming zoophytes, and over which, instead of ivy, seaweed and fucus threw a thick vegetable mantle. But what was this portion of the globe which had been swallowed by cataclysms? Who had placed those rocks and stones like cromlechs of pre-historic times? Where was I? Whither had Captain Nemo's fancy hurried me?

I would fain have asked him; not being able to, I stopped him — I seized his arm. But shaking his head, and pointing to the highest point of the mountain, he seemed to say —

'Come, come along; come higher!'

I followed, and in a few minutes I had climbed to the top, which for a circle of ten yards commanded the whole mass of rock.

I looked down the side we had just climbed. The mountain did not rise more than seven or eight hundred feet above the

276

level of the plain; but on the opposite side it commanded from twice that height the depths of this part of the Atlantic. My eyes ranged far over a large space lit by a violent fulguration. In fact, the mountain was a volcano.

At fifty feet above the peak, in the midst of a rain of stones and scoriae, a large crater was vomiting forth torrents of lava which fell in a cascade of fire into the bosom of the liquid mass. Thus situated, this volcano lit the lower plain like an immense torch, even to the extreme limits of the horizon. I said that the submarine crater threw up lava, but no flames. Flames require the oxygen of the air to feed upon, and cannot be developed under water; but streams of lava, having in themselves the principles of their incandescence, can attain a white heat, fight vigorously against the liquid element, and turn it to vapour by contact.

Rapid currents bearing all these gases in diffusion, and torrents of lava, slid to the bottom of the mountain like an eruption of Vesuvius on another Terra del Greco.

There, indeed, under my eyes, ruined, destroyed, lay a town — its roofs open to the sky, its temples fallen, its arches dislocated, its columns lying on the ground, from which one could still recognise the massive character of Tuscan architecture. Further on, some remains of a gigantic aqueduct; here the high base of an Acropolis, with the floating outline of a Parthenon; there traces of a quay, as if an ancient port had formerly abutted on the borders of the ocean, and disappeared with its merchant vessels and its war-galleys. Further on again, long lines of sunken walls and broad deserted streets — a perfect Pompeii escaped beneath the waters. Such was the sight that Captain Nemo brought before my eyes!

Where was I? Where was I? I must know, at any cost. I tried to speak, but Captain Nemo stopped me by a gesture, and picking up a piece of chalk stone, advanced to a rock of black basalt, and traced the one word — ATLANTIS.

There, under my eyes, ruined, destroyed, lay a town . .

What a light shot through my mind! Atlantis, the ancient Meropis of Theopompus, the Atlantis of Plato, that continent denied by Origen, Jamblichus, D'Anville, Malte-Brun, and Humboldt, who placed its disappearance amongst the legendary tales admitted by Posidonius, Pliny, Ammianus Marcellinus, Tertullian, Engel, Buffon, and D'Avezac. I had it there now before my eyes, bearing upon it the unexceptionable testimony of its catastrophe. The region thus engulfed was beyond Europe, Asia, and Lybia, beyond the columns of Hercules, where those powerful people, the Atlantides, lived, against whom the first wars of ancient Greece were waged.

Thus, led by the strangest destiny, I was treading under foot the mountains of this continent, touching with my hand those ruins a thousand generations old, and contemporary with the geological epochs. I was walking on the very spot where the contemporaries of the first man had walked.

Whilst I was trying to fix in my mind every detail of this grand landscape, Captain Nemo remained motionless, as if petrified in mute ecstasy, leaning on a mossy stone. Was he dreaming of those generations long since disappeared? Was he asking them the secret of human destiny? Was it here this strange man came to steep himself in historical recollections, and live again this ancient life, — he who wanted no modern one? What would I not have given to know his thoughts, to share them, to understand them! We remained for an hour at this place, contemplating the vast plain under the brightness of the lava, which was sometimes wonderfully intense. Rapid tremblings ran along the mountain caused by internal bubblings, deep noises distinctly transmitted through the liquid medium were echoed with majestic grandeur. At this moment the moon appeared through the mass of waters, and threw her pale rays on the buried continent. It was but a gleam, but what an indescribable effect! The Captain rose, cast one last look on the immense plain, and then bade me follow him.

We descended the mountain rapidly, and the mineral forest once passed, I saw the lantern of the *Nautilus* shining like a star. The Captain walked straight to it, and we got on board as the first rays of light whitened the surface of the ocean.

The Ghost Ship

by

RICHARD MIDDLETON

Fairfield is a little village lying near the Portsmouth Road about halfway between London and the sea. Strangers who find it by accident now and then, call it a pretty, old-fashioned place; we, who live in it and call it home, don't find anything very pretty about it, but we should be sorry to live anywhere else. Our minds have taken the shape of the inn and the church and the green, I suppose. At all events we never feel comfortable out of Fairfield.

Of course the Cockneys, with their vast houses and their noise-ridden streets, can call us rustics if they choose, but for all that Fairfield is a better place to live in than London. Doctor says that when he goes to London his mind is bruised with the weight of the houses, and he was a Cockney born. He had to live there himself when he was a little chap, but he knows better now. You gentlemen may laugh — perhaps some of you come from London way — but it seems to me that a witness like that is worth a gallon of arguments.

Dull? Well, you might find it dull, but I assure you that I've listened to all the London yarns you have spun tonight, and they're absolutely nothing to the things that happen at Fairfield. It's because of our way of thinking and minding our own business. If one of your Londoners were set down on the green of a Saturday night when the ghosts of the lads who died in the war keep tryst with the lasses who lie in the churchyard, he couldn't help being curious and interfering, and then the ghosts would go somewhere where it was quieter. But we just let them come and go and don't make any fuss, and in consequence Fairfield is the ghostiest place in all England. Why, I've seen a headless man sitting on the edge of the well in broad daylight, and the children playing about his feet as if he were their father. Take my word for it, spirits know when they are well off as much as human beings.

Still, I must admit that the thing I'm going to tell you about was queer even for our part of the world, where three packs of ghost-hounds hunt regularly during the season, and blacksmith's great-grandfather is busy all night shoeing the dead gentlemen's horses. Now that's a thing that wouldn't happen in London, because of their interfering ways, but blacksmith he lies up aloft and sleeps as quiet as a lamb. Once when he had a bad head he shouted down to them not to make so much noise, and in the morning he found an old guinea left on the anvil as an apology. He wears it on his watch-chain now. But I must get on with my story; if I start telling you about the queer happenings at Fairfield I'll never stop.

It all came of the great storm in the spring of '97, the year that we had two great storms. This was the first one, and I remember it very well, because I found in the morning that it had lifted the thatch of my pigsty into the widow's garden as clean as a boy's kite. When I looked over the hedge, widow — Tom Lamport's widow that was — was prodding for her nasturtiums with a daisy-grubber. After I had watched her for a little I went down to the Fox and Grapes to tell landlord what she had said to me. Landlord he laughed, being a married man and at ease with the sex. 'Come to that,' he said, 'the tempest has blowed something into my field. A kind of ship I think it would be.'

I was surprised at that until he explained that it was only a ghost-ship and would do no hurt to the turnips. We argued that it had been blown up from the sea at Portsmouth, and then we talked of something else. There were two slates down at the parsonage and a big tree in Lumley's meadow. It was a rare storm.

I reckon the wind had blown our ghosts all over England. They were coming back for days afterwards with foundered horses and as footsore as possible, and they were so glad to get back to Fairfield that some of them walked up the street crying like little children. Squire said that his great-grandfather's great-grandfather hadn't looked so dead-beat since the battle of Naseby, and he's an educated man.

What with one thing and another, I should think it was a week before we got straight again, and then one afternoon I met the landlord on the green and he had a worried face. 'I wish you'd come and have a look at that ship in my field,' he said to me; it seems to me it's leaning real hard on the turnips. I can't bear thinking what the missus will say when she sees it.'

I walked down the lane with him, and sure enough there was a ship, in the middle of his field, but such a ship as no man had seen on the water for three hundred years, let alone in the middle of a turnip-field. It was all painted black and covered with carvings, and there was a great bay window in the stern for all the world like the Squire's drawing-room. There was a crowd of little black cannon on the deck and looking out of her port-holes, and she was anchored at each end to the hard ground. I have seen the wonders of the world on picture-postcards, but I have never seen anything to equal that.

'She seems very solid for a ghost-ship,' I said, seeing the landlord was bothered.

'I should say it's a betwixt and between,' he answered, puzzling it over, 'but it's going to spoil a matter of fifty turnips, and missus she'll want it moved.' We went up to her and touched the side, and it was as hard as a real ship. 'Now there's folks in England would call that very curious,' he said.

Sure enough, there was a ship in the middle of his field.

Now I don't know much about ships, but I should think that that ghost-ship weighed a solid two hundred tons, and it seemed to me that she had come to stay, so that I felt sorry for Landlord, who was a married man. 'All the horses in Fairfield won't move her out of my turnips,' he said frowning at her.

Just then we heard a noise on her deck, and we looked up and saw that a man had come out of her front cabin and was looking down at us very peaceably. He was dressed in a black uniform set out with rusy gold lace, and he had a great cutlass by his side in a brass sheath. 'I'm Captain Bartolomew Roberts,' he said, in a gentleman's voice, 'put in for recruits. I seem to have brought her rather far up the harbour.'

'Harbour!' cried landlord; 'why, you're fifty miles from the sea.'

Captain Roberts didn't turn a hair. 'So much as that, is it?' he said coolly. 'Well, it's of no consequence.'

Landlord was a bit upset at this. 'I don't want to be un-neighbourly,' he said, 'but I wish you hadn't brought your ship into my field. You see, my wife sets great store on these turnips.

The captain took a pinch of snuff out of a fine gold box that he pulled out of his pocket, and dusted his fingers with a silk handkerchief in a very genteel fashion. 'I'm only here for a few months,' he said; 'but if a testimony of my esteem would pacify your good lady I would be content,' and with the words he loosed a great gold brooch from the neck of his coat and tossed it down to landlord.

Landlord blushed as red as a strawberry. 'I'm not denying she's fond of jewellery,' he said, 'but it's too much for half a sackful of turnips.' And indeed it was a handsome brooch.

The captain laughed. 'Tut, man,' he said, 'it's a forced sale, and you deserve a good price. Say no more about it,' and nodding good-day to us, he turned on his heel and went into the cabin. Landlord walked back up the lane like a man with a weight off his mind. 'That tempest has blowed me a bit of luck,' he said; 'The missus will be main pleased with that brooch. It's better than the blacksmith's guinea any day.'

Ninety-seven was Jubilee year, the year of the second Jubilee, you remember, and we had great doings at Fairfield, so that we hadn't much time to bother about the ghost-ship, though anyhow it isn't our way to meddle in things that don't concern us. Landlord, he saw his tenant once or twice when he was hoeing his turnips and passed the time of day, and landlord's wife wore her new brooch to church every Sunday. But we didn't mix much with the ghosts at any time, all except an idiot lad there was in the village, and he didn't know the difference between a man and a ghost, poor innocent! On Jubilee Day, however, somebody told Captain Roberts why the church bells were ringing, and he hoisted a flag and fired off his guns like a royal Englishman. 'Tis true the guns were shotted, and one of the round shot knocked a hole in Farmer Johnstone's barn, but nobody thought much of that in such a season of rejoicing.

It wasn't till our celebrations were over that we noticed that anything was wrong in Fairfield. 'Twas shoemaker who told me first about it one morning at the Fox and Grapes. 'You know my great great-uncle?' he said to me.

'You mean Joshua, the quiet lad,' I answered, knowing him well.

'Quiet!' said shoemaker indignantly. 'Quiet you call him, coming home at three o' clock every morning as drunk as a magistrate and waking up the whole house with his noise.'

'Why, it can't be Joshua!' I said, for I knew him for one of the most respectable young ghosts in the village.

'Joshua it is,' said shoemaker; 'and one of these nights he'll find himself out in the street if he isn't careful.'

This kind of talk shocked me, I can tell you; for I don't

like to hear a man abusing his own family, and I could hardly believe that a steady youngster like Joshua had taken to drink. But just then in came butcher Aylwin in such a temper that he could hardly drink his beer. 'The young puppy! the young puppy!' he kept on saying; and it was some time before shoemaker and I found out that he was talking about his ancestor that fell at Senlac.

'Drink?' said shoemaker hopefully, for we all like company in our misfortunes, and butcher nodded grimly.

'The young noodle,' he said, emptying his tankard.

Well, after that I kept my ears open, and it was the same story all over the village. There was hardly a young man among all the ghosts of Fairfield who didn't roll home in the small hours of the morning the worse for liquor. I used to wake up in the night and hear them stumble past my house, singing outrageous songs. The worst of it was that we couldn't keep the scandal to ourselves, and the folk at Greenhill began to talk of 'sodden Fairfield' and taught their children to sing a song about us:

Sodden Fairfield, sodden Fairfield has no use for
bread-and-butter,
Rum for breakfast, rum for dinner, rum for tea, and
rum for supper!

We are easy-going in our village, but we didn't like that.

Of course we soon found out where the young fellows went to get the drink, and landlord was terribly cut up that his tenant should have turned out so badly, but his wife wouldn't hear of parting with the brooch, so that he couldn't give the Captain notice to quit. But as time went on, things grew from bad to worse, and at all hours of the day you would see those young reprobates sleeping it off on the village green. Nearly every afternoon a ghost-wagon used to jolt down to the ship with a lading of rum, and though the older ghosts seemed inclined to give the Captain's hospitality the go-by, the youngsters were neither to hold nor to bind.

So one afternoon when I was taking my nap I heard a knock at the door, and there was parson looking very serious, like a man with a job before him that he didn't altogether relish. 'I'm going down to talk to the Captain about all this drunkenness in the village, and I want you to come with me,' he said straight out.

I can't say that I fancied the visit much myself, and I tried to hint to the parson that as, after all, they were only a lot of ghosts, it didn't very much matter.

'Dead or alive, I'm responsible for their good conduct,' he said, 'and I'm going to do my duty and put a stop to this continued disorder. And you are coming with me, John Simmons.' So I went, parson being a persuasive kind of man.

We went down to the ship, and as we approached her I could see the Captain tasting the air on deck. When he saw parson he took off his hat very politely, and I can tell you that I was relieved to find that he had a proper respect for the cloth. Parson acknowledged his salute and spoke out stoutly enough. 'Sir, I should be glad to have a word with you.'

'Come on board, sir, come on board,' said the Captain, and I could tell by his voice that he knew why we were there. Parson and I climbed up an uneasy kind of ladder, and the Captain took us into the great cabin at the back of the ship, where the bay-window was. It was the most wonderful place you ever saw in your life, all full of gold and silver plate, swords with jewelled scabbards, carved oak chairs, and great chests that looked as though they were bursting with guineas. Even parson was surprised, and he did not shake his head very hard when the Captain took down some silver cups and poured us out a drink of rum. I tasted mine, and I don't mind saying that it changed my view of things entirely. There was nothing betwixt and between about that rum, and I felt that it was ridiculous to blame the lads for drinking too much of stuff like that. It seemed to fill my veins with honey and fire.

Parson put the case squarely to the Captain, but I didn't listen much to what he said; I was busy sipping my drink and looking through the window at the fishes swimming to and fro over landlord's turnips. Just then it seemed the most natural thing in the world that they should be there, though afterwards, of course, I could see that proved it was a ghost-ship.

But even then I thought it was queer when I saw a drowned sailor float by in the thin air with his hair and beard all full of bubbles. It was the first time I had seen anything quite like that at Fairfield.

All the time I was regarding the wonders of the deep, parson was telling Captain Roberts how there was no peace or rest in the village owing to the curse of drunkenness, and what a bad example the youngsters were setting to the older ghosts. The Captain listened very attentively, and only put in a word now and then about boys being boys and young men sowing their wild oats. But when parson had finished his speech he filled up our silver cups and said to parson, with a flourish, 'I should be sorry to cause trouble anywhere where I have been made welcome, and you will be glad to hear that I put to sea tomorrow night. And now you must drink me a prosperous voyage.' So we all stood up and drank the toast with honour, and that noble rum was like hot oil in my veins.

After that Captain showed us some of the curiosities he had brought back from foreign parts, and we were greatly amazed, though afterwards I couldn't clearly remember what they were. And then I found myself walking across the turnips with parson, and I was telling him of the glories of the deep that I had seen through the window of the ship. He turned on me severely. 'If I were you, John Simmons,' he said, 'I should go straight home to bed.' He has a way of putting things that wouldn't occur to an ordinary man, has parson, and I did as he told me.

Well, next day it came on to blow, and it blew harder and harder, till about eight o'clock at night I heard a noise and looked out into the garden. I dare say you won't believe me, it seems a bit tall even to me, but the wind had lifted the thatch of my pigsty into the widow's garden a second time. I thought I wouldn't wait to hear what widow had to say about it, so I went across the green to the Fox and Grapes, and the wind was so strong that I danced along on tip-toe like a girl at the fair. When I got to the inn landlord had to help me shut the door; it seemed as though a dozen goats were pushing against it to come in out of the storm.

'It's a powerful tempest,' he said, drawing the beer. 'I hear there's a chimney down at Dickory End.'

'It's a funny thing how these sailors know about the weather,' I answered. 'When Captain said he was going tonight, I was thinking it would take a capful of wind to carry the ship back to sea, but now here's more than a capful.'

'Ah, yes,' said landlord, 'it's tonight he goes true enough, and, mind you, though he treated me handsome over the rent, I'm not sure it's a loss to the village. I don't hold with gentrice who fetch their drink from London instead of helping local traders to get their living.'

'But you haven't got any rum like his,' I said to draw him out.

His neck grew red above his collar, and I was afraid I'd gone too far; but after a while he got his breath with a grunt.

'John Simmons,' he said, 'if you've come down here this windy night to talk a lot of fool's talk, you've wasted a journey.'

Well, of course, then I had to smooth him down with praising his rum and Heaven forgive me for swearing it was better than Captain's. For the like of that rum no living lips have tasted save mine and parson's. But somehow or other I brought landlord round, and presently we must have a glass of his best to prove its quality.

'Beat that if you can!' he cried, and we both raised our glasses to our mouths, only to stop halfway and look at each other in amaze. For the wind that had been howling outside like an outrageous dog had all of a sudden turned as melodious as the carol-boys of a Christmas Eve.

'Surely that's not my Martha,' whispered landlord; Martha being his great-aunt that lived in the loft overhead.

We went to the door, and the wind burst it open so that the handle was driven clean into the plaster of the wall. But we didn't think about that at the time; for over our heads, sailing very comfortably through the windy stars, was the ship that had passed the summer in landlord's field. Her portholes and her bay-window were blazing with lights, and there was a noise of singing and fiddling on her decks. 'He's gone,' shouted the landlord above the storm, 'and he's taken half the village with him!' I could only nod in answer, not having lungs like bellows of leather.

In the morning we were able to measure the strength of the storm, and over and above my pigsty there was damage enough wrought in the village to keep us busy. True it is that the children had to break down no branches for the firing that autumn, since the wind had strewn the woods with more than they could carry away. Many of our ghosts were scattered abroad, but this time very few came back, all the young men having sailed with Captain; and not only ghosts, for a poor half-witted lad was missing, and we reckoned that he had stowed himself away or perhaps shipped as cabin-boy, not knowing any better.

What with the lamentations of the ghost-girls and the grumblings of families who had lost an ancestor, the village was upset for a while, and the funny thing was that it was the

folk who had complained most of the carryings-on of the
youngsters, who made most noise now that they were gone.
I hadn't any sympathy with shoemaker or butcher, who ran
about saying how much they missed their lads, but it made me
grieve to hear the poor bereaved girls calling their lovers by
name on the village green at nightfall. It didn't seem fair
to me that they should have lost their men a second time,
after giving up life in order to join them, as like as not. Still,
not even a spirit can be sorry for ever, and after a few months
we made up our mind that the folk who had sailed in the ship
were never coming back, and we didn't talk about it any more.

And then one day, I dare say it would be a couple of years
after, when the whole business was quite forgotten, who should
come trapesing along the road from Portsmouth but the daft
lad who had gone away with the ship, without waiting till he
was dead to become a ghost. You never saw such a boy as that
in all your life. He had a great rusty cutlass hanging to a string
at his waist, and he was tattooed all over in fine colours, so
that even his face looked like a girl's sampler. He had a handkerchief in his hand full of foreign shells and old-fashioned
pieces of small money, very curious, and walked up to the well
outside his mother's house and drew himself a drink as if he
had been nowhere in particular.

The worst of it was that he had come back as soft-headed
as he went, and try as we might we couldn't get anything
reasonable out of him. He talked a lot of gibberish about keel-
hauling and walking the plank and crimson murders — things
which a decent sailor should know nothing about, so that it
seemed to me that for all his manners Captain had been more
of a pirate than a gentleman mariner. But to draw sense out
of that boy was as hard as picking cherries off a crab-tree. One
silly tale he had that he kept on drifting back to, and to hear
him you would have thought that it was the only thing that
happened to him in his life. 'We was at anchor,' he would

292

say, 'off an island called the Basket of Flowers, and the sailors had caught a lot of parrots and we were teaching them to swear. Up and down the decks, up and down the decks, and the language they used was dreadful. Then we looked up and saw the masts of the Spanish ship outside the harbour. Outside the harbour they were, so we threw the parrots into the sea and sailed out to fight. And all the parrots were drowned in the sea and the language they used was dreadful.' That's the sort of boy he was, nothing but silly talk of parrots when we asked him about the fighting. And we never had a chance of teaching him better, for two days after he ran away again, and hasn't been seen since.

That's my story, and I assure you that things like that are happening at Fairfield all the time. The ship has never come back, but somehow as people grow older they seem to think that one of these windy nights, she'll come sailing in over the hedges with all the lost ghosts on board. Well, when she comes, she'll be welcome. There's one ghost-lass that has never grown tired of waiting for her lad to return. Every night you'll see her out on the green, straining her poor eyes with looking for the mast-lights among the stars. A faithful lass you'd call her, and I'm thinking you'd be right.

Landlord's field wasn't a penny the worse for the visit, but they do say that since then the turnips that have been grown in it have tasted of rum.

In the Abyss

by

H. G. WELLS

The lieutenant stood in front of the steel sphere and gnawed a piece of pine splinter. 'What do you think of it, Steevens?' he asked.

'It's an idea,' said Steevens, in the tone of one who keeps an open mind.

'I believe it will smash — flat,' said the lieutenant.

'He seems to have calculated it all out pretty well,' said Steevens, still impartial.

'But think of the pressure,' said the lieutenant. 'At the surface of the water it's fourteen pounds to the inch, thirty feet down it's double that; sixty, treble; ninety, four times; nine hundred, forty times; five thousand, three hundred — that's a mile — it's two hundred and forty times fourteen pounds; that's — let's see — thirty hundredweight — a ton and a half, Steevens; *a ton and a half* to the square inch. And the ocean where he's going is five miles deep. That's seven and a half —'

'Sounds a lot,' said Steevens, 'but it's jolly thick steel.'

The lieutenant made no answer, but resumed his pine splinter. The object of their conversation was a huge ball of steel, having an exterior diameter of perhaps nine feet. It looked like the shot for some Titanic piece of artillery. It was elaborately nested in a monstrous scaffolding built into the framework of the vessel, and the gigantic spars that were presently to sling it overboard gave the stern of the ship an appearance that had raised the curiosity of every decent sailor who had sighted it, from the Pool of London to the Tropic of Capricorn. In two places, one above the other, the steel gave place to a couple of circular windows of enormously thick glass, and one of these, set in a steel frame of great solidity, was now partially unscrewed. Both the men had seen the interior of this globe for the first time that morning. It was elaborately padded with air cushions, with little studs sunk between bulging pillows to work the simple mechanism of the affair. Everything was elaborately padded, even the Myers apparatus which was to absorb carbonic acid and replace the oxygen inspired by its tenant, when he had crept in by the glass manhole, and had been screwed in. It was so elaborately padded that a man might have been fired from a gun in it with perfect safety. And it had need to be, for presently a man was to crawl in through that glass manhole, to be screwed up tightly, and to be flung overboard, and to sink down — down — down, for five miles, even as the lieutenant said. It had taken the strongest hold of his imagination; it made him a bore at mess; and he found Steevens, the new arrival aboard, a godsend to talk to about it, over and over again.

'It's my opinion,' said the lieutenant, 'that that glass will simply bend in and bulge and smash, under a pressure of that sort. Daubree has made rocks run like water under big pressures — and, you mark my words —'

'If the glass did break in,' said Steevens, 'what then?'

'The water would shoot in like a jet of iron. Have you ever felt a straight jet of high pressure water? It would hit as hard as a bullet. It would simply smash him and flatten him. It would tear down his throat, and into his lungs; it would blow in his eyes —'

'What a detailed imagination you have!' protested Steevens, who saw things vividly.

'It's a simple statement of the inevitable,' said the lieutenant.

'And the globe?'

'Would just give out a few little bubbles, and it would settle down comfortably against the day of judgment, among the oozes and the bottom clay — with poor Elstead apread over his own smashed cushions like butter over bread.'

He repeated this sentence as though he liked it very much. 'Like butter over bread,' he said.

'Having a look at the jigger?' said a voice, and Elstead stood behind them, spick and span in white, with a cigarette between his teeth, and his eyes smiling out of the shadow of his ample hat-brim. 'What's that about bread and butter, Weybridge? Grumbling as usual about the insufficient pay of naval officers? It won't be more than a day now before I start. We are to get the slings ready today. This clean sky and gentle swell is just the kind of thing for swinging off a dozen tons of lead and iron, isn't it?'

'It won't affect you much,' said Weybridge.

'No. Seventy or eighty feet down, and I shall be there in a dozen seconds, there's not a particle moving, though the wind shriek itself hoarse up above, and the water lifts halfway to the clouds. No. Down there' — He moved to the side of the ship and the other two followed him. All three leant forward on their elbows and stared down into the yellow-green water.

'*Peace*,' said Elstead, finishing his thought aloud.

'Are you dead certain that clockwork will act?' asked Weybridge presently.

'It has worked thirty-five times,' said Elstead. 'It's bound to work.'

'But if it doesn't.'

'Why shouldn't it?'

'I wouldn't go down in that confounding thing,' said Weybridge, 'for twenty thousands pounds.'

'Cheerful chap you are,' said Elstead, and spat sociably at a bubble below.

'I don't understand yet how you mean to work the thing,' said Steevens.

'In the first place, I'm screwed into the sphere;' said Elstead, 'and when I've turned the electric light off and on three times to show I'm cheerful, I'm swung out over the stern by that crane, with all those big lead sinkers slung below me. The top lead weight has a roller carrying a hundred fathoms of strong cord rolled up, and that's all that joins the sinkers to the sphere, except the slings that will be cut when the affair is dropped. We use cord rather than wire rope because it's easier to cut and more buoyant — necessary points, as you will see.

'Through each of these lead weights you notice there is a hole, and an iron rod will be run through that and will project six feet on the lower side. If that rod is rammed up from below, it knocks up a lever and sets the clockwork in motion at the side of the cylinder on which the cord winds.

'Very well. The whole affair is lowered gently into the water, and the slings are cut. The sphere floats — with the air in it, it's lighter than water — but the lead weights go down straight and the cord runs out. When the cord is all paid out, the sphere will go down too, pulled down by the cord.'

'But why the cord?' asked Steevens. 'Why not fasten the weights directly to the sphere?'

'Because of the smash down below. The whole affair will go rushing down, mile after mile, at a headlong pace at last. It would be knocked to pieces on the bottom if it wasn't for that cord. But the weights will hit the bottom, and directly they do, the buoyancy of the sphere will come into play. It will go on sinking slower and slower; come to a stop at last, and then begin to float upward again.

'That's where the clockwork comes in. Directly the weights smash against the sea bottom, the rod will be knocked through and will kick up the clockwork, and the cord will be rewound on the reel. I shall be lugged down to the sea bottom. There I shall stay for half an hour, with the electric light on, looking about me. Then the clockwork will release a spring knife, the cord will be cut, and up I shall rush again, like a soda-water bubble. The cord itself will help the flotation.'

'And if you should chance to hit a ship?' said Weybridge.

'I should come up at such a pace, I should go clean through it,' said Elstead, 'like a cannon ball. You needn't worry about that.'

'And suppose some nimble crustacean should wriggle into your clockwork —

'It would be a pressing sort of invitation for me to stop,' said Elstead, turning his back on the water and staring at the sphere.

They had swung Elstead overboard by eleven o'clock. The day was serenely bright and calm, with the horizon lost in haze. The electric glare in the little upper compartment beamed cheerfully three times. Then they let him down slowly to the surface of the water, and a sailor in the stern chains hung ready to cut the tackle that held the lead weights and the sphere together. The globe, which had looked so large in deck, looked the smallest thing conceivable under the stern of the ship. It rolled a little, and its two dark windows, which floated uppermost, seemed like eyes turned up in round wonderment at the people who crowded the rail. A voice wondered how Elstead liked the rolling. 'Are you ready?' sang out the commander. 'Ay, ay, sir!' 'Then let her go!'

The rope of the tackle tightened against the blade and was cut, and an eddy rolled over the globe in a grotesquely helpless fashion. Someone waved a handkerchief, someone else tried an ineffectual cheer, a middy was counting slowly, 'Eight, nine, ten!' Another roll, then with a jerk and a splash the thing righted itself.

It seemed to be stationary for a moment, to grow rapidly smaller, and then the water closed over it, and it became visible, enlarged by refraction and dimmer, below the surface.

Before one could count three it had disappeared. There was a flicker of white light far down in the water, that diminished to a speck and vanished. Then there was nothing but a depth of water going down into blackness, through which a shark was swimming.

Then suddenly the screw of the cruiser began to rotate, the water was crickled, the shark disappeared in a wrinkled confusion, and a torrent of foam rushed across the crystalline clearness that had swallowed up Elstead. 'What's the idea?' said one A. B. to another.

'We're going to lay off about a couple of miles, 'fear he should hit us when he comes up,' said his mate.

The ship steamed slowly to her new position. Aboard her almost everyone who was unoccupied remained watching the breathing swell into which the sphere had sunk. For the next half-hour it is doubtful if a word was spoken that did not bear directly or indirectly on Elstead. The December sun was now high in the sky, and the heat very considerable.

'He'll be cold enough down there,' said Weybridge. 'They say that below a certain depth sea-water's always just about freezing.'

'Where'll he come up?' asked Steevens. 'I've lost my bearings.'

'That's the spot,' said the commander, who prided himself on his omniscience. He extended a precise finger southeastward. 'And this, I reckon, is pretty nearly the moment,' he said. 'He's been thirty-five minutes.'

'How long does it take to reach the bottom of the ocean?' asked Steevens.

'For a depth of five miles, and reckoning — as we did — an acceleration of two feet per second, both ways, is just about three-quarters of a minute.'

'Then he's overdue,' said Weybridge.

'Pretty nearly,' said the commander. 'I suppose it takes a few minutes for that cord of his to wind in.'

'I forgot that,' said Weybridge, evidently relieved.

And then began the suspense. A minute slowly dragged itself out, and no sphere shot out of the water. Another followed, and nothing broke the low oily swell. The sailors explained to one another that little point about the winding-in of the cord. The rigging was dotted with expectant faces. 'Come up, Elstead!' called one hairy-chested salt impatiently, and the others caught it up, and shouted as though they were waiting for the curtain of a theatre to rise.

The commander glanced irritably at them.

'Of course, if the acceleration is less than two,' he said, 'he'll be all the longer. We aren't absolutely certain that was the proper figure. I'm no slavish believer in calculations.'

Steevens agreed concisely. No one on the quarterdeck spoke for a couple of minutes. Then Steevens' watchcase clicked.

When, twenty-one minutes after, the sun reached the zenith, they were still waiting for the globe to reappear, and not a man aboard had dared to whisper that hope was dead. It was Weybridge who first gave expression to that realisation. He spoke while the sound of eight bells still hung in the air. 'I always distrusted that window,' he said quite suddenly to Steevens.

'Good God!' said Steevens; 'you don't think — ?'

'Well!' said Weybridge, and left the rest to his imagination.

'I'm no great believer in calculations myself,' said the commander dubiously, 'so that I'm not altogether hopeless yet.' And at midnight the gunboat was steaming slowly in a spiral round the spot where the globe had sunk, and the white beam of the electric light fled and halted and swept discontentedly onward again over the waste of phosphorescent waters under the little stars.

'If his window hasn't burst and smashed him,' said Weybridge, 'then it's a cursed sight worse, for his clockwork has gone wrong, and he's alive now, five miles under our feet, down there in the cold and dark, anchored in that little bubble of his, where never a ray of light has shone or a human being lived, since the waters were gathered together. He's there without food, feeling hungry and thirsty and scared, wondering whether he'll starve or stifle. Which will it be? The Myers apparatus is running out, I suppose. How long do they last?'

'Good heavens!' he exclaimed; 'what little things we are! What daring little devils! Down there, miles and miles of water — all water, and all this empty water about us and this sky. Gulfs!' He threw his hands out, and as he did so, a little white streak swept noiselessly up the sky, travelled more slowly, stopped, became a motionless dog, as though a new star had fallen up into the sky. Then it went sliding back again and lost itself amidst the reflections of the stars and the white haze of the sea's phosphorescence.

At the sight he stopped, arm extended and mouth open. He shut his mouth, opened it again, and waved his arms with an impatient gesture. Then he turned, shouted 'El-stead ahoy!' to the first watch, and went at a run to Lindley and the searchlight. 'I saw him,' he said. 'Starboard there! His light's on, and he's just shot out of the water. Bring the light round. We ought to see him drifting, when he lifts on the swell.'

But they never picked up the explorer until dawn. Then they almost ran him down. The crane was swung out and a boat's crew hooked the chain to the sphere. When they had shipped the sphere, they unscrewed the manhole and peered into the darkness of the interior (for the electric light chamber was intended to illuminate the water about the sphere, and was shut off entirely from its general cavity).

The air was very hot within the cavity, and the india-rubber at the lip of the manhole was soft. There was no answer to their eager questions and no sound of movement within.

Elstead seemed to be lying motionless, crumpled up in the bottom of the globe. The ship's doctor crawled in and lifted him out to the men outside. For a moment or so they did not know whether Elstead was alive or dead. His face, in the yellow light of the ship's lamps, glistened with perspiration. They carried him down to his own cabin.

He was not dead, they found, but in a state of absolute nervous collapse, and besides cruelly bruised. For some days he had to lie perfectly still. It was a week before he could tell his experiences.

Almost his first words were that he was going down again. The sphere would have to be altered, he said, in order to allow him to throw off the cord if need be, and that was all. He had had the most marvellous experience. 'You thought I should find nothing but ooze,' he said. 'You laughed at my explorations, and I've discovered a new world!' He told his story in disconnected fragments, and chiefly from the wrong end, so that it is impossible to re-tell it in his words. But what follows is the narrative of his experience.

It began atrociously, he said. Before the cord ran out the thing kept rolling over. He felt like a frog in a football. He could see nothing but the crane and the sky overhead, with an occasional glimpse of the people on the ship's rail. He couldn't tell a bit which way the thing would roll next. Suddenly he would find his feet going up, and try to step, and over he went rolling, head over heels, and just anyhow, on the padding. Any other shape would have been more comfortable, but no other shape was to be relied upon under the huge pressure of the nethermost abyss.

Suddenly the swaying ceased; the globe righted, and when he had picked himself up, he saw the water all about him greeny-blue, with an attenuated light filtering down from above, and a shoal of little floating things went rushing up past him, as it seemed to him, towards the light. And even as he looked, it grew darker and darker, until the water above was as dark as the midnight sky, albeit of a greener shake, and the water below black. And little transparent things in the water developed a faint tint of luminosity, and shot past him in faint greenish streaks.

And the feeling of falling! It was just like the start of a lift, he said, only it kept on. One has to imagine what that means, that keeping on. It was then of all times that Elstead repented his adventure. He saw the chances against him in an altogether new light. He thought of the big cuttle-fish people knew to exist in the middle waters, the kind of things they find half digested in whales at times, or floating dead and rotten and half eaten by fish. Suppose one caught hold and wouldn't let go. And had the clockwork really been sufficiently tested? But whether he wanted to go on or to go back mattered not the slightest now.

In fifty seconds everything was as black as night outside, except where the beam from his light struck through the waters, and picked out every now and then some fish or scrap of sinking matter. They flashed by too fast for him to see what they were. Once he thinks he passed a shark. And then the sphere began to get hot by friction against the water. They had under-estimated this, it seems.

The first thing he noticed was that he was perspiring, and then he heard a hissing growing louder under his feet, and saw a lot of little bubbles — very little bubbles they were — rushing upward like a fan through the water outside. Steam! He felt the window and it was hot. He turned on the minute glow-lamp that lit his own cavity, looked at the padded watch by the studs, and saw he had been travelling now for two minutes. It came into his head that the window would crack through the conflict of temperatures, for he knew the bottom water is very near freezing.

Then suddenly the floor of the sphere seemed to press

against his feet, the rush of bubbles outside grew slower and slower, and the hissing diminished. The sphere rolled a little. The window had not cracked, nothing had given, and he knew that the dangers of sinking, at any rate, were over.

In another minute or so he would be on the floor of the abyss. He thought, he said, of Steevens and Weybridge and the rest of them five miles overhead, higher to him than the very highest clouds that ever floated over land are to us, steaming slowly and staring down and wondering what had happened to him.

He peered out of the window. There were no more bubbles now, and the hissing had stopped. Outside there was a heavy blackness — as black as black velvet — except where the electric light pierced the empty water and showed the colour of it — a yellow-green. Then three things like shapes of fire swam into sight, following each other through the water. Whether they were little and near or big and far off he could not tell.

Each was outlined in a bluish light almost as bright as the lights of a fishing smack, a light which seemed to be smoking greatly, and all along the sides of them were specks of this, like the lighter portholes of a ship. Their phosphorescence seemed to go out as they came within the radiance of his lamp, and he saw then that they were little fish of some strange sort, with huge heads, vast eyes, and dwindling bodies and tails. Their eyes were turned towards him, and he judged they were following him down. He supposed they were attracted by his glare.

Presently others of the same sort joined them. As he went on down, he noticed that the water became of a pallid colour, and that little specks twinkled in his ray like motes in a sunbeam. This was probably due to the clouds of ooze and mud that the impact of his leaden sinkers had disturbed.

By the time he was drawn down to the lead weights he was

in a dense fog of white that his electric light failed altogether to pierce for more than a few yards, and many minutes elapsed before the hanging sheets of sediment subsided to any extent. Then, lit by his light and by the transient phosphorescence of a distant shoal of fishes, he was able to see under the huge blackness of the superincumbent water an undulating expanse of greyish-white ooze, broken here and there by tangled thickets of a growth of sea lilies, waving hungry tentacles in the air.

Farther away were the graceful, translucent outlines of a group of gigantic sponges. About this floor there were scattered a number of bristling flattish tufts of rich purple and black, which he decided must be some sort of sea-urchin, and small, large-eyed or blind things having a curious resemblance, some to wood-lice, and others to lobsters, crawled sluggishly across the track of the light and vanished into the obscurity again, leaving furrowed trails behind them.

Then suddenly the hovering swarm of little fishes veered about and came towards him as a flight of starlings might do. They passed over him like a phosphorescent snow, and then he saw behind them some larger creature advancing towards the sphere.

At first he could see it only dimly, a faintly moving figure remotely suggestive of a walking man, and then it came into the spray of light that the lamp shot out. As the glare struck it, it shut its eyes, dazzled. He stared in rigid astonishment.

It was a strange vertebrated animal. Its dark purple head was dimly suggestive of a chameleon, but it had such a high forehead and such a braincase as no reptile ever displayed before; the vertical pitch of its face gave it a most extraordinary resemblance to a human being.

Two large and protruding eyes projected from sockets in chameleon fashion, and it had a broad reptilian mouth with hoary lips beneath its little nostrils. In the position of the ears were two huge gill-covers, and out of these floated a branching tree of coralline filaments, almost like the tree-like gills that very young rays and sharks possess.

But the humanity of the face was not the most extraordinary thing about the creature. It was a biped; its almost globular body was poised on a tripod of two frog-like legs and a long thick tail, and its fore limbs, which grotesquely caricatured the human hand, much as a frog's do, carried a long shaft of bone, tipped with copper. The colour of the creature was variegated; its head, hands, and legs were purple; but its skin, which hung loosely upon it, even as clothes might do, was a phosphorescent grey. And it stood there blinded by the light.

At last this unknown creature of the abyss blinked its eyes open, and, shading them with its disengaged hand, opened its mouth and gave vent to a shouting noise, articulate almost as speech might be, that penetrated even the steel case and padded jacket of the sphere. How a shouting may be accomplished without lungs Elstead does not profess to explain. It then moved sideways out of the glare into the mystery of shadow that bordered it on either side, and Elstead felt rather than saw it was coming towards him. Fancying the light had attracted it, he turned the switch that cut off the current. In another moment something soft dabbed upon the steel, and the globe swayed.

Then the shouting was repeated, and it seemed to him that a distant echo answered it. The dabbing recurred, and the globe swayed and ground against the spindle over which the wire was rolled. He stood in the blackness and peered out into the everlasting night of the abyss. And presently he saw, very faint and remote, other phosphorescent quasi-human forms hurrying towards him.

Hardly knowing what he did, he felt about in his swaying prison for the stud of the exterior electric light, and came by accident against his own small glow-lamp in its padded recess.

The sphere twisted, and then threw him down; he heard shouts like shouts of surprise, and when he rose to his feet, he saw two pairs of stalked eyes peering into the lower window and reflecting his light.

In another moment hands were dabbing vigorously at his steel casing, and there was a sound, horrible enough in his position, of the metal protection of the clockwork being vigorously hammered. That, indeed, sent his heart into his mouth, for if these strange creatures succeeded in stopping that, his release would never occur. Scarcely had he thought as much when he felt the sphere sway violently, and the floor of it press had against his feet. He turned off the small glow-lamp that lit the interior, and set the ray of the large light in the separate compartment out into the water. The sea-floor and the man-like creatures had disappeared, and a couple of fish chasing each other dropped suddenly by the window.

He thought at once that these strange denizens of the deep sea had broken the rope, and that he had escaped. He drove up faster and faster, and then stopped with a jerk that sent him flying against the padded roof of his prison. For half a minute, perhaps he was too astonished to think.

Then he felt that the sphere was spinning slowly, and rocking, and it seemed to him that it was also being drawn through the water. By crouching close to the window, he managed to make his weight effective and roll that part of the sphere downward, but he could see nothing save the pale ray of his light striking down ineffectively into the darkness. It occurred to him that he would see more if he turned the lamp off, and allowed his eyes to grow accustomed to the profound obscurity.

In this he was wise. After some minutes the velvety blackness became a translucent blackness, and then, far away, and as faint as the zodiacal light of an English summer evening, he saw shapes moving below. He judged these creatures had detached his cable, and were towing him along the sea bottom.

And then he saw something faint and remote across the undulations of the submarine plain, a broad horizon of pale luminosity that extended this way and that way as far as the range of his little window permitted him to see. To this he was being towed, as a balloon might be towed by men out of the open country into a town. He approached it very slowly, and very slowly the dim irradiation was gathered together into more definite shapes.

It was nearly five o'clock before he came over this luminous area, and by that time he could make out an arrangement suggestive of streets and houses grouped about a vast roofless erection that was grotesquely suggestive of a ruined abbey. It was spread out like a map below him. The houses were all roofless enclosures of walls, and their substance being, as he afterwards saw, of phosphorescent bones, gave the place an appearance as if it were built of drowned moonshine.

Among the inner caves of the place waving trees of crinoid stretched their tentacles, and tall, slender, glassy sponges shot like shining minarets and lilies of filmy light out of the general glow of the city. In the open spaces of the place he could see a stirring movement as of crowds of people, but he was too many fathoms above them to distinguish the individuals in those crowds.

Then slowly they pulled him down, and as they did so, the details of the place crept slowly upon his apprehension. He saw that the courses of the cloudy buildings were marked out with beaded lines of round objects, and then he perceived that at several points below him, in broad open spaces, were forms like the encrusted shapes of ships.

Slowly and surely he was drawn down, and the forms below him became brighter, clearer, more distinct. He was being pulled down, he perceived, towards the large building in the centre of the town, and he could catch a glimpse ever and again of the multitudinous forms that were lugging at his cord.

Slowly and surely they pulled him down into their world.

He was astonished to see that the rigging of one of the ships, which formed such a prominent feature of the place, was crowded with a host of gesticulating figures regarding him, and then the walls of the great building rose about him silently, and hid the city from his eyes.

And such walls they were, of water-logged wood, and twisted wire-rope, and iron spars, and copper, and the bones and skulls of dead men. The skulls ran in zigzag lines and spirals and fantastic curves over the building; and in and out of their eye-sockets, and over the whole surface of the place, lurked and played a multitude of silvery little fishes.

Suddenly his ears were filled with a low shouting and a noise like the violent blowing of horns, and this gave place to a fantastic chant. Down the sphere sank, past the huge pointed windows, through which he saw vaguely a great number of these strange, ghostlike people regarding him, and at last he came to rest, as it seemed, on a kind of altar that stood in the centre of the place.

And now he was at such a level that he could see these strange people of the abyss plainly once more. To his astonishment, he perceived that they were prostrating themselves before him, all save one, dressed as it seemed in a robe of placoid scales, and crowned with a luminous diadem, who stood with his reptilian mouth opening and shutting, as though he led the chanting of the worshippers.

A curious impulse made Elstead turn on his small globe-lamp again, so that he became visible to these creatures of the abyss, albeit the glare made them disappear forthwith into night. At this sudden sight of him, the chanting gave place to a tumult of exultant shouts; and Elstead, being anxious to watch them, turned his light off again, and vanished from before their eyes. But for a time he was too blind to make out what they were doing, and when at last he could distinguish them, they were kneeling again. And thus they continued worshipping him, without rest or intermission, for a space of three hours.

Most circumstantial was Elstead's account of this astounding city and its people, these people of perpetual night, who have never seen sun or moon or stars, green vegetation, nor any living, air-breathing creatures who know nothing of fire, nor any light but the phosphorescent light of living things.

Startling as is his story, it is yet more startling to find that scientific men, of such eminence as Adams and Jenkins, find nothing incredible in it. They tell me they see no reason why intelligent, water-breathing, vertebrated creatures, inured to a low temperature and enormous pressure, and of such a heavy structure, that neither alive nor dead would they float, might not live upon the bottom of the deep sea, and quite unsuspected by us, descendants like ourselves of the great Theriomorpha of the New Red Sandstone age.

We should be known to them, however, as strange meteoric creatures, wont to fall catastrophically dead out of the mysterious blackness of their watery sky. And not only we ourselves, but our ships, our metals, our appliances, would come raining down out of the night. Sometimes sinking things would smite down and crush them, as if it were the judgment of some unseen power above, and sometimes would come things of the utmost rarity or utility, or shapes of inspiring suggestion. One can understand, perhaps, something of their behaviour at the descent of a living man, if one thinks what a barbaric people might do, to whom an enhaloed, shining creature came suddenly out of the sky.

At one time or another Elstead probably told the officers of the *Ptarmigan* every detail of his strange twelve hours in the abyss. That he also intended to write them down is certain, but he never did, and so we have to piece together the discrepant fragments of his story from the reminiscences of Commander Simmons, Weybridge, Steevens, Lindley and the others.

We see the thing darkly in fragmentary glimpses — the huge ghostly building, the bowing, chanting people, with their dark chameleon-like heads and faintly luminous clothing, and Elstead, with his light turned on again, vainly trying to convey to their minds that the cord by which the sphere was held was to be severed. Minute after minute slipped away, and Elstead looking at his watch, was horrified to find that he had oxygen only for four hours more. But the chant in his honour kept on as remorselessly as if it was the marching song of his approaching death.

The manner of his release he does not understand, but to judge by the end of cord that hung from the sphere, it had been cut through by rubbing against the edge of the altar. Abruptly the sphere rolled over, and he swept up, out of their world, as an ethereal creature clothed in a vacuum would sweep through our own atmosphere back to its native ether again. He must have torn out of their sight as a hydrogen bubble hastens upward from our air. A strange ascension it must have seemed to them.

The sphere rushed up with even greater velocity than, when weighted with the lead sinkers, it had rushed down. It became exceedingly hot. It drove up with the windows uppermost, and he remembers the torrent of bubbles frothing against the glass. Every moment he expected this to fly. Then suddenly something like a huge wheel seemed to be released in his head, the padded compartment began spinning about him, and he fainted. His next recollection was of his cabin, and of the doctor's voice.

But that is the substance of the extraordinary story that Elstead related in fragments to the officers of the *Ptarmigan*. He promised to write it all down at a later date. His mind was chiefly occupied with the improvement of his apparatus, which was effected at Rio.

It remains only to tell that on February 2, 1896, he made his second descent into the ocean abyss, with the improvements his first experience suggested. What happened we shall probably never know. He never returned. The *Ptarmigan* beat about over the point of his submersion, seeking him in vain for thirteen days. Then she returned to Rio, and the news was telegraphed to his friends. So the matter remains for the present. But it is hardly probable that no further attempt will be made to verify his strange story of these hitherto unsuspected cities of the deep sea.

Laffey *and the* Kamikazes

by

COMMANDER JOHN KERANS D. S. O., R. N.

When the radar operator's urgent voice called out: 'Kamikazes — too many to count — coming in fast!' Commander Frederick Becton of the destroyer U. S. S. *Laffey* knew he and his men were in for a tough time.

The date was 16 April, 1945, and the place fifty miles north of the Japanese fortress island of Okinawa. Since 1 April the 10th U. S. Army, with massive fleet support, had been engaged in a desperate assault on Okinawa. From the bitterness of the Japs' resistance it was obvious this was going to be the most murderous battle of all the Pacific islands' campaign. The enemy were fully aware once Okinawa was captured the Americans would have a base only 325 miles from the Japanese mainland.

That the fanaticism already widespread among the Japanese fighting men flamed even more ferociously when their homeland was threatened with invasion, was already terribly apparent. The cult of the Kamikaze — the young men who gloried in sacrificing themselves in suicide attacks — was at its peak. Kamikaze pilots were diving their bomb-loaded planes squarely on to warships, supply ships and troop transports; suicide swimmers and boatmen were ramming contact-detonated high-explosive against ships; shore soldiers crouched in fox holes, clutching big bombs which they detonated when tanks or armoured carriers passed over them. At Okinawa there were more Jap suicide attacks made by land, sea and air than any other battlefield.

The reason why the U. S. S. *Laffey* was where she was, at station Roger Peter One, on this calm sunny April morning, was because she was operating as a radar picket ship to give warning of approaching Kamikazes. She was in fact, the forward picket ship, nearly one hundred miles closer to Japan than the main force attacking Okinawa. Inevitably she would be the first of the hated enemy the Japs would see as they flew out on their desperate one-way missions. And now the first wave was approaching: 'Range 17,000 — still coming fast and impossible to count!' called the breathless voice of the radar operator.

Commander Becton, a quietly-spoken, intense man who became suddenly dynamic when action was required, sounded the general alarm. Down the voice pipe to the Chief Engineer he called for speed: 'Henke we want every turn you've got!' Although the *Laffey* had not been attacked or in action yet, her men had a good idea what happened when the Kamikazes came. In the Hagushi anchorage of Okinawa, seized in the opening assault and now thronged with the multitude of vessels of the invading force, there had been many victims of the power-diving suicide planes. Contorted metal, gaping holes in decks, smouldering wreckage, gruesome remains of what had been men and already ashore a cemetery which daily expanded... All was grim testimony to the fact that many a Jap pilot had taken far more than one enemy with him when he died. While the *Laffey* was briefly in that graveyard anchorage being equipped with the complicated radar installation of an early-warning ship, they had been tersely advised by a gun captain from a battle-scarred destroyer: 'You guys will have a fighting chance — you'll knock a lot of them down and you'll think you're doing fine but they'll just keep on coming until one of them gets you!'

The *Laffey*, a powerfully-gunned destroyer of 2,200 tons, had been on extreme forward duty exactly twenty-four hours when the scanning radar first registered the swarming cluster of blips. The seas were calm, so that she gently rocked as she cruised beneath a sky smiling and blue by day and soft star-spangled velvet by night. Pacific seemed the right name for this ocean and there was nothing to indicate it would be different until the threshing propellers churned up the bloated body of a Jap pilot and the charred wreckage of his plane.

Now the lean, grey destroyer was a-shudder with the pulse of her engines as the men below responded to the orders for full speed. Still the wide blue heavens were innocent of anything at all that could be deemed hostile. High-powered glasses on the bridge intently scanning the sky to the north, searched for something that at first would look like a swarm of gnats. Although still invisible to the naked eye, the approaching Kamikazes were coming up bigger and bigger on the radar screen. Then: 'Seem to be opening out — but they're still coming on!' came the operator's report.

That Jap suicide planes were heading her way did not necessarily mean the *Laffey* was their target. It was more likely they had been ordered to crash with their bomb-loads on to the decks of the huge American aircraft carriers which were playing such a great part in the island-hopping advance on Japan. Other priority targets would be the battleships, cruisers and big transports whose destruction must bring death to large numbers of Americans. 'Most likely they'll go over us,' suggested one of the *Laffey*'s officers. 'Maybe they will get shot down by our combat air patrols before they can do any damage.' But Lieutenant Challen McCune, the Executive Officer, reported that the American fighter patrol was at the moment being relieved; it would be some little time before the relieving fighters could get to the area.

Suddenly Captain Becton's binoculars picked out the Jap

The planes dived to certain death for the destruction of their enemies.

planes! 'Bogies ahead — coming fast!' a sailor shouted from the look-out platform at that moment. The Kamikazes were coming! (Afterwards the survivors learned there were no fewer than 165 Jap suicide planes in that approaching cloud!) 'Lieutenant Smith requests permission to fire;' came in excited tones from the forward five-inch guns. 'Fire when ready!' rapped the Captain. The murmur of the approaching enemy could now be heard; with each second it swelled until it was an angry hornet-like drone. Suddenly the forward guns belched fire and smoke. The whole ship shuddered. 'Hard left rudder! All guns commence fire!' roared Captain Becton. And the azure morning erupted into one vast bellowing, flaming inferno.

The roar of the *Laffey*'s big guns was joined by insistent throbbing from forty millimetre guns and pulsing whip-cracks from twenty millimetre cannons. The sky ahead was full of Jap planes. Crackling smoke puffs of the destroyer's first salvo were planted blackly in their path. Then four Aichi Ninety-nine dive bombers peeled off and power-dived at the *Laffey*. Engines bellowing they hurtled down, down, down like thunderbolts, two at the bows and two at the stern. Their fanatical pilots were giving every atom of engine power, every taut, strained fibre of their own dedicated beings. They dived to certain death for the destruction of their enemies.

A stream of smoke whirled back from one of the bombers forward. Suddenly it was a fire-streaked comet plunging straight into the sea. The five-inch guns had claimed their first victim. The water still frothed where it had vanished when the other bomber diving at the bows lurched, cartwheeled dramatically, shattered into fragments as it struck the sea. All around and above her now the *Laffey* was surrounded by the black smoke of her bursting shells. Then the red and white tracer streams of her close-range automatic weapons leaped out and up. Abruptly a billow of smoke and flame aft told the ending of another of the attackers: shells from No. 3 turret had destroyed it. The tail of the fourth was spectacularly whipped away by a cannon-shell stream; it disintegrated in mid-air and was gone. Momentarily man looked at man in speechless wonderment at what they had done — then the next attack was coming in.

Two Kamikaze bombers streaked in headlong, then parted and peeled off left and right for flank attacks. Boiling the sea into foam behind her, flinging out great spumes of white water forward, the *Laffey* heeled to port and then to starboard as she dodged and weaved. One Jap plane tearing in at 2,000 yards range was suddenly the centre of shell bursts and criss-cross tracer streams. It had its wings torn off in mid-air, and a great water spout climbed up where it vanished into the sea. The Kamikaze on the other side twisted frantically, got within fifty yards, then was caught by a salvo of the destroyer's big guns which blew it apart. Although the pilot was dead the big bomb he had intended to take with him to his death on the *Laffey's* deck tumbled from the smoke cloud and burst alongside. The ship lurched violently at the concussion, her nearest escape yet, but although men were flung down none was wounded.

'God! How long can our luck hold!' gasped a gunner. The men of the Laffey were well aware that most of the savagely-torn ships they had seen in Hagushi Bay had each been victim of no more than one Kamikaze. Yet already the *Laffey* had survived six separate attacks and destroyed the attackers. The roar above them now was deafening; the Kamikaze swarm seemed to be milling round waiting to take it in turns to dive bomb. Surely there could be no hope of surviving if the Kamikazes did not press on to other targets?

'Hard right!' By both voice and gesture Commander Becton gave the order urgently. Another Jap bomber was coming, skimming the sea on the port bow. The destroyer keeled over, steeper and steeper, until the frothing sea surged along her slanting deck, until she was round with the Kamikaze howling over her stern instead of attacking her broadside. The pilot missed his death crash but barely clipped the top of one of the five-inch guns and killed one of the crew instantly. The *Laffey* had suffered her first casualty. The ensuing lull was just long enough for the dead man to be dragged away, and hasty repairs to be made to the broken signal wires, then the eighth Kamikaze was coming at them.

This Jap torpedo bomber also dodged in at sea level, on the starboard beam. But a deadly concentration of tracer fastened on to it, its fuel tank exploded and it was a funeral pyre rushing toward them. Then the whole thing disintegrated and vanished, leaving only a sinister patch on the sea. Without any respite the ninth attacker screamed down. Down, down, down it plunged then zoomed in a short shattering climb, levelled out, and was at them. Every gun that the twisting, turning *Laffey* could bring to bear thundered and cracked and rattled, but to no avail. As he hurtled towards the thunderous death he had chosen the Kamikaze pilot bore a charmed life. Some men who glimpsed his face in the last split seconds swore it had a set, dedicated look, as though he were already not of this world; which he wasn't an instant later, when the plane smashed into the destroyer amongst a nest of guns amidship. With a horrible 'whoof' a great tower of smoke and flame boiled up from the destroyer. 'Fire amidships!' the dread call went out. 'Damage control and fire fighting parties needed topside on the double!'

With this pillar of smoke and fire standing up from the ocean to make the *Laffey* a target that could be seen for miles, the Jap suicide pilots were spurred to an absolute frenzy. Despite all the variety of targets beyond at Okinawa, all the great warships and transport whose destruction was so vital to the Japanese soldiers fanatically defending the island, the Kami-

320

kaze pilots seemed obsessed with a desire to obliterate this one American destroyer. Perhaps it was because this warship was the closest enemy to their homeland, perhaps it was the unreasoning inflexibility which so often caused the Japs to squander fighting men on comparatively unimportant outposts which they should have by-passed. Whatever it was, the blind, furious persistance with which the Kamikazes kept attacking the *Laffey* undoubtedly saved countless American lives at Okinawa.

Weaving and writhing through the sea like a living thing in extreme pain, the destroyer was now amidst a swarm of plunging Japanese warplanes piloted by fanatics seeking death and glory. Fortunately there were still sufficient guns working, and men to serve them, to put up a formidable curtain of exploding steel. But the tenth Kamikaze also got home, and even more devastatingly than the previous one. Wave-hopping and jinking it burst through the fire curtain and crashed terrifyingly on to the after five-inch gun mounting. Almost immediately an eleventh, hot on its heels, shattered down on to almost exactly the same place. A huge billow of flame, like sudden engulfment by a prairie fire, enveloped the destroyer from end to end. One complete side of the turret had been blown out, great holes gaped in the main deck, and flaming fuel spewed through into the living space below. The *Laffey* shuddered as though in her death throes as the forty millimetre ammunition magazine took fire and shells began to explode deep down within her, blowing men there to bits.

As though that were not enough yet another attacker, the twelfth, glided in silently on the portside, masked by the billowing smoke. He dropped a bomb near the stern and it tore through the ship's side, exploded in a machine gun magazine and jammed the rudder. Listing, blazing, crippled, the *Laffey* could now only circle on the one course. She was an absolute-sitting target. In the inferno below a damage control party worked heroically. Dr Mathew Darnell, Jnr, the ship's M.O., plucked live ammunition from amidst red hot metal and tossed it overboard. Commander Becton, still in complete control of an almost indescribably desperate situation, kept the destroyer flat out on its jammed circular course.

The thirteenth Kamikaze plunged down with the fourteenth hot on its tail. They crashed on to the after deckhouse almost simultaneously. The terrifying impact coupled with the shattering explosion of the bombs nearly power-punched the *Laffey* beneath the sea. But she rode up again, with yet another terrible fire adding to her shroud of black smoke and leaping flames. High-octane fuel released by the smashing of watertight hatches added to the roaring conflagration.

A brave attempt was now made by Lieutenant Ted Runk and three enlisted men to repair the damaged steering. They fought their way through smoke and flame without breathing masks and struggled to clear the rudder. But the flames were licking closer all the time and they were forced back. On their way out they walked straight into an unexploded Japanese bomb ringed by flames and quickly rolled it overboard. Meanwhile, on a wrecked forty millimetre gun aft with flames leaping around him, Lieutenant Joe Youngquist tossed live hot ammunition into the sea.

The attacking Jap bombers could now only be glimpsed through rifts in the pall of smoke that enveloped the destroyer. Suddenly the fifteenth Kamikaze was plunging down upon them, but as they saw it they saw also there was a Corsair fighter of the U. S. Navy tearing after it with guns blazing. The *Laffey's* forward machine guns opened up on the Jap and at the last minute its nose lifted and it howled over the ship instead of on to it, just clipping the radar mast. Seconds later it disintegrated, struck by a concentration of fire. The Corsair could not pull out and also hit the radar mast, rolled over as it zoomed, and the pilot bailed out.

Yet another Kamikaze roared in, this time to port, again with a Corsair hammering away on its tail. It burst into flames before reaching the destroyer but dropped a bomb which burst so close that splinters struck down some of the gunners still tirelessly serving the now nearly red hot forty-millimetre and twenty-millimetre guns. It also destroyed the communications to the two five-inch guns still in action. The fate of the seventeenth Kamikaze proved that the destruction of communications had not put these guns out of action. One of them, now manually trained, blasted the Jap suicide plane out of the sky as it came in head on.

The next two Kamikazes to attack were just too easy to be true. They were two Nakajima army fighters fitted out with bombs. The destroyer's remaining big guns just blasted them out of the sky — one — two — at long range. But the twentieth suicide bomber was far more formidable. Dropping down from a steep glide out of the sun, it twisted and turned to present the most difficult target possible, then opened up its engine and howled down upon the ship. But yet again a Corsair came swooping in with all guns blazing, braving the curtain of fire put up by the destroyer's guns. Shots ripped the Jap plane from above and below as it thundered over, so close as to clip off the one remaining yardarm. It plummeted into the water just beyond the *Laffey*'s stern. Still the Kamikazes came! And still the half-sunken destroyer fought back! The twenty-first Jap bomber was blasted out of the sky by the forward five-inch guns and the last remaining forty-millimetre gun. The twenty-second howled in through a hail of shell-fire and machine-gun bullets, then abruptly reeled, spun and disintegrated in a great puff of smoke.

Then suddenly all the brave men aboard the *Laffey* who still could listen stood stock still. Their eyes and ears strained out and upwards towards a new sound that was filling the sky. It was a crescendo of engine song of a great number of diving warplanes, pitched in a key they recognised as American. At last the combat air patrol had arrived! Squadrons of Marine-piloted Corsair fighters hurtled upon the milling Kamikazes. Now the *Laffey* plunged clear of her smoke shroud — and high above her could be seen the downrush of the attacking fighters and the twisting flaming downfall of their victims. It was as though a band of shining angels had suddenly rescued them from the hell that enveloped them. For a moment the men stood in bewilderment, as though they could hardly comprehend that they were going to live after all. Then cheer after cheer rose from the destroyer and the bloodstained, sweat-stained, smoke-blackened men shouted exultingly: 'Get the bastards! — Rip 'em up! — Give 'em hell!'

A great silence descended upon the Pacific Ocean fifty miles north of Okinawa. The crippled, heroic *Laffey* wallowed there amidst the wreckage of the unbelievable battle through which she had just fought. For seventy-nine minutes non-stop she had been subjected to relentless Kamikaze attacks, no fewer than twenty-two of them pressed right home. Yet still she was afloat, still prepared to fight on. She had lost thirty-one killed, seventy-two wounded and was a mass of tortured, smoking wreckage, but she was still indomitable.

Early that afternoon another warship steamed up, warned of the *Laffey's* condition by the figher pilots who had terminated the battle. She took the gallant destroyer in tow, back to Hagushi Bay. In that harbour of Kamikaze victims the *Laffey* caused wonderment and admiration, for the minds of men who had experienced the terror of suicide bombers boggled at the thought of the *Laffey's* twenty-two attacks and could not imagine how she had still fought on and lived to tell the tale.

In due course the destroyer was patched up at Pearl Harbor, then moved back to be rebuilt in the great Todd shipyards at San Francisco. While there she was for five days put on display so that the American people could appreciate what their sailors had to face from the Kamikaze suicide attacks. Commander Frederick Becton — who is now Rear Admiral Becton — was awarded the Navy Cross for his great heroism and devotion to duty. Many said he should have received America's highest award for valour, the Congressional Medal.

It is of interest to record that Captain Frank Manson, one of the *Laffey's* surviving officers, is now known the world over as the man who thought up the idea of the Great White Fleet. This project envisages a 'mercy task force' of obsolete warships and other vessels not in use to take aid anywhere in the world that disease, hunger and disaster requires it. Britain's own bomber hero Group Captain Leonard Cheshire, V. C., is associated with Manson in this. The American officer was obsessed with the idea after becoming convinced of the futility of the slaughter he had witnessed. He determined that warships 'in their retirement' should be used to alleviate some of the world's misery, particularly in South-east Asia, of which he had experience.

You'll Never Make a Sailor

by

ROBERT BATEMAN

This was the best moment of the day, Bill Jory thought as he scrambled up the ladder to the bridge of the 'Tahiti Star', hanging on with one hand while with the other he carried three steaming hot mugs of coffee. His fingers were jammed tightly through the handles of the thick mugs, and he held them out beyond the rail of the ladder, so that if the 'Tahiti Star' gave a sudden lurch in a high sea there was no risk of being half-drowned in hot coffee.

It was the best moment because up high on the bridge he could watch the bows rise up on the huge Atlantic waves and then drop down, down, down into the troughs that followed. Salt spray whipped up as the bows crashed into the seas cascading over the foredeck.

'Hello, Bill, there you are! Is that my coffee? Good lad.'

The Second Mate, Harry Rawston, was broad as a barn door, red-faced, and at least a foot taller than Bill. Ever since the start of the trip he had been leg-pulling about Bill's small size. But at least it *was* leg-pulling. Even though it was his first voyage, even though for a week he had been too seasick to work, everybody from Captain Fallon downwards had told him, 'Never mind. You'll make a good sailor.'

Bill opened the wheelhouse door and fought his way inside as the 'Tahiti Star' rolled and made the deck into a steep hill.

'Brought my coffee?' Captain Fallon grinned at him.

'Thanks, Bill. You haven't spilled it. That's pretty good — it's blowing up rough.' As he spoke, the 'Tahiti Star' plunged between two waves, and Bill had to grab a stanchion in order not to be flung straight at him.

'Better give the helmsman his coffee before you drop it,' the Captain laughed.

Still hanging on to the stanchion, Bill reached out and handed over the coffee.

Suddenly the door in the back of the wheelhouse swung open. Captain Fallon turned his head. 'Hello, Sparks, what's the matter?'

The Radio Officer held out a scrap of paper. 'Ship in distress, sir. I've just picked up this S. O. S. message. She's about thirty miles ahead of us, I reckon, just off the Irish coast.'

The Captain glanced at the piece of paper. 'Bill, ask the Second Mate to come in here, will you?'

'Aye, aye, sir.' Bill opened the wheelhouse door, chose his moment when the ship was on an even keel, and went out to the wing of the bridge. Harry Rawston was crouching behind the canvas weatherscreen with his sextant raised to his eyes, trying to take a bearing to work out the ship's position. Bill clutched the bridge rail and hung on tight, waiting for him to finish. Then he said, 'There's a ship in trouble, Mr Rawston. Captain Fallon wants you in the wheelhouse.'

He hoped to be able to go in again and hear what was said, but the Second Mate shook his head. 'Sorry, Bill, you'd be in the way. And you've got your own work to do, haven't you?'

That made Bill jump to the ladder. He had forgotten about the six other mugs of coffee on the tray in the steward's pantry. Dodging as a heavy sea smashed its way up on to the boat deck, he went down below and took coffee to the First and Third Mates and the Engineers.

Then he was free for an hour. He stood on deck, braced against the 'midships cargo hatch, and looked at the rough sea to starboard.

'You'll never make a sailor.'

That was what he had heard at home ever since he was eight years old. His father, tough and leathery after twenty years as bo'sun of the old *Corymer*, would come home on leave and look at him scornfully. 'What's up with the boy, mother? Looks like a midget to me. Better get him a good safe shore job. He'll *never* make a sailor.'

But here he was, on the way home after his first Atlantic crossing. All right — so he was small. But he'd show his father — he'd make his father admit that he, too, could be tough enough for a lifetime on cargo ships in the rough north Atlantic.

'Bill!'

He looked up towards the bridge. The Second Mate was beckoning to him, so he raced up the ladders, halting only once when the *Tahiti Star* rolled so far to starboard that if he had not clung on rightly with both hands he would have been swept over the side. Below him, on the midships deck he had just left, a giant wave crashed through the rails, roared over the hatchtop with a welter of white foam, and caught the Steward, soaking him to the waist.

Bill reached the top of the ladder. 'Yes, sir?'

'Bill, tell the Steward to get out extra bedding. Get the galley to make up a big pan of hot soup. We may have two boatloads of cold and hungry survivors.'

'What ship is she, sir?'

'Oh just another old tramp ship like this one. Her name's the *Corymer*.'

Bill froze at the head of the ladder,

'What's the matter, boy?'

'That's my father's ship, sir.'

Harry Rawston looked at him sharply. 'You're sure of that?' Bill nodded. 'Dead sure, sir. He's been bo'sun on the *Corymer* for years.' He swallowed. 'Sir, what's happened to the '*Corymer*'? Is she sinking?'

The Second Mate braced himself against the bridge rail as the *Tahiti Star* nose-dived between waves. Bill looked down as water seemed for a moment to be clmbing the ladder below him. He stared at it, thinking differently about it now. Up to now the gale and the huge white-crested waves had been exciting; now he saw them as a menace. He glanced across to the boat deck. The lifeboats looked small and frail. He tried to imagine them packed with men, battling to keep afloat, struggling not to be swamped by every wave. He thought of his father, and shivered.

'We don't know whether she's sinking,' said the Second Mate. 'She hit an underwater wreck.'

Bill looked at him wildly. 'Don't we know any more than that?'

He saw that the Second Mate was looking at him, as if weighing him up. 'I suppose you'd better know the truth,' said Harry Rawston. 'We've only had one message from the *Corymer*.'

'But why haven't they gone on sending signals?'

The Second Mate drew in his breath. 'She's carrying iron ore.'

'I don't understand, sir.'

'Iron ore's one of the heaviest cargoes a ship ever carries, Bill. When an ore-ship gets a hole in her, she goes down... well, pretty fast.'

Bill felt cold panic inside him. 'How long?'

'It could be only two or three minutes. Just long enough to get the boats away.' He paused for a moment. 'When we pick them up they'll need that hot soup and the warm bunks. Better get on your way and see the Steward.'

'Aye, aye, sir.'

Bill went down to the 'midships deck in a daze.

If it had been any other ship it would have been different. But the very idea of the *Corymer* going down seemed impossible. For as long as he could remember, his father had been crossing the Atlantic aboard her. 'Tough old tub,' his father had said. 'They really knew *how* to build ships in the old days when she came out of the yards. An iceberg couldn't sink her.'

Suddenly the steady throb of the *Tahiti Star's* engines speeded up. The whole ship vibrated as she hurled herself at the seas, breaking a passage through them, but pitching fore and aft so steeply that Bill went slithering along the deck to fetch up with a crash against the galley door, making the steel plating ring like a gong.

The door opened, and the Steward put his head out. Bill gave him the message.

Then he went back to the bridge ladder. Up aloft, the First Mate had now joined Captain Fallon and Harry Rawston. He was wedged tightly in the starboard wing of the bridge, peering out across the crests of the giant waves.

It was now three hours since the S. O. S. message. If the *Tahiti Star* had been doing her usual eight knots, then by now she must be only a few miles from the *Corymer* — if the *Corymer* was still afloat. But remembering what Rawston had said, Bill realised the First Mate wasn't searching for the ship.

He was searching for tiny black specks rising high on each mountainous wave, then dropping with sickening force into the trough while the drenched, half frozen men aboard struggled to bale out the water.

He was searching for lifeboats.

Bill had an excuse to go back on the bridge. He went up the ladders, and into the chartroom behind the wheelhouse, where the Second Mate was bending over a chart with a ruler and pencil.

'Sir, the Steward said to tell you there's enough hot soup for forty men, and solid food to follow.'

Harry Rawston did not look up. 'Good lad, What about bedding?'

'He can't manage enough for forty, sir, but he's found enough blankets for twenty.'

The Second Mate straightened himself up. 'Then the rest of them will have to use our bunks. They'll need 'em more than we shall.' He glanced through the porthole. 'We should be sighting something any time now. Don't worry, Bill — we'll have your father safe aboard in an hour or two.'

Bill swallowed hard.

It was funny, he thought. His father was tough. They'd had rows — plenty of them. He still felt angry whenever he thought of those sarcastic words, 'You'll never make a sailor.' It was only now, when there was danger, that he realised how much he cared about his father.

The shout from outside on the bridge came suddenly. 'Boat on the port quarter!'

Before Bill could move, Harry Rawston had leaped past him, throwing the cartroom door opened. The wind screamed in, lifting charts from the table and scattering them across the floor. Bill dashed out after the Second Mate, and joined him on the port wing of the bridge.

At first he could see nothing. The gale was now so fierce that stinging spray slammed into his face like a rainstorm the moment he raised it above the weathershield. Ahead, the sea was a vast boiling mass of white foam.

His heart sank. Surely lifeboats could not stay afloat in that wilderness?

Shielding his eyes with his hands, he strained to pick out the dark outlines of boats against the background of churning water.

The Second Mate shouted to the helmsman, and down below, near the engine room, the steering engine clanked busily, swinging the bows of the *Tahiti Star* to port.

Immediately, with the seas no longer dead ahead, the ship lurched violently as a giant wave hit her starboard flank. Hundreds of tons of water swept across the decks, tearing away tarpaulin hatch covers. Just forward of the bridge one of the off-duty sailors, darting to his tea in the forecastle, was caught and thrown against the rail. He stood, holding on, pinned to it by the terrific force of rushing water, with only his head visible. Then, as the sea fell away, he clambered to safety.

The Second Mate was beside Bill. 'Quick, boy, get below and warn the Steward and the Engineers. Secure everything. This is going to be rough!'

Bill was half way down the ladder when the next wave struck. He saw it climb towards him at tremendous speed as the whole port side of the *Tahiti Star* disappeared beneath it. Then, icy cold, it was on him like an avalanche, sweeping his legs from under him so that he hung outwards from the ladder with only the ocean below him, and his hands taking his full weight.

For what seemed hours the *Tahiti Star* lay on her beam ends. Bill's wrists ached with the agony of holding on. Then, terribly slowly and with a groan of strained metal, she righted herself, and he swung back to regain a foothold on the ladder.

Water was streaming off him, but Bill grinned. 'Huh!' he said softly to himself. 'So you'll never make a sailor?'

And then, only a few hundred yards away, he saw the boats. Only they were not boats — just rafts, each with black dots of heads around them, the heads of men clinging desperately to the safety ropes as they struggled not to be torn away by each wave. As he looked, a raft rose high on the crest of a wave, then dropped like a stone into what seemed like a bottomless trough beyond. Before he could see what happened to it, another great sea struck the *Tahiti Star*, and once again he had to cling on as she was flung over on her side by a thundering torrent of water. This time his head went under, for he was lower down the ladder. He held his breath to keep his lungs from filling with water, then, as the wave fell away, he scrambled down to the deck and raced along the rail. No use now to pass on the Second Mate's orders — if they hadn't been carried out already, it was too late. Everything that could move would have moved. That giant pan of hot soup would have raced the full length of the galley stove, then raced back again, with the cook darting out of the way as it chased him. Every loose cup and saucer aboard would have been smashed.

No, he knew what he was doing. There was only one way of saving the men on the rafts, and that was by managing to lower the port lifeboat in one of the gaps between the great seas.

And when they did that, he intended to be aboard.

He looked over his shoulder as he reached the narrow iron ladder to the boat deck, but nobody was watching him. Nobody had any time at a moment like this except for the job of keeping the *Tahiti Star* from turning turtle in the next big sea.

He was up the ladder just in time to miss another battle with a giant wave. From behind him came a crash; looking back he saw the galley door fly open and the cook come racing out, grabbing at the door handle just in time to avoid being swept over the rail into the water.

Then Bill was beside the lifeboat, heaving at the lines holding the tarpaulin cover. He loosened them just enough to be able to wriggle over the gunwale into the boat, and then, as he heard shouts and the tramp of feet on the boat deck, he scrambled under the loose cover of the engine.

There was more shouting, then bangs like pistol shots when men pulled off the tarpaulin cover and the wind caught it, beating it out of their hands with savage force.

The boat jerked upwards as it was swung out on the davits. Somebody crashed into the side of the engine cover only inches away from Bill. The boat rocked wildly as the *Tahiti Star* lurched in another big wave, and then, when once again she was on her beam ends, there was a shout from the Second Mate and a rattle of pulleys. Down went the lifeboat, so fast that Bill's stomach seemed to come up into his throat.

Men piled into the boat. 'Cast off!' yelled the Second Mate.

And then the engine cover was ripped away.

Bill straightened up.

The Second Mate stared at him in astonishment. 'What are you doing here, Bill? Get back aboard.'

But as they looked up at the rusty, heaving flank of the *Tahiti Star* they both knew it was impossible. The Second Mate looked angry for a moment, then he smiled grimly. 'All right, Bill. I understand. Get in the stern and keep down low.'

The petrol engine burst into life. The Second Mate swung the tiller, bringing the lifeboat round in a tight curve as the *Tahiti Star* came back from her steep roll. For a horrible moment, perched high on a wave the lifeboat seemed to hang above the ship, threatening to slide down and crash on the midships hatch, then the pull of the little engine dragged her away from the brink and out of danger.

'There they are!' somebody shouted, pointing to a spot dead ahead.

The raft at which he was pointing was very low in the water, weighed down by at least twenty men clinging to the safety ropes. One of them raised his arm and waved it feebly.

'Engine dead slow,' shouted the Second Mate.

The fast roar of the petrol engine slowed to a grumbling

murmur, speeding up only as each wave lifted the lifeboat and took the propeller high out of the water. A wave carried them up and up, until they towered above the raft, then, with superb steering, the Second Mate brought the boat sliding down the flank of the wave, with her gunwale just above the water, to a point only six feet from the raft.

Now, as Bill could see, was the most dangerous moment. The exhausted men had to cross the six feet of heaving water to the safety ropes of the lifeboat before the next wave slammed their heavy raft into the wooden sides of the boat.

Six of them made it, grabbing frantically at the safety ropes, then gasping with relief as the boat's crew reached down and hauled them aboard.

That left fourteen — and no chance for any of them to make another move. From the direction of the *Tahiti Star* another giant wave began to life the lifeboat once again. Bill hung on beside the Second Mate as the lifeboat rose higher and higher, canting over steeply until her crew flung themselves like yachtsmen to the other side. Even their combined weight had hardly any effect. The Second Mate reached down, wrenched open a locker door, and flung out three bailing tins. Bill grabbed one of them and began scooping water out of the bottom of the boat. As he did so he could see the raft down at the bottom of what looked like an immense pit, but rising rapidly to meet them.

It came up only three feet away, and stayed there, just long enough for the remaining men to leap across to the safety ropes. Then, as the raft began drifting away, they were dragged aboard. Anxiously Bill looked at every face, but there was none with that familiar quarter inch of stubble, none with the heavy eyebrows and the huge square chin.

His father must be on the second raft.

The lifeboat's engine picked up speed again, and the bows slammed hard into a heavy sea. Harry Rawston brought her round full circle, judging his turn cleverly to avoid being caught broadside on by the next wave.

The second raft was no more than a hundred yards away, but to Bill it seemed like ten miles as the boat crept up towards it, changing course every few seconds to dodge being swamped. The Second Mate squatted at the tiller, his eyes on every movement of the seas, watching for treacherous waves that could catch them on the flank.

Bill caught only one glimpse of the raft until they were almost alongside. Then, without warning, it rose up ahead of them on a wave, and tobogganned down at them — half a ton of timber and metal buoyancy tanks. Yelling, men let go of the safety ropes and flung themselves clear to avoid being crushed as the raft hit the boat.

The crash came with a rending, tearing shock that sent Bill flying over the stern, hanging on by one hand while he fought to keep his feet from being hit by the spinning propeller. He heaved himself back aboard, and grabbed the tiller from the Second Mate, who was crouched forward with his hands half covering a wound on his face. In the bows, water was pouring in through a ragged hole torn by the raft, and men came stumbling into the stern of the boat to weigh it down and lift the hole above water level.

Two men flung from the raft thrust their hands up over the gunwale close to Bill. Locking one leg over the tiller bar to keep it in check, Bill grabbed one pair of hands and pulled. He felt his muscles crack with the strain, then the man below managed to get his elbows over the gunwale.

Bill looked round, and shouted for help, but every man in sight was busy on the same task. He shook the Second Mate by the shoulder, but Harry Rawston was too dazed to do more than shake his head.

He looked back at the exhausted man clinging to the gunwale. Somehow he would have to manage the weight alone.

Bill thrust both hands under the man's shoulders.

The man's eyes were closing; Bill seized his hair and pulled it. The sudden tug was painful enough to jerk the man back into consciousness; when Bill took his hands he summoned up a last reserve of strength, hauled his body upwards, and toppled forward into the boat.

Bill glanced hurriedly towards the bows as he heard the engine cough, splutter, and then unexpectedly pick up speed again. He almost let out a cheer when he saw that the raft had remained wedged in the hole, keeping the bows afloat. He swung the tiller slightly, heading the boat back towards the heaving flank of the *Tahiti Star*, then once again locked the tiller under his leg, and reached out for the second pair of hands of the gunwale.

This time it took a greater heave than before. The man below was a heavyweight. He seemed to be too far gone to do anything to help himself. Agonisingly slowly, inch by inch, he came up, then feebly hooked his forearms over the gunwale.

Bill stretched out as far as he dared, and thrust both hands under the man's shoulders. With an effort, the man looked up. Water was streaming down his face, which was pinched and white with exposure. His eyes were only half open.

In a frenzy Bill heaved again. He released his leg from the tiller, planted both feet firmly in the bottom boards, stood up, and wrenched himself backwards as the next wave tipped the boat. A huge figure in oilskins came up out of the water like a cork from a bottle and crashed down on top of him, knocking him flat in the bottom of the boat.

Dazed, Bill sat up. They were on the crest of the wave now; he looked down what seemed a sheer wall of water, then as the lifeboat and the raft, locked together, slid down into the trough, he saw the *Tahiti Star's* other lifeboat coming in a wide circle towards them.

It looked as though it would be only just in time. With nearly fifty men crowded aboard, their own boat was wallowing, shipping gallons of water every second — far faster than the men with baling tins could hurl it back. He jumped for the tiller, to put the boat head on into the seas again.

But the giant in oilskins was already there, heaving the tiller with strong, skilled hands, placing the wrecked boat so that the other lifeboat could come safely alongside.

Bill let out a gasp of exhaustion and relief.

Forgetting they were balanced on the crest of a wave, he stood up again, and cheered.

The man in the oilskins caught him just in time, as a sudden violent lurch sent him flying towards the gunwale. Only then did Bill recognise him.

A great horny hand came out from an oilskin-covered sleeve. It shook his. For a moment Bill thought his father was going to say thanks — thanks for a strong haul up out of the sea.

What his father did was to shake his head, and look at the gunwale over which Bill had nearly plunged. 'You'll never make a sailor!' he said.

But he said it differently now.

He said it with a grin!

The Stranger from the Sea

by

JOHN DAVIES

The fog had come down suddenly, in the middle of the afternoon. Through the clammy greyness glided a trim little sailing dinghy with two boys in it. The slim, dark, quiet-looking one sitting amidships handling the jib-sheets was Jeremy Hamilton. The stockier, red-haired boy at the tiller was Simon Ward, and the dinghy belonged to him. Its name was *Seaspray*.

'Lost at sea!' Jeremy said. 'What fun!'

Simon grinned. 'We aren't really.'

'You mean you can find your way through this stuff?'

'I reckon so. We've just passed the West Shoal Buoy, so the harbour's only a mile ahead.'

Seaspray sailed slowly on. Jeremy couldn't help being excited by this latest development in a day of excitements. He was a Londoner and not used to boats or the sea. His cousin Simon, on the other hand, had been born in the little Cornish village of Towan, and had been sailing nearly all his life.

Jeremy was spending a holiday with Simon, and, though they were very different in temperament, the two boys had quickly become the best of friends.

'The only thing we've got to look out for is the oil-rig platform,' Simon said. He peered out over the bows. 'Hullo — what's this?'

Jeremy stared into the fog. He said, 'It's a boat.'

The dinghy sailed nearer the vague, pale shape ahead.

'A motor-cruiser,' Simon said. A biggish job too.' He kept his eyes on the boat as *Seaspray* glided nearer. 'I don't recognise her. She doesn't belong to Towan.'

'Is she moving?'

'If she is, she's going dead slow.' Simon was puzzled. 'I wonder if the people aboard her know where they are? On that course she'll end up on West Bay rocks.'

'Perhaps they're lost, if they're strangers?'

'They could be. We'd better give them a hail and find out.' Simon raised his voice and shouted, 'Motor cruiser ahoy!'

The call drifted away into the greyness. There was no response from the motor cruiser. In fact there was no sign of life aboard her at all.

Jeremy said, 'She's at anchor — I can see the chain. Maybe they're waiting for the fog to clear?'

'Maybe,' Simon said. 'But why don't they answer?' He called again. 'Motor cruiser ahoy! Are you in trouble?'

No reply. Simon frowned, and altered course directly towards the other boat.

Jeremy looked back at him quickly. 'What are you going to do?'

'There's something funny about this,' Simon said, I'm going alongside to check up. There may be somebody ill or something.'

A minute or so later he brought the dinghy gently alongside the cruiser. She was a big, white, powerful-looking craft. Standing up and hanging on to her well-coaming, he called again, 'Anybody aboard?'

No answer.

Jeremy said, 'There must be somebody.'

'I don't believe there is,' Simon said. 'I think she's deserted.' He took a firm grip on the coaming. Hang on to her a moment while I have a look.'

341

'O. K.'

Simon stepped up on to *Seaspray's* transom. Then, with a jump and a heave, he hauled himself over the motor-cruiser's side. Jeremy saw him stand there for a moment, then move forward and disappear.

He felt a little shiver run down his spine.

What would Simon find? Somebody ill, he had said. Supposing it was somebody dead? A body?

A little while passed, then Simon reappeared. He was looking more puzzled than ever.

'I was right,' he said. 'This is a very funny business indeed. Chuck me up the painter — you'd better come aboard too.'

While Simon tied *Seaspray* up astern, Jeremy climbed aboard the motor cruiser. Then Simon led the way through the wheelhouse and into the saloon.

There was nobody there, but Jeremy at once noticed signs of very recent occupation. On the table were the remains of a meal, and on one of the settees a shirt, sweater and a pair of jeans lay in an untidy heap, as though they had recently been thrown down there.

Simon nodded towards the table. 'Feel the teapot.'

Jeremy did so, then stared at his friend. 'It's still warm!'

'Exactly,' Simon said.

They stood there in the cruiser's saloon, trying to work it out.

Jeremy said, 'Perhaps she's broken down and they've gone ashore in their dinghy to get help?'

'The dinghy's still in its chocks on the foredeck,' Simon said. 'I noticed it as we came alongside.'

'Then I don't know,' Jeremy said. 'I . . .'

He broke off as Simon gripped his arm. The motor-cruiser had just given a little lurch to starboard, as though a weight had been put on that side.

'Someone coming aboard!' Simon hissed.

The two boys stood stock still, watching the entrance to the saloon. Who was it? And where had he come from? There had been no sound of a boat approaching.

The lurch was followed by a commotion in the water somewhere alongside the cruiser. Then they heard someone moving about in the well aft... someone coming forward through the wheelhouse... someone — or something — moving with a slithering flapping sound...

A figure appeared in the entrance to the saloon, a tall, weird figure, clothed from head to foot in glistening black. As he caught sight of the boys, he stopped, blocking the doorway. His face was pale, and he stared at them expressionlessly. He looked like a visitant from another world.

The man in black said, 'What are you doing here?'

Simon almost laughed. The 'apparition' wasn't in fact anything more frightening than a frogman. He was wearing a frogman's black rubber suit, with a compass on his wrist, and was carrying his mask in his hand.

'I'm sorry,' he said. 'We didn't get any reply when we hailed, so we wondered if you were in trouble.'

The man grunted. 'Good of you to bother.' He didn't sound very friendly.

Jeremy said, 'We thought that, with the fog...'

'That's why I anchored,' the man in the rubber suit said. 'And I thought that while I was stuck here I might as well try for a fish for my supper.' He paused. 'No luck, though, I'm afraid.'

There was an awkward silence. Then Simon said, 'Well, I suppose we'd better be on our way...'

The man didn't try to stop them. He followed them out into the well.

'It seems to be thinning a bit,' he said. 'So I think I'll be on my way too.'

Simon glanced quickly round the well of the cruiser, but he

343

couldn't see what he was looking for. He felt the frogman's eyes on him and said, as casually as he could, 'Where are you heading for?'

'Paenporth. If I can get there, I'll have my supper ashore instead'.

Five minutes later the two boys were back in *Seaspray* again, heading for Towan harbour. The motor-cruiser had disappeared in the fog astern.

Jeremy said, 'So it wasn't such a mystery after all.'

'Wasn't it?' Simon retorted.

Jeremy gave him a quick, surprised look. 'What do you mean?'

'I mean I think it was all very fishy.' Simon paused. 'Talking of that, he said he'd been trying to get a fish for his supper, didn't he? But he hadn't a spear gun when he came into the saloon — and he didn't leave it outside. I looked.'

'You could have missed it.'

'All right. Perhaps I did. But he was lying about something else too.'

'What?'

'He said if he could get to Paenporth, he'd go ashore for supper. He couldn't do that because the harbour at Paenporth is dry at low tide, and with the tide the way it is today, he won't be able to get in until about three o'clock tomorrow morning.'

'Perhaps he doesn't know that,' Jeremy said. But he too was now convinced that there had been something suspicious about the frogman.

They were silent for a while. Then Simon said, 'I was a silly fool. I ought to have noticed the cruiser's name.'

'I did,' Jeremy said. 'It was *Amaryllis*.'

'Good for you,' Simon said. 'Was there anything to say where she belonged to — any yacht club initials or anything?'

'I don't think so,' Jeremy said. 'I didn't notice any.'

A little later they passed the oil-rig platform. It was as yet only half completed, and rose like a gaunt skeleton out of the sea. Simon had already told Jeremy that a big drilling operation was planned for this area. Then the breakwater of Towan harbour appeared ahead. They sailed in, and half an hour later they were ashore and heading for home.

That night Simon lay in bed listening to the grunt of the Outer Bank foghorn, which meant there was still fog out at sea. He kept thinking about the strange incident of the frogman and the motor cruiser. Before he finally dropped off to sleep he resolved to find out a bit more about that boat, if he could...

In the morning the weather was clear and sunny again. Before he and Jeremy left the house, Simon phoned the harbour-master at Paenporth, who told him there was no motor-cruiser named *Amaryllis* based there.

It was a perfect day for sailing, but they couldn't go out that morning because *Seaspray* was due to have her rigging tuned up for the weekend's racing. They went along to the yacht yard where a weatherbeaten old man known as Rigger was busily at work on the dinghy. No one knew whether that was really his name or just his job.

They watched for a while. Then Simon said, 'Rigger — do you know a motor-cruiser named *Amaryllis?*'

Rigger knew most of the boats along that bit of coast, but he shook his head. 'Never heard of her.' Then he thought again. 'Wait a minute — there's that charter firm along at Polwen. They've got a lot of boats, all beginning with A. Might be one of them.'

'Thanks,' Simon said. 'Thanks, Rigger.'

He and Jeremy wandered along to the end of the harbour wall and stood there looking out to sea.

'Where's Polwen?' Jeremy asked.

'About twenty miles along the coast to the westward,'

Simon said. The opposite way from Paenporth, where that chap said he was going.' He paused thoughtfully. 'I could ring up the charter firm and ask them about the *Amaryllis*, I suppose.' Suddenly his face lightened. 'Or we could sail over there. We could take sleeping bags and a primus and make a short cruise of it. What do you think?'

Jeremy said, 'I think it's a smashing idea!'

They were both excited now, and couldn't wait to get cracking. They decided to start off as soon as the dinghy was ready.

The first thing was to ask permission from Simon's parents and then get the necessary gear together. They dashed home. Simon's mother said she thought it would be all right, but that he ought to ask his father. So Simon got on the phone to Dad at his office in Plymouth — and Dad, as usual turned up trumps. The weather forecast was good, and he didn't believe in boys being mollycoddles. The only thing he asked was that Simon should look after Jeremy, and Simon said he would; thought he felt, privately, that Jeremy was quite capable of looking after himself.

Simon's mother turned up trumps too. She put on an early lunch for them, and drove them down to the harbour with their gear. The dinghy was ready, and by two o'clock they were under way.

They had a marvellous sail. The dinghy sped along before a fresh breeze, over a sparkling sea. Simon was prepared to drop anchor for the night, if necessary, in Mawn Creek, which was half way between Towan and Polwen, but by the time they got there they were making such good progress that he decided to press on to Polwen.

An hour later their progress was almost too good. In spite of the forecast of fair weather, the wind had strengthened, and a great bank of black cloud was climbing up in the sky behind them. The dinghy was roaring along, her rigging humming.

'It looks as though we're in for a blow,' Simon said. 'It's a good job we've got the wind behind us.'

Jeremy did not answer. This was his first experience of rough weather, and the thrill of it took his breath away.

They made one of the fastest passages even Simon had ever known. Just before seven that evening they charged in past the small lighthouse on the Polwen harbour breakwater.

They spotted the motor-cruiser almost at once. Neither of them could believe it at first, for up till then she had seemed so mysterious and elusive. She was lying alongside the harbour wall, near its outer end, some distance away from any other craft. They thought they recognised her as they approached and when they passed her and looked back, there was proof positive — the name *Amaryllis* plainly visible on her stern. There was no sign of life aboard.

'We'd better take a closer look at her as soon as we can,' Simon said. 'In case she puts to sea and we lose her.'

'She wouldn't go out in this, would she?' Jeremy asked.

'She might,' Simon said. 'Bad weather can be useful cover, if you're up to no good.'

They sailed on across the harbour, and Simon brought *Seaspray* expertly alongside the Town Quay. In a matter of minutes the little boat was securely moored to the quay with her sails lowered.

'She'll be all right there until we get back,' Simon said.

He didn't, of course, know just how long it would be before they got back. Neither did Jeremy...

An iron ladder led up to the top of the quay. Jeremy followed Simon up it. The *Amaryllis* was lying about a couple of hundred yards away round the curve of the harbour wall. With their hands in the pockets of their jeans they strolled casually towards her.

It was an easy enough stalk. The motor cruiser was lying well below the level of the harbour wall, and they had only

347

to stay back from the edge to keep out of sight. On the wall a few yards short of the *Amaryllis* there was a large red buoy which had been brought in from sea for servicing and this made a first-rate observation point. If anyone came out from below decks on the motor cruiser, they had only to move back into the shelter of the buoy.

They watched from the lee of the buoy. For a long time nothing happened. Then a short, fat man came out into the well with a plastic bowl in his hand. As they drew back they heard him tip the contents over the side. A moment later some potato parings floated into the boy's range of vision.

'He's been peeling spuds,' Simon whispered. 'Seems harmless enough.'

A voice said, 'I wouldn't be too sure about that.'

Both the boys had been so intent on watching the motor cruiser that they were taken completely by surprise. Their heads jerked round. Behind them, not more than three yards away, stood a tall man. He was wearing a white roll-necked sweater and khaki drill trousers today, but they recognised him at once.

It was the frogman.

'You two seem very interested in my boat,' the tall man said. 'A little too interested, shall we say?'

Both Simon and Jeremy could only stare, speechlessly.

They were staring at the thing the man was holding in his hand. It was a snub-nosed, wicked-looking little gun.

'Perhaps you'd like to come on board again?' the man said. 'In fact, you're going to, whether you like it or not.' The gun jerked in his hand and his voice sharpened. 'All right — down that ladder! Get moving — and no nonsense!

Mechanically, the boys obeyed. To both of them this seemed like a dream — or a nightmare. They couldn't really believe that they were at the wrong end of a gun, but they were. They couldn't believe the man would use it; and yet that wouldn't

348

have been any more incredible than the rest of the situation.

His head in a whirl, Simon climbed down the iron ladder abreast of the motor-cruiser. Jeremy followed. The man already aboard heard them and came out from below. When he saw the boys, his face was almost comical with surprise.

'Peters!' he exclaimed. 'What...?' His voice was guttural and he spoke with a foreign accent.

Peters followed Jeremy down the ladder into the motor-cruiser's well.

'These are the two nosey little devils I told you about,' he said. The gun jerked at Simon and Jeremy again. 'Get below — and be quick about it!'

In a daze, the two boys stumbled through the wheelhouse into the saloon. Peters was hard at their heels. The little fat man was saying something, protesting, but Peters took no notice. He drove the boys right forward, into the forepeak. Then, almost before they knew what was happening, the forepeak door was slammed and they heard the grating of the key in the lock. They were prisoners, in a cramped, dark little compartment right up in the bows of the boat.

They were still stunned.

'Simon,' Jeremy said. He tried to keep his voice steady, but didn't quite succeed. 'What are they going to...?'

'Shut up a minute,' Simon said. There were raised voices in the saloon. 'Let's see if we can hear what they are saying.'

The two men — they heard Peters call the other one Margolis — were quarrelling.

'Why did you bring them aboard?' Margolis demanded.

'I told you,' Peters said. 'They're the two I found on the boat yesterday. They must have got wind of something, or they wouldn't have turned up here the way they did. And I'm not going to risk my neck for a couple of kids.'

'But they couldn't have done anything!'

'I'm not so sure they couldn't,' Peters retorted. 'Anyway,

they're coming with us now. We're not taking any chances,'

'But' — Margolis repeated the question Jeremy had started to ask — 'what are we going to do with them?'

'I don't know,' Peters said. 'We'll see about that later.'

The tone of his voice was ominous.

Margolis seemed to accept the situation then, and the quarrel died away into ordinary talk. It was harder to hear what the men were saying, and they weren't talking about the boys any more, but what little Simon could make out made him almost as alarmed as if they had been. He heard Peters say something about 'the charge on the rig,' and then Margolis asked anxiously about the 'cable to the plunger.'

In the gloom of the forepeak Simon turned urgently to Jeremy.

'You know what?' he whispered hoarsely. 'They're going to blow up the oil platform!'

The men's voices droned on.

'We've got to get out of here!' Jeremy said. 'We must warn somebody!'

But how?

'Perhaps if we shouted?' Simon said. 'Someone ashore might hear us and...'

But it was already too late. At that moment the motor-cruiser's engine roared into life. There were footsteps on the deck overhead as one of the men cast off. The engine sound settled to a steady throb, and they could hear the rush of water past the boat's bows. They were under way.

In a few minutes the boys' prison began to lift and fall. They were out of the harbour. The motion became more violent, and soon the cruiser's bows were soaring sickeningly and crashing down again into the sea.

'It's a gale, isn't it?' Jeremy said. Where they had previously been whispering, he now had to raise his voice against the noise outside.

350

'It's a gale all right,' Simon said. He added bitterly. 'If they don't know what they're doing, we may all go to the bottom together!'

Jeremy didn't say any more. The idea of being shut up in that horrible little compartment when the *Amaryllis* sank was not very pleasant.

Neither of them spoke again for a long while after that. The motor-cruiser soared and plunged on. Then at last her motion seemed to get easier. Some time later she was in comparatively smooth water.

Later still they heard footsteps overhead again. The anchor chain rattled out, the cruiser's engine was cut, and all was silence except for the sound of the wind and the gentle wash of the sea.

Simon looked at the luminous dial of his watch and was amazed to see that the time was nearly midnight. He and Jeremy had been shut up there in the forepeak for five hours. Where were they now? Were they back in Towan? He realised at once that they couldn't be since Towan harbour was very small and they had been in fairly calm water for some time. His guess was that they had run into one of the lonely creeks somewhere along that stretch of coast.

He and Jeremy listened intently, trying to hear what the two men were doing. They heard muffled movements, a faint creaking, and then a sudden throaty whine which Simon recognised immediately.

'An outboard!' he exclaimed. 'They've gone off in the dinghy!'

The knowledge that the two men had gone gave a great lift to the boys' spirits.

Jeremy said, 'Now we've got to get out of her! Fast!'

The question remained — how? The door was still locked and there was nothing in the forepeak to batter it down with. Simon had already explored and found nothing except a couple of coils of rope and one or two tins of paint.

Then he had an inspiration and began to pull at the floor-boards. They should be loose, so that you could get at the bilges. They were. He pulled the centre one up, and underneath it he found what he had been desperately hoping would be there: a heavy chunk or 'pig' of cast iron which was part of the cruiser's ballast.

He told Jeremy excitedly about his find and hauled the pig out. It was all he could do to lift it.

He was about to attack the door with it when Jeremy stopped him.

'Wait,' he said. It'll make a devil of a noise, so let them get well clear first.'

They waited impatiently until the sound of the outboard had faded right away, and for five minutes after that. Then Simon went to work on the door. The lock gave as he crashed the pig against it the second time. They were free!

They rushed out through the saloon into the well of the cruiser. Simon stared around him, trying to get his bearings. As it happened, it was easy. The night, though rough, was not really dark. A full moon was racing through ragged clouds, and by its light he saw a great black headland which he recognised immediately. It was the Barrow. On the other side of it was Towan harbour.

He told Jeremy where they were.

'We're about five miles from the oil rig,' he said. 'We've got to get there before anything happens!'

Jeremy said blankly, 'How?'

'In this boat, of course! How else? If I start the engine, can you get the anchor up?'

'Yes.'

Simon was already groping around the controls. He wasn't used to motor-cruisers, but he did know a bit about engines. He found the starter, and the engine roared into life. Jeremy

352

was already up on the bows, hauling on the anchor chain. He shouted as the anchor came free... Simon shoved the engine in gear and took the wheel. They were under way!

A quarter of an hour later they were out in the open sea again. The night was as wild as ever, and the motor cruiser surged and rolled crazily, dashing great sheets of spray up over her bows.

Hanging on beside Simon, Jeremy said, 'Why do you think those two went ashore?'

Simon said, 'From that talk about a cable and plunger, I reckon they're planning to blow up the rig from somewhere on land — and the other side of the Barrow would be the nearest point. But they must have known they couldn't land on that side in this weather, so they ran in behind. My guess is they're making their way over the headland on foot.' He laughed shortly. 'They've got a rough walk.'

'How long will it take them?'

'A good hour. It must be three miles, and there's a lot of marshland first.

'Oughtn't we to have gone after them — to try to stop them?'

Simon said, 'I thought about that, but we couldn't risk it. We might not have been able to catch them up, or even find them, in the dark. And there may be someone on the rig. Sometimes they work all night, and there's always a watchman.' His tone became suddenly more urgent. 'We've got to get there before the whole thing goes sky-high!'

The motor-cruiser plunged on. Jeremy marvelled that anyone could navigate in that wild waste of waters, but Simon had the fleeting light of the moon and the dim glow of the compass in front of him to help him...

A gaunt black skeleton tower appeared ahead, in the middle of a great smother of breaking seas.

'The rig!' Jeremy yelled. 'And there's someone on it! I can see a light!'

Simon took the cruiser round to the leeward side of the rig, where the sea was a little calmer and there was an embarkation ladder. There were several lights on the rig, and one of them came bobbing down the ladder. Simon brought the cruiser in as close as he dared, and the man clinging to the ladder shone a torch on his face.

'Young Simon!'

The voice was deep, with a strong Scottish accent. The man on the ladder was the rig boss, Bob Mclean, whom Simon had got to know well during the time the oil platform had been under construction.

'Bob?' Simon yelled. 'How many of you on there?'

'Six,' Bob shouted back. 'We got cut off by the storm!'

'You've got to come off now — quick!' Simon shouted. 'The rig may go any moment!'

'But what...'

'Don't waste time!' Simon yelled desperately. 'It's sabotage!'

On the way to the rig he had been terribly afraid that, even if he raised the alarm, no one would believe him. He need not have worried. The rig boss climbed quickly back up the ladder, and a few moments later the two boys saw a line of men descending it. Simon nudged the cruiser in until, one by one, they had all jumped aboard.

Bob McLean came last. He grabbed the well-coaming beside Simon.

'Now, then,' he said sharply, 'what's all the fuss?'

Simon told him. He added, 'It's my guess they're planning to blow her from the nearest point on the Barrow' — he pointed — 'somewhere over there.'

'O. K.' Bob said grimly. 'We've got to get there.' He hesitated. 'But how?'

'There's only one way,' Simon said. 'We haven't got time to muck about. We'll have to run the boat on the beach.'

Bob still hesitated. The whole weight of the storm was

The cruiser rolled over on her beam ends, spilling everyone out.

pounding on the long beach on this side of the Barrow. There was no telling what might happen to the cruiser if she was deliberately run ashore there.

But as Simon had said, it was the only way...

'Verra gude,' Bob said. He looked around him at the other dark figures crowded into the cruiser's well. 'You know what we're after!' he told them and divided them into two parties, one to search the beach in each direction. 'And,' he added, 'when she grounds, it's every man for himself!'

Now, with the storm behind her, the *Amaryllis* was rushing towards the beach, surging and slewing dizzily. There were breakers ahead...

The cruiser struck and swung broadside on. A great sea lifted her and flung her shorewards. She struck again, with a cracking splintering sound and rolled over on her beam ends, spilling everyone out of her.

The sea closed over Jeremy's head. He held his breath and tried to swim. Then there was sand underfoot. He stumbled, gasping. Another wave picked him up and flung him shoreward. He was in the shallows. He floundered out on to the beach.

There were dark figures running, spreading out. He thought he saw Simon and was about to follow him when he spotted something else; something up near the flat coarse grass of the dunes which might have been a small rock, except that it moved, or seemed to.

He dashed towards the 'rock'. It moved again. The moon shone suddenly out and he saw two men crouching over a sort of box. One of them saw him and shouted a warning. Jeremy flung himself forward. He fell on the box in a flurry of sand and hugged it to him. Hands grabbed at him and someone was cursing. Then someone else rushed up. He heard a sharp Scots voice exclaim, 'No ye don't, ye devil!' Then there was a dull thumping sound, and a yell of pain.

356

It was Saturday morning two days after the storm, and the weather was sparkling again. Simon and Jeremy had sailed the dinghy home, arriving back the previous evening. This morning they had come out to the oil platform, at Bob McLean's invitation, to have a look round.

Peters and Margolis were safe under lock and key, and Bob had explained what they had been up to. If oil was found off the coast of Britain, less would have to be brought in from abroad, and one of the foreign companies most likely to suffer had bribed the two men to try and sabotage the rig. They had failed.

Thanks to Simon and Jeremy.

This morning the rig was swarming with men and everyone was in high spirits. Since the sabotage bid had been foiled, everyone felt sure they must strike oil soon.

Simon and Jeremy spent an hour on the rig. Then Simon said 'I'm afraid we must be off.'

'Racing this afternoon?' Bob asked.

'Yes'.

Bob turned to Jeremy. 'Well — at least you've had a lively holiday so far.'

Jeremy grinned. And Simon said. 'He's sailing with me in the race this afternoon. He'll get a bit of *real* excitement then!'

ACKNOWLEDGEMENTS

The publishers wish to express their thanks to authors and publishers for permission to include the following stories.

'Famous Ships' from *Stories of Famous Ships* (Oliver & Boyd) © copyright Frank Knight 1962.

'Strange Tales of the Coast' by George Goldsmith-Carter © copyright Odhams Periodicals 1960-61.

'Jackdaw Baits the Trap' © copyright John E. Edwards 1965.

'*Laffey* and the Kamikazes' from *The World's Greatest Sea Adventures* (Odhams) © copyright Commander John Kerans 1964.

'Hornblower and the Man who felt Queer' from *Mr Midshipman Hornblower* © copyright C. S. Forester 1950. Reprinted by permission of A. D. Peters & Co.

'Captain Sharkey: How the Governor Of Saint Kitt's Came Home' from *The Conan Doyle Stories*. Reprinted by permission of John Murray (Publishers) Ltd and the Estate of Sir Arthur Conan Doyle.

'In the Abyss' from *The Short Stories of H. G. Wells*. Reprinted by permission of the Executors of H. G. Wells.